RANDALL LIBRARY

W9-BKQ-297

RANDALL L. FRANK

PROBLEM-SOLVING METHODS IN ARTIFICIAL INTELLIGENCE

McGRAW-HILL COMPUTER SCIENCE SERIES

RICHARD W. HAMMING
Bell Telephone Laboratories

EDWARD A. FEIGENBAUM
Stanford University

BELL AND NEWELL COMPUTER STRUCTURES: READINGS AND EXAMPLES
COLE INTRODUCTION TO COMPUTING
GEAR COMPUTER ORGANIZATION AND PROGRAMMING
GIVONE INTRODUCTION TO SWITCHING CIRCUIT THEORY
HAMMING INTRODUCTION TO APPLIED NUMERICAL ANALYSIS
HELLERMAN DIGITAL COMPUTER SYSTEM PRINCIPLES
KOHAVI SWITCHING AND FINITE AUTOMATA THEORY
LIU INTRODUCTION TO COMBINATORIAL MATHEMATICS
NILSSON PROBLEM-SOLVING METHODS IN ARTIFICIAL INTELLIGENCE
RALSTON INTRODUCTION TO COMPUTER SCIENCE
ROSEN PROGRAMMING SYSTEMS AND LANGUAGES
SALTON AUTOMATIC INFORMATION ORGANIZATION AND RETRIEVAL
WATSON TIMESHARING SYSTEM DESIGN CONCEPTS
WEGNER PROGRAMMING LANGUAGES, INFORMATION STRUCTURES,
            AND MACHINE ORGANIZATION

NILS J. NILSSON Artificial Intelligence Group
Stanford Research Institute, Menlo Park, California

PROBLEM-SOLVING METHODS IN ARTIFICIAL INTELLIGENCE

McGRAW-HILL BOOK COMPANY
New York   San Francisco   St. Louis   Düsseldorf
Johannesburg   Kuala Lumpur   London   Mexico   Montreal
New Delhi   Panama   Rio de Janeiro
Singapore   Sydney   Toronto

**PROBLEM-SOLVING
METHODS IN
ARTIFICIAL
INTELLIGENCE**

Copyright © 1971 by McGraw-Hill, Inc. All rights reserved.
No part of this publication may be reproduced, stored in a
retrieval system, or transmitted, in any form or by any means,
electronic, mechanical, photocopying, recording, or otherwise,
without the prior written permission of the publisher.

Printed in the United States of America.

Library of Congress catalog card number: 74-136181

567890   KPKP   79876543

07-046573-8

TO MY PARENTS
WALTER AND PAULINE NILSSON

PREFACE

The goal of work in artificial intelligence is to build machines that perform tasks normally requiring human intelligence. Thus, prominent topics in the field include automatic methods for solving problems, "understanding" and translating languages, proving theorems, and recognizing speech sounds and visual objects. Although many of these tasks are exceedingly difficult, several computer programs have been written whose performance begins to match that of humans.

Future progress in this field will depend on the development of both practical and theoretical knowledge. The practical knowledge of technique will gradually accumulate as practitioners learn by experience how to construct ever more complex information processing systems. We can expect that the technology of the digital computer and of computer languages (especially list-processing languages) will continue to form the foundation for the growth of the necessary new practical knowledge.

As regards theoretical knowledge, some have sought a unified theory of artificial intelligence. My view is that artificial intelligence is (or soon will be) an engineering discipline since its primary goal is to *build* things. Thus it makes no more sense to look for a theory of artificial intelligence than it does to look for a theory of civil engineering. Instead of a central theory, there are many theoretical subjects that are relevant and should be studied by students specializing in artificial intelligence. Some of these include mathematical logic, computational linguistics, theory of computation, information structures, control theory, statistical classification theory, graph theory, and theory of heuristic search. The last named subject, *heuristic search,* is the main topic of this book.

Solving problems by heuristically guided, trial-and-error search in a space of possible solutions is a dominant theme in artificial-intelligence research, yet there is no single textbook devoted to explaining the underlying theoretical ideas of these search processes. This book has been written in an attempt to fill that need. It covers thoroughly the major heuristic search methods used in automatic problem solving, theorem proving, and game playing.

These search methods are explained using a uniform vocabulary, and several theoretical results about the properties of heuristic search are presented. Several simple examples are used to illustrate the techniques. Although efficient utilization of heuristic search methods in large-scale "practical" problems is just beginning, in many cases these techniques have been successfully applied to problems much more complex than those represented by our examples. I have referenced some of these applications, but I suspect that there are many more.

The book includes three chapters dealing with resolution-based theorem proving in the predicate calculus and its applications to problem solving. Even though these techniques have not yet enjoyed practical applications, my guess is that ultimately they will. Furthermore, most of the literature on this subject is quite difficult to read, so I thought it worthwhile to attempt a simple explanation illustrated with many examples.

In my early plans for the book, I wanted to include a chapter discussing problem-solving methods using machine-learning techniques. I concluded that the subject was not yet well enough developed for inclusion in a textbook.

The level of presentation is such that the book could be used as a senior or first-year graduate text. A course in mathematical logic would provide helpful but not necessary background. The reader having some familiarity with the vocabulary of sets and combinatorial mathematics should have no difficulty in following any of the arguments. Exercises are included at the end of each chapter. These serve three purposes: Some merely test the reader's comprehension of the material, others bring out important ideas not explicitly discussed in the text, and some would make suitable term projects. Those in the last category are identified by a dagger (†).

Each chapter also contains a section entitled Bibliographical and Historical Remarks. In these I have listed and briefly discussed some of the more important references related to the subject of the chapter. All of these references are then combined in an alphabetical list at the end of the book.

Many organizations and individuals have helped me immensely with this book. I want to acknowledge especially the primary sponsorship of the Information Systems Branch of the Office of Naval Research (contract N0014–68–C–0266). Additional support came from the Information Processing Techniques group of the Advanced Research Projects Agency through its sponsorship of artificial intelligence projects at the Stanford Research Institute and at Stanford University (where I spent part of the academic year 1968–69). The Artificial Intelligence Group at Stanford Research Institute, of which I am a member, provided the all-important base (physically and intellectually) to support this effort.

Dr. Peter Hart of Stanford Research Institute devoted a great amount of effort to reading and criticizing several versions of the manuscript. His help notably improved the clarity of the presentation. Talks with Professors Edward Feigenbaum and Arthur Samuel of the Computer Science Department of Stanford University helped me in deciding on the organization of the book. I also want to thank Professor David Luckham of Stanford for attempting to teach me logic. Many of the Computer Science Department graduate students at Stanford, especially Rev. J. Kenneth Siberz, S.J., suggested several improvements.

NILS J. NILSSON

CONTENTS

CHAPTER SIX
THEOREM-PROVING IN THE PREDICATE CALCULUS 156

CHAPTER SEVEN
APPLICATIONS OF THE PREDICATE CALCULUS IN PROBLEM SOLVING 187

PROBLEM-SOLVING
METHODS IN
ARTIFICIAL
INTELLIGENCE

CHAPTER ONE

INTRODUCTION

1-1   PROBLEM SOLVING AND ARTIFICIAL INTELLIGENCE

Many human activities, such as solving puzzles, playing games, doing mathematics, and even driving an automobile, are said to demand "intelligence." If computers could perform tasks such as these, then presumably these computers (together with their programs) would possess some degree of "artificial intelligence." Many experts believe that the artificial intelligence of computers will eventually surpass the natural intelligence of humans, although there is a growing realization that the processes required to perform even some of the most routine human tasks will have to be extremely complex. In this book we shall treat in detail some of the processes involved in intelligent *problem solving*.

Problem solving might seem to be an extremely vague topic, but nevertheless much of the artificial-intelligence research has concentrated on it. In its broadest sense, problem solving encompasses *all* of computer science because any computational task can be regarded as a problem to be solved. For our purposes, however, we desire a somewhat narrower definition, one that excludes routine computational methods such as those used in inverting a 50×50 matrix or in solving a set of linear differential equations.

If we examine those problem-solving methods studied in artificial-intelligence research we find that many of them use the notion of trial-and-error *search*. That is, these methods solve problems by searching for a solution in a *space* of possible solutions. The purpose of this book is to explain the major search-based problem-solving methods.

There are, of course, other important topics in artificial intelligence. Typical of those that have received special attention (besides problem solving) are:

Processing sensory data (especially visual images and speech sounds)

Sophisticated information storage and retrieval systems

Processing natural languages

Unfortunately, no one has yet been able to say anything very helpful about how these elements might fit together in a general "intelligence" (whatever that might be). In fact, upon close analysis, any supposed "fundamental" component of intelligent behavior seems to have aspects of other fundamental components within it. Thus, sensory perception may require sophisticated problem solving which may require efficient information retrieval which may require additional problem solving, and so on.

Our experience with these complex processes is still insufficient to propose a unified theory of the organization of intelligence. Indeed, at present there are no grounds for believing that there might be such a theory. Some researchers believe that intelligent behavior by computers can only be produced by a combination of specialized programs each incorporating many ad hoc tricks (or programming "hacks" as they are often called) and accessing encyclopedic data bases of well-indexed facts. But it is not our purpose here to take a position on this issue. Instead we shall describe those problem-solving techniques that appear to have some general utility.

1-2 PUZZLES AND GAMES AS EXAMPLE PROBLEMS

We have not yet been precise about what it means to solve a problem by search methods. Neither have we defined what we mean by a problem.

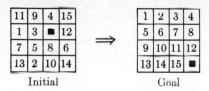

FIG. 1-1   *The* 15-*puzzle.*

Probably no one has produced a simple definition of the word *problem* that captures completely the intuitive meaning that we wish to use here. So rather than attempt a formal definition we shall begin our discussion by considering a typical example problem.

Puzzles and games provide a rich source of example problems useful for illustrating and testing problem-solving methods. Computer programs have been written to solve many types of puzzles that humans find difficult. Other programs have been written that beat expert human players at board games such as checkers and chess. As Minsky[1] says, "It is not that the games and mathematical problems are chosen because they are clear and simple; rather it is that *they give us, for the smallest initial structures, the greatest complexity,* so that one can engage some really formidable situations after a relatively minimal diversion into programming." Research on solving puzzles and games has generated and refined many problem-solving ideas that are also genuinely useful on less frivolous tasks.

A puzzle that we shall use frequently to illustrate problem-solving concepts is the 15-*puzzle.* The 15-puzzle consists of 15 numbered, movable tiles set in a 4×4 frame. One cell of the frame is always empty, making it possible to move an adjacent numbered tile into the empty cell, thus "moving" the empty cell also. Such a puzzle is illustrated in Fig. 1-1. Two configurations of tiles are given. Consider the problem of changing the initial configuration into the goal configuration. A solution to the problem is an appropriate sequence of moves, such as "Move tile 12 to the left, move tile 15 down, . . . , etc."

The 15-puzzle is an excellent example of one class of problem for which the methods of this book are best suited. In this problem there is a precisely defined initial situation and a precisely defined goal. There is also a set of operations or moves that change one situation into another. We shall begin by introducing some fundamental problem-solving concepts as they might be employed in finding a solution to the 15-puzzle.

---

[1] Minsky (1968), p. 12.

1-3 PROBLEM STATES AND OPERATORS

Perhaps the most straightforward approach to finding a solution to the 15-puzzle would be to try out various moves until we happened to produce the goal configuration. Such an attempt involves essentially a trial-and-error search. (We assume, of course, that such a search can be carried out conceptually, say with a computer, rather than by using an actual 15-puzzle.) Starting with the initial configuration, we might compute the configurations resulting from each of the applicable moves, then compute the next set of configurations produced by one more move, and so on until the goal configuration is reached.

To discuss solution methods of this sort it is helpful to introduce the notions of problem *states* and *operators*. For the 15-puzzle, a problem state is just a particular configuration of tiles. The initial and goal configurations are the initial and goal states, respectively. The *space* of states reachable from the initial state consists of all of those tile configurations that can be produced by moving tiles around in the legal manner. Many of the problems with which we shall be concerned will have extremely large (if not infinite) state spaces.[1]

An *operator* transforms one state into another state. The 15-puzzle is most naturally interpreted as having four operators corresponding to the moves: Move empty space (blank) to the left, move blank up, move blank to the right, and move blank down. Sometimes an operator cannot be applied to a state; thus "move blank to the right" cannot be applied to the goal state of Fig. 1-1. In our language of states and operators, a solution to a problem is a sequence of operators that transforms an initial state into a goal state.

It is useful to imagine the space of states reachable from the initial state as a graph containing nodes corresponding to the states. The nodes of this graph are linked together by arcs that correspond to the operators. We illustrate a small part of the graph for the 15-puzzle in Fig. 1-2. In this graph each node is labeled by the tile configuration it represents.

A solution to the 15-puzzle could be obtained by a *search* process that first applies operators to the initial state to produce new states, then applies operators to these, and so on until the goal state is produced. Methods for organizing such a search for the goal state are most conveniently explained in terms of the graph representation of Fig. 1-2.

Any problem-solution method that relies on these ideas of states and operators could be said to use a *state-space* approach to problem solving. We shall generally reserve the term to denote those methods

---

[1] In the 15-puzzle there are 16! different configurations of the 15 tiles and the blank space. One-half of these (or approximately 10.5×10^{12}) are reachable from a given initial configuration.

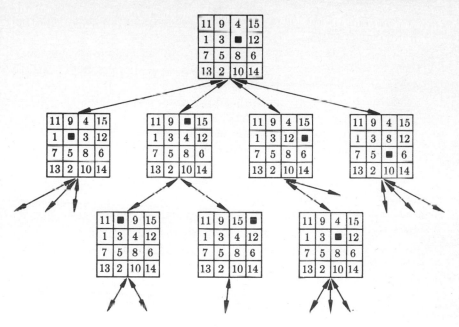

FIG. 1-2 *A portion of the graph for the 15-puzzle.*

that build up trial sequences of operators incrementally by starting with some initial operator and then adding one operator at a time until the goal state is reached.

We shall return to discuss state-space methods further in the next two chapters.

1-4 REDUCING PROBLEMS TO SUBPROBLEMS

A somewhat more sophisticated problem-solving approach involves the notion of *subproblems*. In this approach, an analysis is made of the original problem in order to produce a set of subproblems such that solutions to some particular subset of the subproblems would imply a solution to the original problem. For example, consider the problem of driving an automobile from Palo Alto, California, to Cambridge, Massachusetts. This problem could be reduced to, say, the following subproblems:

Subproblem 1   Drive from Palo Alto to San Francisco.

Subproblem 2   Drive from San Francisco to Chicago, Illinois.

Subproblem 3   Drive from Chicago to Albany, New York.

Subproblem 4   Drive from Albany to Cambridge.

Here a solution to all four of the subproblems would produce a solution to the original problem.

Each of the subproblems can be solved by any method whatsoever. They might be attacked by state-space methods or they themselves might be analyzed to produce sub-subproblems and so on. If one continues to break the resulting subproblems down into smaller problems, eventually some *primitive* problems will be reached whose solutions are regarded as trivial.

Any method that solves problems by generating and then solving subproblems will be said to employ a *problem-reduction* approach. Note that, strictly speaking, the state-space approach can be regarded as a trivial case of a problem-reduction approach: Each operator application reduces a problem to a slightly simpler subproblem. Usually, though, we shall be concerned with cases in which the subproblems created by the problem-reduction approach are less trivially obtained.

It is important to note that trial-and-error search still plays an important role in the problem-reduction approach. At any stage there may be several alternative sets of subproblems to which some given problem may be reduced. Since some of these sets might not ultimately lead to a final solution, one typically needs to search through a space of subproblem sets in order to solve the original problem. We shall return to discuss problem-reduction methods in Chapters 4 and 5.

1-5 THE USE OF LOGIC IN PROBLEM SOLVING

Frequently the solution to a problem either requires or is aided by a certain amount of logical analysis. Sometimes such an analysis shows that certain problems are insoluble. In the 15-puzzle, for example, it is possible to *prove*[1] that one cannot produce the goal configuration

1	2	3	4
5	6	7	8
9	10	11	12
13	14	15	■

[1] This contention follows from a logical analysis of the 15-puzzle that reveals that the set of all configurations can be partitioned into two disjoint subsets, A and B. No member of A can be transformed into a member of B and vice versa.

from the initial configuration

15	14	13	12
11	10	9	8
7	6	5	4
3	2	1	■

The need to perform logical deductions can arise in both the state-space and problem-reduction approaches. In the state-space approach, the test used to determine whether or not a state is a goal state might require logical deductions. Additionally, one may have to make logical deductions to determine which operators are applicable in a given state. As we have already seen, sometimes a problem can be proven to be insoluble. In the problem-reduction approach, such a proof would allow us to eliminate futile attempts to solve insoluble subproblems. In addition to these applications, we also desire to be able to solve problems which themselves are problems of proof. For example, we may want to find a proof for some mathematical theorem expressed in a formal system, such as the first-order predicate calculus.

Thus a complete treatment of problem-solving techniques must include a discussion of mechanical proof-finding methods. Some of these methods use search strategies that are similar to those we shall be discussing in connection with the state-space and problem-reduction approaches. Although many choices of logical formalism exist, we shall discuss the recently developed resolution theorem-proving techniques for first-order predicate calculus and their applications to problem solving. These will be explained in Chapters 6, 7, and 8.

In our discussion of automatic theorem proving we shall point out that even nonmathematical problems can be formulated as theorems to be proved. Many of the puzzles that we shall consider as well as many real-life problems requiring common-sense analysis can in principle be posed in a logical formalism and then solved by proof-finding techniques. The use of formal logic and proof-finding methods encourages one to think of a truly "general purpose" problem solver. Such a problem solver could be told new information merely by adding axioms to its memory rather than by reprogramming it. It could solve problems in a wide variety of domains since logical formalisms exist that are sufficiently general to express any information and any problem.

1-6 TWO ELEMENTS OF PROBLEM SOLVING: REPRESENTATION AND SEARCH

Each of the approaches to problem solving that we have mentioned requires some sort of search for a solution. This book is largely about how to conduct these searches as efficiently as possible. But before a search process can begin, the problem must be set up, either in a state-space or problem-reduction formulation or as a theorem to be proved. Usually one applauds a human problem solver not for conducting a fast and orderly search through all solution possibilities, but for looking at the problem in such a clever way that its solution seems elegantly simple.

In the next chapter we shall consider the problem of setting up or representing a problem so that it can be solved by a state-space approach. We shall see that there are alternative representations for the same problem, some with much smaller state spaces than others. Since even the most efficient search methods will be inadequate if the space to be searched is too large, it is important to be able to represent a problem in as economical a way as possible. The problem of representation is common to any problem-solving approach, but unfortunately, research in artificial intelligence has not yet produced any general automatic method for skillfully formulating problems. So although there are two aspects to automatic problem solving—representation and search—this book must of necessity be concerned mainly with search.

1-7 BIBLIOGRAPHICAL AND HISTORICAL REMARKS

The "intelligence" of computers

The question of whether or not machines can (or ever will be able to) "think" still provokes lively debate even among those who concede that man himself is a machine. Turing (1950) disposes of many of the standard arguments against intelligent machines. To decide whether or not a machine is intelligent, he proposes what has come to be called the *Turing test*.

Selfridge and Kelly (1962) debate about the magnitude of the practical problems in creating intelligent machines after agreeing that there are no known theoretical barriers. Hubert Dreyfus (1965) stated that digital computers arc *inherently* incapable of such necessities of intelligence as "fringe consciousness" and "perspicuous grouping." His arguments are systematically refuted by Papert (1968).

Overviews of artificial intelligence

Attempts to organize the field of artificial intelligence have never been wholly successful. The subtopics of search, pattern recognition, learning, problem solving, and induction have been suggested by Minsky (1961a) in an important survey article. This breakdown is still useful even though its taxonomic value is challenged by the plethora of statements in the literature that have the form "The problem of X is basically a problem of Y," where X and Y could be any pair of Minsky's subtopics. More recently, Minsky (1968) has written another thoughtful article on the foundations of artificial intelligence and concludes that a major problem is that of acquiring, maintaining, and accessing a large knowledge base.

Approaches to artificial intelligence

In attempting to build intelligent machines one naturally asks "What is the secret of animal intelligence?" People have had a variety of adventures pursuing this question but no one has yet found the secret. Rosenblatt (1962) suggested brain models called *perceptrons;* these were networks of artificial neurons based on the neuron models of McCulloch and Pitts (1943). The study of perceptrons stimulated early pattern-recognition research and led to some elegant mathematical results on computational geometry by Minsky and Papert (1969). The complex processes of intelligence, however, were beyond the power of these simple perceptron models.

Another biologically based strategy was the rather grandiose attempt to simulate evolution itself. Since evolution produced intelligent man in two billion years or so, why not simulate the processes of evolution at high speed on the computer? Fogel et al. (1966) describe experiments involving the production of many generations of finite-state machines using the strategies of mutation and selective survival. Although this technique may be capable of condensing the first few million years of evolution to a few days of computer time, it seems that the important middle and later stages of evolution involve structures already so complex (though not yet "intelligent") that their evolution cannot be speeded up by computer simulation. Thus the "artificial evolution" approach has not succeeded in producing adequately complex machines either.

Another way to learn about intelligence from animals is to study their behavior, particularly the problem-solving behavior of man. Travis (1963, 1967) discusses the role of introspection in the design of problem solvers. Newell, Shaw, and Simon (1959) describe a "general problem solver" that is supposed to attack problems in much the same way that humans do. A rich source of ideas about how humans attack problems is found in Polya (1957).

In the problem-solving methods based on analysis of human behavior, we find that trial-and-error search at some level plays a key role. Campbell (1960) calls the *unguided* search process a "blind-variation-and-selective-survival process." He concludes:

> A blind-variation-and-selective-survival process is fundamental to all inductive achievements, to all genuine increases in knowledge, to all increases in fit of system to environment.

> The processes which shortcut the full blind-variation-and-selective-survival process are in themselves inductive achievements containing wisdom about the environment achieved originally by a blind-variation-and-selective survival process.

> In addition, such substitute processes contain in their own operation a blind-variation-and-selective-survival process at some level.

We agree with Campbell about the ultimate primacy of search. The real trick in designing an efficient automatic problem solver is to search at the highest level permitted by the available information about the problem and about how it might be solved. Thus in this book we are primarily concerned with search techniques and with how they can be made more efficient by using all available information.

Problem-solving methods

There have been only a few attempts to study problem-solving processes abstractly in order to catalog the different methods and to deduce general properties of these methods. In this book we attempt to isolate some of the major problem-solving concepts and to present some sort of coherent discussion about them. A slightly different way of organizing a discussion of problem-solving methods is suggested by Newell (1969). The organization of the present book has been much influenced by a series of difficult but worthwhile papers by Amarel (1965, 1967, 1969). A paper by Sandewall (1969) formalizes some of the same problem-solving ideas that we treat in this book. A book by Banerji (1969) contains a highly formal treatment of problem solving and game playing.

The state-space approach to problem solving gets its name from the use of state spaces for similar purposes in control theory. It is also used extensively in operations research. Some of the state-space search methods that we shall be discussing later are identical to those called *branch and bound methods* in operations research. Lawler and Wood (1966) give a survey of branch and bound methods and their applications.

Our predilection to distinguish between state-space and problem-reduction methods derives from the different search strategies used by each method. The distinction is precisely the same as that made by Amarel (1967) between "production type" and "reduction type" methods. Slagle (1963a) also finds the problem-reduction formulation useful in describing his program for symbolic integration. In our opinion, the operation of the general problem solver (GPS) of Newell and his coworkers [Ernst and Newell (1969)] can be understood most clearly if it is described as a problem-reduction type problem solver.

The use of formal methods for making logical deductions in automatic problem solving can be traced to the "advice-taker" memoranda of McCarthy (1958, 1963). The advice taker was to be a system that deduced the solutions to problems from a large set of axioms representing the problem solver's knowledge base. It could be given "advice" merely by adding new axioms. Some early work related to this idea was undertaken by Black (1964). We shall mention some of the later work in this field in Chapter 7.

Some excellent ideas on solving large combinatorial problems have been suggested by Shen Lin (1965, 1970). Lin presents some powerful strategies for breaking problems into subproblems.

Applications of problem-solving programs

It is fair to ask whether or not any of these methods that work so well on puzzles and games has been usefully employed on "real" problems. State-space methods have been employed in the solution of operations research problems such as the well-known traveling-salesman problem. An example is a state-space method proposed in a Ph.D. dissertation by Shapiro (1966) and discussed by Bellmore and Nemhauser (1968). Although the traveling-salesman problem may appear as frivolous as do puzzles and games, it is a model for problems of economic importance in scheduling and production design.

Other applications of the state-space method have been made in the control of remote manipulators by Whitney (1969), in sequential decoding by Jelinek (1969), and in chromosome matching by Montanari (1970). Problem-reduction methods have been employed in a system that performs symbolic integration [Slagle (1963a)] and in a system that analyzes mass spectrograph data [Feigenbaum, Buchanan, and Lederberg (1971)].

Important source materials for artificial intelligence

Artificial intelligence is a much-surveyed field, and there are many bibliographies. An early annotated one is that of Minsky (1961b). Later surveys by Feigenbaum (1963) and Solomonoff (1966) include many additional references. A recent survey by Feigenbaum (1969) lists more articles and also speculates about the future of the field.

A volume that is often referenced because it contains many of the early papers is entitled "Computers and Thought," edited by Feigenbaum and Feldman. D. Michie and others have edited a series of books called "Machine Intelligence." These contain papers delivered at the Machine Intelligence Workshops held annually in Edinburgh. Another important book is called "Semantic Information Processing," edited by Minsky; it contains complete versions of several Ph.D. dissertations dealing with language processing and "understanding."

Artificial Intelligence is a journal devoted exclusively to artificial intelligence; it began publishing in 1970. Also, the *Journal of the Association for Computing Machinery* occasionally publishes articles on artificial intelligence subjects.

In the United States, artificial intelligence activities are coordinated through a Special Interest Group on Artificial Intelligence (SIGART) of the Association for Computing Machinery (ACM). SIGART publishes a newsletter that occasionally contains reference material not published elsewhere. The Artificial Intelligence and Simulation of Behavior (AISB) group of the British Computer Society publishes a European newsletter.

Problem-solving programs have sharpened their techniques on a variety of puzzles and games. Some good general books of puzzles are those of Martin Gardner (1959, 1961), who edits a puzzle column in *The Scientific American.* Also see the books of puzzles by Dudeney (1958, 1967), who was a famous British puzzle inventor. A puzzle book by Schuh (1968) specifically mentions the strategies of trial-and-error search and problem reduction. The 15-puzzle has a long history and is discussed by Martin Gardner (1964, 1965a,b,c) and by Ball (1931).

For completeness, we shall occasionally reference unpublished memoranda and reports in this book. The authors of such material will sometimes provide copies upon request.

PROBLEMS

1-1   Read the article by Newell (1969) and compare his organization of problem-solving methods with the one presented in this chapter. Which of Newell's methods can be described as state-space search methods? For these, what are the states and operators?

1-2 Many problem solving activities involve performing an incremental computation and then testing to see if the problem is completed. If it is not completed, an additional increment is performed, and so on. An example is the following process for adding a list of numbers:

Compute $\sum_{i=1}^{n} x_i$

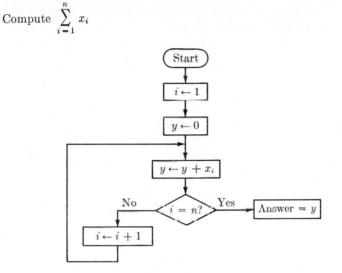

Can this process be represented as a state-space problem-solving method? If so, what are the states and operators? Is there any trial-and-error search involved in this process? (Might the process ever need to back up and follow an alternative path to the goal?)

1-3 List some everyday mental activities that are characterized by some sort of trial-and-error search. (Examples might be deciding what to wear, what to prepare for dinner, etc.)

1-4 Read the paper on the Logic Theory Machine [Newell, Shaw, and Simon (1957)] and describe its operation both from a state-space and from a problem-reduction viewpoint.

REFERENCES

Amarel, S. (1965): Problem Solving Procedures for Efficient Syntactic Analysis, *ACM 20th Nat. Conf.* [Also printed as *Sci. Rept.* no. 1, AFOSR Contr. no. AF49(638)–1184, 1968.]
———— (1967): An Approach to Heuristic Problem-Solving and Theorem Proving in the Propositional Calculus, in J. Hart and S. Takasu (eds.), "Systems and Computer Science," University of Toronto Press, 1967.
———— (1969): On the Representation of Problems and Goal Directed Procedures for Computers, *Commun. Am. Soc. Cybernetics*, vol. 1, no. 2, 1969.

Ball, W. (1931): "Mathematical Recreations and Essays," 10th ed., Macmillan & Co., Ltd., London, 1931. (15-puzzle, pp. 224–228; Tower-of-Hanoi, pp. 228–229.)

Banerji, R. (1969): "Theory of Problem Solving: An Approach to Artificial Intelligence," American Elsevier Publishing Company, Inc., New York, 1969.

Bellmore, M. and G. Nemhauser (1968): The Traveling Salesman Problem: A Survey, *Operations Res.*, vol. 16, no. 3, pp. 538–558, May–June 1968.

Black, F. (1964): A Deductive Question-Answering System, Ph. D. dissertation, Harvard, June 1964. Reprinted in M. Minsky (ed.), "Semantic Information Processing," pp. 354–402, The M.I.T. Press, Cambridge, Mass., 1968.

Campbell, D. (1960): Blind Variation and Selective Survival as a General Strategy in Knowledge-Processes, in M. Yovits and S. Cameron (eds.), "Self-Organizing Systems," pp. 205–231, Pergamon Press, New York, 1960.

Collins, N. and D. Michie (eds.) (1967): "Machine Intelligence 1," American Elsevier Publishing Company, Inc., New York, 1967.

Dale, E. and D. Michie (eds.) (1968): "Machine Intelligence 2," American Elsevier Publishing Company, Inc., New York, 1968.

Dreyfus, H. (1965): Alchemy and Artificial Intelligence, Rand Corporation Paper P3244 (AD 625 719), December 1965.

Dudeney, H. (1958): "The Canterbury Puzzles," Dover Publications, Inc., New York, 1958. (Originally published in 1907.)

———— (1967): "536 Puzzles and Curious Problems," Martin Gardner (ed.), Charles Scribner's Sons, New York, 1967. (A collection from two of Dudeney's books: "Modern Puzzles," 1926, and "Puzzles and Curious Problems," 1931.)

Ernst, G. and A. Newell (1969): "GPS: A Case Study in Generality and Problem Solving," ACM Monograph Series, Academic Press, Inc., New York, 1969.

Feigenbaum, E. (1963): Artificial Intelligence Research, *IEEE Trans. Info. Theory*, vol. IT-9, no. 4, pp. 248–261, October 1963.

———— (1969): Artificial Intelligence: Themes in the Second Decade, in A. J. H. Morrell (ed.), "Information Processing 68," vol. 2, pp. 1008–1022, North-Holland Publishing Company, Amsterdam, 1969. (Also printed as *Stanford University Artificial Intelligence Project* Memo no. 67, Aug. 15, 1968.)

————, B. Buchanan, and J. Lederberg (1971): Generality and Problem Solving: A Case Study Using the DENDRAL Program, in B. Meltzer and D. Michie (eds.), "Machine Intelligence 6," American Elsevier Publishing Company, Inc., New York, 1971.

———— and J. Feldman (1963): "Computers and Thought," McGraw-Hill Book Company, New York, 1963.

Fogel, L., A. Owens, and M. Walsh (1966): "Artificial Intelligence Through Simulated Evolution," John Wiley & Sons, Inc., New York, 1966.

Gardner, M. (1959): "The Scientific American Book of Mathematical Puzzles and Diversions," Simon and Schuster, New York, 1959.

———— (1961): "The Second Scientific American Book of Mathematical Puzzles and Diversions," Simon and Schuster, New York, 1961.

———— (1964, 1965a,b,c): Mathematical Games, *Sci. Am.*, vol. 210, no. 2, pp. 122–130, February 1964; vol. 212, no. 3, pp. 112–117, March 1965; vol. 212, no. 6, pp. 120–124, June 1965; vol. 213, no. 3, pp. 222–236, September 1965.

Jelinek, F. (1969): Fast Sequential Decoding Algorithm Using a Stack, *IBM J. Res. Develop.*, vol. 13, no. 6, pp. 675–685, November 1969.

Lawler, E. and D. Wood (1966): Branch and Bound Methods: A Survey, *Operations Res.*, vol. 14, no. 4, pp. 699–719, July–August 1966.

Lin, Shen (1965): Computer Solutions of the Traveling Salesman Problem, *Bell Sys. Tech. J.*, vol. XLIV, no. 10, December 1965.

———— (1970): Heuristic Techniques for Solving Large Combinatorial Problems on a Computer, in R. Banerji and M. Mesarovic (eds.), "Theoretical Approaches to Non-Numerical Problem-Solving," pp. 410–418, Springer-Verlag New York, Inc., New York, 1970.

McCarthy, J. (1958): Programs with Common Sense, in "Mechanization of Thought Processes," vol. I, pp. 77–84, *Proc. Symp. Natl. Phys. Lab.*, London, Nov. 24–27, 1958. Reprinted in M. Minsky (ed.), "Semantic Information Processing," pp. 403–410, The M.I.T. Press, Cambridge, Mass., 1968.

———— (1963): Situations, Actions and Causal Laws, *Stanford University Artificial Intelligence Project Memo. No. 2*, 1963. Reprinted in M. Minsky, (ed.), "Semantic Information Processing," pp. 410–418, The M.I.T. Press, Cambridge, Mass., 1968.

McCulloch, W. S. and W. Pitts (1943): A Logical Calculus of the Ideas Immanent in Neural Nets, *Bull. Math. Biophys.*, vol. 5, pp. 115–137, 1943.

Meltzer, B. and D. Michie (eds.) (1969): "Machine Intelligence 4," American Elsevier Publishing Company, Inc., New York, 1969.

———— and ———— (eds.) (1970): "Machine Intelligence 5," American Elsevier Publishing Company, Inc., New York, 1970.

———— and ———— (eds.) (1971): "Machine Intelligence 6," American Elsevier Publishing Company, Inc., New York, 1971.

Michie, D. (ed.) (1968): "Machine Intelligence 3," American Elsevier Publishing Company, Inc., New York, 1968.

Minsky, M. (1961a): Steps Toward Artificial Intelligence, *Proc. IRE*, vol. 49, pp. 8–30, January 1961. Reprinted in E. Feigenbaum and J. Feldman (eds.), "Computers and Thought," pp. 406–450, McGraw-Hill Book Company, New York, 1963.

———— (1961b): A Selected Descriptor-Indexed Bibliography to the Literature on Artificial Intelligence, *IRE Trans. Human Factors Electron.*, HFE-2, pp. 39–55, March 1961. A revision is reprinted in E. Feigenbaum and J. Feldman (eds.), "Computers and Thought," pp. 453–523, McGraw-Hill Book Company, New York, 1963.

———— (ed.) (1968): "Semantic Information Processing," The M.I.T. Press, Cambridge, Mass., 1968.

———— and S. Papert (1969): "Perceptrons: An Introduction to Computational Geometry," The M.I.T. Press, Cambridge, Mass., 1969.

Montanari, U. (1970): Heuristically Guided Search and Chromosome Matching, *Artificial Intelligence*, vol. 1, no. 4, 1970.

Newell, A. (1969): Heuristic Programming: Ill-Structured Problems, in J. Aronofsky (ed.), "Progress in Operations Research," vol. 3, John Wiley & Sons, Inc., New York, 1969.

———, J. Shaw, and H. Simon (1959): Report on a General Problem-Solving Program, *Proc. Intern. Conf. Inform. Process.*, UNESCO House, Paris, pp. 256–264, 1959.

Papert, S. (1968): The Artificial Intelligence of Hubert L. Dreyfus. A Budget of Fallacies, *M.I.T. Artificial Intelligence Memo no.* 54, January 1968.

Polya, G. (1957): "How to Solve It," 2d ed., Doubleday & Company, Inc., Garden City, N.Y., 1957.

Rosenblatt, F. (1962): "Principles of Neurodynamics," Spartan Books, New York, 1962.

Sandewall, E. (1969): Concepts and Methods for Heuristic Search, in Donald E. Walker and Lewis M. Norton (eds.), *Proc. Intern. Joint Conf. Artificial Intelligence*, Washington, D.C., 1969.

Schuh, F. (1968): "The Master Book of Mathematical Recreations," W. J. Thieme & Cie, Zutphen, 1943 (in Dutch); English translation, F. Göbel, Dover Publications, Inc., New York, 1968.

Selfridge, O. and J. Kelly, Jr. (1962): Sophistication in Computers: a Disagreement, *IRE Trans. Inform. Theory*, vol. IT-8, no. 2, pp. 78–80, February 1962.

Shapiro, D. (1966): "Algorithms for the Solution of the Optimal Cost Traveling Salesman Problem," Sc.D. thesis, Washington University, St. Louis, Mo., 1966.

Slagle, J. (1963a): A Heuristic Program that Solves Symbolic Integration Problems in Freshman Calculus, *J. ACM*, vol. 10, no. 4, pp. 507–520, October 1963. [Also in E. Feigenbaum and J. Feldman (eds.), "Computers and Thought," pp. 191–203, McGraw-Hill Book Company, New York, 1963.]

Solomonoff, R. (1966): Some Recent Work in Artificial Intelligence, *Proc. IEEE*, vol. 54, no. 112, December 1966.

Travis, L. (1963): The Value of Introspection to the Designer of Mechanical Problem-Solvers, *Behav. Sci.*, vol. 8, no. 3, pp. 227–233, July 1963.

Travis, L. (1967): Psychology and Bionics: Many Old Problems and a Few New Machines, *Conf. Record 1967 Winter Conv. Aerospace Electron. Sys. (WINCON)*, IEEE Publication No. 10-C-42, vol. VI, February 1967.

Turing A. M. (1950): Computing Machinery and Intelligence, *Mind*, vol. 59, pp. 433–460, October 1950. Reprinted in E. Feigenbaum and J. Feldman (eds.), "Computers and Thought," pp. 11–35, McGraw-Hill Book Company, New York 1963.

Whitney, D. (1969): State Space Models of Remote Manipulation Tasks, in Donald E. Walker and Lewis M. Norton (eds.), *Proc. Intern. Joint Conf. Artificial Intelligence*, pp. 495–507, Washington, D.C., 1969.

CHAPTER TWO

STATE-SPACE REPRESENTATIONS

2-1 STATE DESCRIPTIONS

In the last chapter we introduced the concepts of *states* and *operators*. Here we shall elaborate on these ideas and present several example state-space formulations of problems.

In setting up a state-space formulation of a problem, we must first have some idea of what the states of the problem are. In the 15-puzzle, tile configurations were the obvious choice. But a problem-solving process that finds a solution without actually moving the physical tiles around must work with some *description* of the configurations rather than with the configurations themselves. Thus an important part of any state-space problem formulation is the selection of some particular *form* of description for the states of the problem.

Virtually any kind of data structure can be used to describe states. These include symbol strings, vectors, two-dimensional arrays, trees, and lists. The form of the data structure selected often bears a resemblance to some physical property of the problem being solved. Thus in the 15-puzzle, a 4×4 array might be a natural state-description form. One must also take care to select a state-description form that permits easy computations on it by the operators that transform one state description into another.

We shall illustrate the selection of a state-description form with a simple example. Consider the problem of transforming the algebraic expression $(AB + CD)/BC$ into the simpler expression $A/C + D/B$. The problem states here obviously ought to be algebraic expressions, but we must still decide on the form of the state description.

A commonly used description employs binary trees. The non-terminal nodes of the description tree represent the arithmetic signs $(+, -, \times,$ and $\div)$, and the terminal nodes represent the variable or constant symbols (A,B,C,D) appearing in the expression. Thus a description tree for $(AB + CD)/BC$ would be

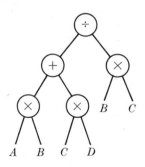

Where the left-hand branch out of a $\div$ node represents the numerator and the right-hand branch represents the denominator. Applications of the laws of algebra (the state-space operators) would transform this state description into other descriptions. Our problem is to transform it into a state described by the following tree:

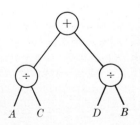

Another common description form is a linear string. A possible string description for $(AB + CD)/BC$ is $\div+\times AB \times CD \times BC$. Here the arithmetic operators ($\div$, $+$, and $\times$) are called *prefix operators* because they precede their operands in the string. Because we know that each of these operators takes precisely two operands, punctuation of the string is not necessary. The operands of the $+$ symbol in the string, for example, must be the two immediately following substrings that describe well-formed algebraic expressions: $\times AB$ and $\times CD$. Using the string-form description, we can state our problem as one of transforming the string $\div+\times AB \times CD \times BC$ into the string $+\div AC \div DB$.

2-2 OPERATORS

Operators change one state into another. Thus they can be considered functions[1] whose domain and range are sets of states. Since our problem-solving processes will be working with state descriptions, we shall assume that the operators are functions of these descriptions whose values are new descriptions. We could, of course, define our operator functions by a table that paired an "output" state description with every possible "input" state description. For large problems a table is obviously impractical, so we shall generally assume that the operators are *computations* that transform state descriptions into other state descriptions.

When the state descriptions are in the form of strings, we have a very convenient method for representing operator computations. This method uses the idea of *rewriting rules* (sometimes called *productions*).

A set of rewriting rules defines the ways in which one string can be transformed into another one. Rewriting rules are all of the form $S_i \rightarrow S_j$, meaning that the string S_i can be transformed into the string S_j. An example of a rewriting rule is:

$$A\$ \rightarrow B\$$$

meaning that the symbol A occurring as the first symbol of a string may be replaced by the symbol B. The $\$$ sign stands for an arbitrary substring (including the empty string). In this rewriting rule, the $\$$ sign is used to indicate that the rest of the string (whatever it is) following the A is not altered when the A is replaced by the B.

Several $\$$ signs may be used in rewriting rules to indicate several different substrings. Thus we have the following additional examples

---

[1] Actually they are partial functions, since an operator may not be applicable in all states.

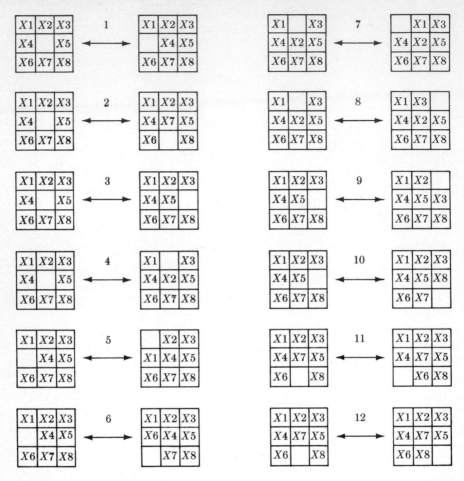

FIG. 2-1 *Rewriting rules for the 8-puzzle.*

of possible rewriting rules:

1. $A\$A \to A$ (a string beginning and ending with A may be replaced by a single occurrence of A)

2. $\$_1 BAB\$_2 \to \$_1 BB\$_2$ (a single A occurring between two B's may be eliminated)

3. $\$_1\$_2\$_3 \to \$_1\$_2\$_2\$_3$ (any substring may be replicated)

4. $\$_1\$_2\$_2\$_3 \to \$_1\$_2\$_3$ (any adjacent repetition of a substring may be eliminated)

Using the last two of these rules, for example, we can convert the string $ABCBABC$ into the string ABC as follows:

$$ABCBABC \xrightarrow{3} ABABCBABC \xrightarrow{4} ABABC \xrightarrow{4} ABC$$

Often a rewriting rule can be applied to a string in many different ways. Thus in the example above, rule 4 cannot be applied to *ABCBADC* at all, but rule 3 can be applied in several ways. It is, of course, a *specific* application of a rewriting rule that corresponds to an operator. Because a single rewriting rule can be used to represent a large number of different operators, rewriting rules are used frequently in problem-solving methods.

The representation of operators by rewriting rules does not necessarily have to be limited to situations in which states are described by strings. Similar ideas can be used in the 15-puzzle, for example, where a natural state description is a 4×4 array. Let us illustrate this generalized notion of rewriting rules by considering the 8-puzzle, a simplified version of the 15-puzzle. In the 8-puzzle, 8 numbered tiles are set in a 3×3 array.

One way to represent the legal moves in the 8-puzzle is by a set of rewriting rules on arrays. These rules define the ways in which 3×3 arrays can be transformed into other 3×3 arrays. A set of rewriting rules for the 8-puzzle is shown in Fig. 2-1. To save space, each rule is really two (as shown by the double arrowheads); in each case either the left-hand expression can be replaced by the right-hand one, or vice versa. For each rewriting rule, a legal move is obtained by assigning numbers 1, 2, . . . , 8 to the variables X_1, X_2, . . . , X_8 on either side of the arrow (with no $X_i = X_j$). Thus

2	1	6
4	■	8
7	5	3

can be transformed to

2	1	6
4	8	■
7	5	3

by application of rule **3**.

2-3 GOAL STATES

Our procedures for searching the state space will all involve generating new state descriptions from old ones and then checking the new ones to see if they describe the goal state. Often this check will merely amount to testing to see if a state description matches a given goal state description, but sometimes more complex goal tests must be made. For example, in the 15-puzzle the goal might be to produce a configuration of tiles in which no tile having a number greater than 12 is in the top two rows. In any case the *property* that a state description must satisfy in order that it describe a goal must be described precisely.

In certain optimization problems it is not sufficient merely to find any path to a goal; it is also necessary to find some path optimizing some criterion (such as minimizing the number of operator applications). Such problems are most easily handled by making sure that search does not terminate until an optimal solution is found. The state-space search methods to be discussed in the next chapter are capable of finding optimal solutions.

Thus we see that to complete a state-space representation of a problem, we must specify three things: (*a*) the form of the state description and, in particular, the description of the initial state, (*b*) the set of operators and their effects on state descriptions, and (*c*) the properties of a goal state description.

We have already mentioned that it is useful to conceive of a state space as a directed graph. The graph representation is particularly useful for discussing the various methods for searching a state space. In the next section we shall introduce some appropriate graph terminology.

2-4 GRAPH NOTATION

In Chapter 1, we used a graph to illustrate the state space for the 15-puzzle. Our discussion of graphs so far has been intuitive, and in this section we shall introduce some useful formal notation about graphs.

A graph consists of a (not necessarily finite) set of *nodes*. Certain pairs of nodes are connected by *arcs*, and these arcs are directed from one member of the pair to the other. Such a graph is called a *directed graph*. If an arc is directed from node n_i to node n_j, then node n_j is said to be a *successor* of node n_i, and node n_i is said to be a *parent* of node n_j. A pair of nodes may be successors of each other; in this case the pair of directed arcs is sometimes replaced by an *edge*. When a graph is used to represent a state space, the nodes of the graph are labeled by state descriptions, and the arcs are labeled by operators.

A sequence of nodes $n_{i1}, n_{i2}, \ldots, n_{ik}$ with each n_{ij} a successor of n_{ij-1} for $j = 2, \ldots, k$ is called a *path* of length k from node n_{i1} to node n_{ik}. If a path exists from node n_i to node n_j, then node n_j is said to be *accessible* from node n_i or a *descendant* of node n_i. In this case we also say that node n_i is an *ancestor* of node n_j. We see that the problem of finding a sequence of operators transforming one state into another is equivalent to the problem of finding a path in a graph.

Often it will be convenient to assign costs to arcs, to represent the cost of applying the corresponding operator. We shall use the notation $c(n_i,n_j)$ to denote the cost of an arc directed from node n_i to n_j. The cost of a path between two nodes is then the sum of the costs of all of the arcs connecting the nodes on the path. In optimization problems, we shall be wanting to find that path having minimal cost between two nodes.

In the simplest type of problem, we desire to find a path (perhaps having minimal cost) between a specified node s (representing the initial state) and another specified node t (representing the goal state). Two obvious elaborations of this simplest problem are:

Find a path between a node s and *any* member of a set of nodes $\{t_i\}$.

Find a path between any member of a set $\{s_i\}$ and any member of a set $\{t_i\}$.

The set $\{t_i\}$, called the goal set, does not have to be given explicitly. Instead it might be implicitly defined by the properties possessed by the corresponding goal-state descriptions.

A graph may be specified either explicitly or implicitly. In an explicit specification, the nodes and arcs (with associated costs) are explicitly given (say) in a table. The table might list every node in the graph, its successors, and the costs of the associated arcs. Obviously, an explicit specification is impractical for large graphs and impossible for those having an infinite set of nodes.

In an implicit specification, a finite set $\{s_i\}$ of nodes is given as *start* nodes. In addition, a *successor operator* Γ is given that can be applied to any node to give *all* of the successors of that node and the costs of the associated arcs. (In our state-space terminology, the successor operator is defined in terms of the set of operators applicable to a given state description.) The application of Γ to the members of $\{s_i\}$, to their successors, and so on indefinitely, then makes explicit the graph implicitly defined by Γ and $\{s_i\}$.

The process of searching through a state space for a solution sequence of operators then corresponds to making explicit a sufficient portion of an implicit graph to include a goal node. Searching graphs in this manner is therefore a central element of state-space problem solving.

We shall postpone until the next chapter our discussion of graph-searching techniques.

2-5 REPRESENTATION OF STATE SPACES BY NONDETERMINISTIC PROGRAMS[1]

The process for generating a state space can be represented by the flow chart in Fig. 2-2. There we use the notation **x** and **y** to represent arbitrary data structures. Notice that the assignment statement "Set **y** to *some* member of the set $\Gamma(\mathbf{y})$ of successors of **y**" is *nondeterministic* in the sense that, at execution, *any* member of $\Gamma(\mathbf{y})$ may be selected. The (perhaps infinite) set of all possible executions of the program represented by this flow chart then encompasses the complete state space. (In this formulation, the states are described by the possible values of the program variable **y**, which may be arbitrarily complex data structures.)

Programs that have assignment (and other) statements allowing nondetermined choices at execution time have been called nondeterministic[2] programs. It is often convenient to represent implicitly the state space of a problem by some nondeterministic program flowchart. The flowchart may be as simple as the canonical version of Fig. 2-2 or it

---

[1] This section may be omitted in a first reading.
[2] The phrase *nondeterministic* as used here is not at all synonymous with stochastic; it does not imply the operation of any chance device.

FIG. 2-2 *Representation of a state-space by a nondeterministic program.*

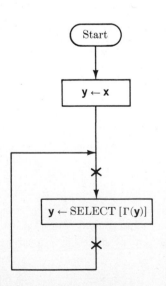

INITIALIZATION   A program variable **y** (ranging over state descriptions) is set equal to an input data structure **x** describing the initial state

ASSIGNMENT   The new value of the program variable **y** is set equal to some member of the set $\Gamma(\mathbf{y})$ of the successors of the old value of **y**

may be in a more complex form with several nondeterministic as well as deterministic elements.

[Strictly speaking, in our flow chart of Fig. 2-2, we should have provided for termination conditions and disposed of other fine points such as a test to see if $\Gamma(\mathbf{y})$ is empty or not. Termination checks might occur at either of the points marked "X" in the flow chart. In the next chapter we shall define precise algorithms for generating and searching the state space.]

In general, nondeterministic programs involve broadening the definitions of the conventional assignment and branching operations of deterministic programs. We have already seen how a nondeterministic assignment statement can be used. This type of assignment statement, called a *SELECT statement*, is represented in flow charts by the notation:

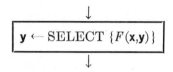

Here, the data structure **x** is the input to the program. The function F is a total function mapping the cross domain of **x** and **y** into a nonempty subset of the domain of **y**. We use the notation $\{F\}$ to represent this subset, and SELECT $\{F\}$ selects one member (any member) of the subset. This member is then assigned as the new value of **y**. (Note that we allow the assignment to depend on the value of the input variable **x** as well as on the present value of the program variable **y**.)

In addition, we broaden the notion of a branching operation. An n-way $\vee$-branch uses n predicates $p_1(\mathbf{x},\mathbf{y})$, . . . , $p_n(\mathbf{x},\mathbf{y})$, which have the value T (true) or F (false) over the cross domain of **x** and **y**, but the value of at least one of the predicates must be T. Each predicate corresponds to a branch, and one branch (any one) for which the corresponding predicate has value T is then selected. This type of nondeterministic branch, called a $\vee$-branch, is represented in flow charts by the notation

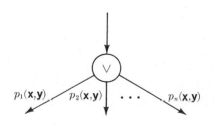

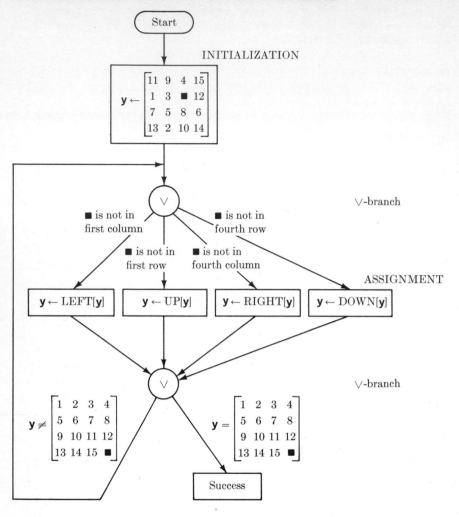

FIG. 2-3 *Setting up the 15-puzzle as a nondeterministic program.*

Notice that ordinary deterministic assignments and branches are simple special cases of the nondeterministic ones.

A particular *execution* of a nondeterministic program makes specific selections at ∨-branches and at SELECT statements. The set of all possible executions then defines the state space. If for any input there exists at least one execution that terminates, then the program is said to be well defined.

As an example of the way in which a problem can be set up as a nondeterministic program, we present one possible program for the 15-puzzle in Fig. 2-3. Here the state is described by the value of a program variable y ranging over the domain of 4×4 arrays. The elements of the 4×4 arrays are the integers 1 through 15 and ■ (representing the blank square). The functions LEFT, UP, RIGHT, and DOWN correspond to the operators. They change arrays by moving ■ to the left, up, right, or down, respectively.

It happens that additional elements of nondeterministic programs can also be defined and that these are useful in discussing problem-reduction formulations. We shall introduce them in Chapter 4.

2-6   SOME EXAMPLE PROBLEM REPRESENTATIONS

A wide variety of problems can be given a state-space representation. For some problems it is possible to select a quite natural state-space representation, while for others, any state-space representation seems forced. The reader should not assume that any of the formulations given in this section are uniquely the best among all alternatives. Neither should he be surprised if he concludes that he would solve the problem by representing it in a different way. Our purpose here is merely to illustrate that several different kinds of problems 'can be set up in a state-space representation.

The traveling-salesman problem

The traveling-salesman problem is a classic combinatorial problem. A salesman must plan a trip so that he visits each of n cities just once and returns to the starting city. A minimal-mileage trip is desired. Several efficient solution methods have been devised that are feasible for fewer than 50 or so cities. Approximate methods give good solutions (although not necessarily minimal-mileage ones) for as many as 200 cities. The traveling-salesman problem is useful for illustrating state-space representations, as shown by the following simple example.

A salesman has to visit each of the five cities shown in the map of Fig. 2-4. There is a road between every pair of cities, and the mileage is shown next to the road. Starting at city A, find a minimal-mileage route that visits each of the cities once only and returns to A.

To set up a state-space representation for this problem we specify the following:

The state descriptions. We shall describe the states by a list of cities visited so far. Thus the initial state is described by the list (A). We do not allow lists that name any city more than once except that after all of the other cities have been named, A can be named again.

The operators. The operators are computations corresponding to the actions (1) go to city A next, (2) go to city B next, . . . , and (5) go to city E next. An operator is not applicable to a state description unless it transforms it into some legal description. Thus operator number 1 (corresponding to "go to city A next") is not applicable to any description not naming all of the cities.

The goal criterion. Any state description beginning and ending with A and naming all of the other cities also is a goal-state description.

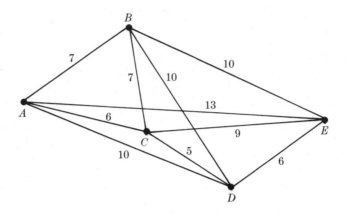

FIG. 2-4 *A map for the traveling-salesman problem.*

The graph representation of the state space is shown in Fig. 2-5. (Only some of the nodes are shown explicitly.) The numbers adjacent to the arcs in the graph are the costs of the arcs. In this case we let the costs equal the mileages between pairs of cities, as given in Fig. 2-4. Nodes in the graph are labeled by the state descriptions they represent. An advantage of the graph representation is that assigning costs to arcs allows us a convenient method of computing the total mileage of a tour and thus a means for searching for the shortest tour. In this case the shortest tour (34 miles) is indicated by the dark branch in the graph.

The traveling-salesman problem is an example of one in which information contained in the problem statement is presented in graphical form (the mileage chart). One should be careful not to confuse any graphs used in the problem statement with the state-space graph set up for solving the problem.

Syntax-analysis problems

A commonly occurring problem in language processing is the problem of *syntax analysis*. In these problems a formal definition is first given

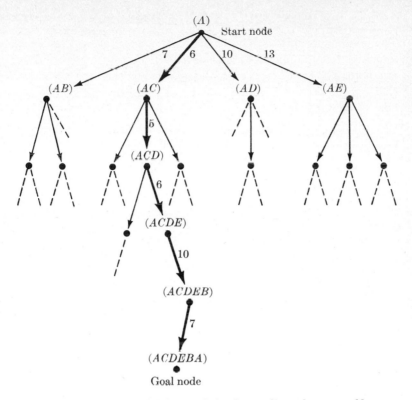

FIG. 2-5 *A portion of the graph for the traveling-salesman problem.*

by means of a *grammar* that defines a certain class of symbol strings. We are then asked to decide whether some arbitrary string is in the class or not. The following example illustrates this type of problem.

The grammar Suppose we define a *sentence* to be one of the following kinds of strings:

the symbol *a* followed by the symbol *b*
the symbol *a* followed by a sentence
a sentence followed by the symbol *b*
a sentence followed by another sentence

Some examples of sentences are: *aab, abaabab, aaaaab*. Some strings that are not sentences are: *aaa, aba, abaa*.

Suppose we want to determine whether or not the string *abaabab* is a sentence. A state-space formulation of this problem is then given by:

The state descriptions. One method of formulating this problem assumes that the initial state is described by the string in question, *abaabab*. The set of legal state descriptions is then the set of strings that can be produced by application of those rewriting rules (given below) defining the operators.

The operators. We define the operators in terms of the following rewriting rules:

$\$_1 ab \$_2 \rightarrow \$_1 S \$_2$ (the substring *ab* may be replaced by the name S for a sentence)

$\$_1 aS \$_2 \rightarrow \$_1 S \$_2$

$\$_1 Sb \$_2 \rightarrow \$_1 S \$_2$

$\$_1 SS \$_2 \rightarrow \$_1 S \$_2$

We see that these rules simply embody the grammar defining sentences.

The goal criterion. The goal state is described by the string consisting of the single symbol S.

A sequence of states representing a solution to this problem is then as follows:

abaabab
Saabab
SaSab
SSab
SSS
SS
S

A graph showing the state space for this problem is shown in Fig. 2-6. In this problem it happens that we could have logically deduced from the grammar the fact that any string beginning with an *a* and ending with a *b* is a sentence. This knowledge obviously would greatly have reduced the effort needed to determine whether an arbitrary string is a sentence or not. It sometimes happens that a given grammar has an equivalent and simpler specification. Finding such simplifications then allows smaller search spaces to be set up.

Distribution problems

The following simple problem typifies a class sometimes called *distribution problems*. Two fluid sources, A with a capacity of 100 gal/min

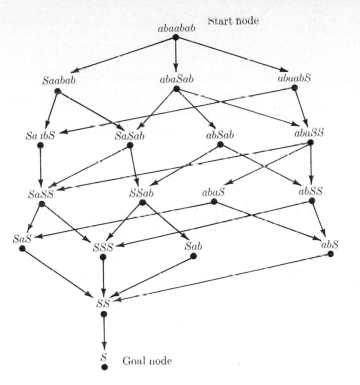

FIG. 2-6 *Graph for the syntax-analysis problem.*

and B with a capacity of 50 gal/min, must supply two sinks C and D with requirements of 75 gal/min each. The means of delivering fluid from source to sink is through pipes of maximum transmission capacity of 75 gal/min. If the physical locations of sources and sinks are as shown in Fig. 2-7, and if we allow pipe connections only at source or sink locations, how should the pipe be connected so as to use the least amount of pipe?

A state-space representation of this problem is as follows:

The state descriptions. The states are described by lists of the amounts of extra fluid per minute available at A, B, C, and D. Thus the initial state is described by the list $(A = 100, B = 50, C = 0, D = 0)$.

The operators. The operators correspond to transferring an increment of "fluid per minute" from one point to another. In problems like this, a greatest common divisor of the capacities and requirements of the various points and pipes serves as an appropriate

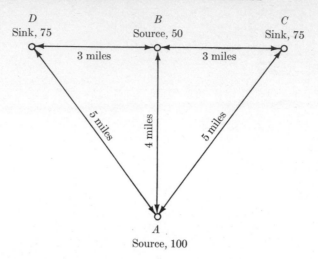

FIG. 2-7 *Locations of fluid sources and sinks.*

increment. Thus we have the operators:

1. Transfer 25 gal/min from A to B.
2. Transfer 25 gal/min from A to C.
   .
   .
   .
12. Transfer 25 gal/min from B to A.

Of course operators are only applicable if there is sufficient extra fluid at the point from which fluid is to be transferred. Also, with each transfer, appropriate pipe must be committed to effect it.

The goal criterion. The goal state is described by the list $(A = 0, B = 0, C = 75, D = 75)$.

We show part of the graph for the resulting state space in Fig. 2-8. The notation such as $A \rightarrow D$ on the arcs of the graph indicate that the corresponding operator transfers an increment of 25 gal/min from A to D. The costs written adjacent to each arc show the miles of pipe that must be committed to handle this increment; the number zero means that no extra pipe needs to be committed because there was already sufficient extra capacity available from a previous commitment. The graph in Fig. 2-8 is incomplete; many of the nodes are not shown. If the complete graph were searched, one would find that the least costly path from initial node to goal node involved **12** miles of pipe.

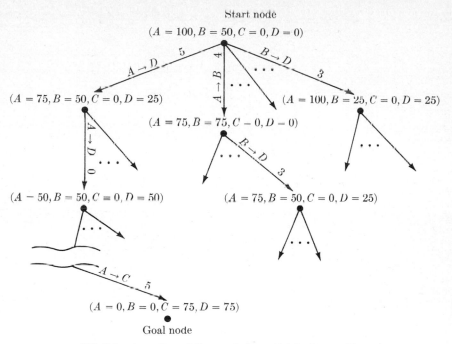

Start node
$$(A = 100, B = 50, C = 0, D = 0)$$

$A \to D$ 5 $A \to B$ $B \to D$ $\cdots$ 3

$(A = 75, B = 50, C = 0, D = 25)$

$\cdots$

$A \to B$ 4

$(A = 75, B = 75, C - 0, D - 0)$

$(A = 100, B = 25, C = 0, D = 25)$

$A \to D$ 0

$\cdots$

$(A - 50, B = 50, C = 0, D = 50)$

$R \to D$ 3 $\cdots$

$(A = 75, B = 50, C = 0, D = 25)$

$\cdots$

$A \to C$ 5

$$(A = 0, B = 0, C = 75, D = 75)$$

Goal node

FIG. 2-8   *A portion of the graph for a distribution problem.*

Control problems

In a typical *control* problem we have a process represented by a system of "plant" variables that must be controlled by the application of the appropriate control from a set of control variables.

An interesting example is provided by the *inverted pendulum* on a cart, illustrated in Fig. 2-9. In this problem a mass M rests on top of a rod of length ℓ that pivots in one plane on top of a wheeled cart. The plant variables are the angle of the rod θ, the position of the cart x, and the time derivative $\dot\theta$. It is desired that each of these variables be maintained within some preset limits. The control variable is the velocity of the cart $\dot x$, which is allowed to have one of two values, $+v$ and $-v$. (We assume for simplicity that these values can be changed instantaneously.) The main problem here is to decide at a given instant of time whether the cart should move to the right with speed v or to the left with speed v.

> The state descriptions. If the variables θ, $\dot\theta$, and x were quantized sufficiently finely we could let the vector composed of these three variables describe a state. (The space of states is then a lattice of points in the three-dimensional space of θ, $\dot\theta$, and x.)

RANDALL L. FRANK

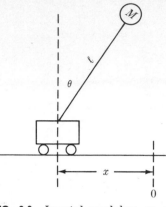

FIG. 2-9 *Inverted pendulum on a cart.*

The operators. We have just two operators:

1. Apply control $+v$.
2. Apply control $-v$.

The state resulting after applying one of these operators is just that state described by the $(\theta,\dot{\theta},x)$ vector resulting Δt seconds later. (In many typical control problems, the effects of the operators can be compactly represented by differential equations.)

The goal criterion. Let us suppose that the goal state is described by the vector $(\theta = 0, \dot{\theta} = 0, x = 0)$. Our problem then is to find a sequence of operators that will transform any given state into the goal state. Of course such a sequence will avoid any states described by values of θ, $\dot{\theta}$, and x for which ultimate collapse of the system is inevitable. (Collapse occurs when $\theta = \pm 90°$.)

In some types of control problems, one can often calculate (by analytic means) equations of separating surfaces that divide the vector space of states into disjoint regions such that for all vectors in a given region, the same control (or operator) should be the first to be applied. In these cases a routine calculation can be used to obtain the answer that otherwise would be produced by a search process. The reader should understand that our purpose here is not to recommend search processes over other, more direct problem-solving methods when the direct ones are known. Rather we emphasize that efficient search methods can often be used to solve problems for which no direct methods have yet been discovered.

2-7 SELECTING "GOOD" REPRESENTATIONS

The selection of a state-space representation for a problem has a great influence on the search effort needed to solve it. Obviously one prefers representations with small state spaces (that is, ones whose graphs have a small number of nodes). There are many examples of seemingly difficult problems that, when looked at appropriately, have trivially small state spaces. Sometimes a given state space can be "collapsed" by recognizing that certain operators can be discarded or that other operators can be combined into more powerful ones. Even when such simple transformations cannot be achieved, it is possible that a complete reformulation of the problem, changing the very notion of what a state is, will result in a smaller space.

The processes required to represent problems initially and to improve given representations are very poorly understood. It seems that desirable shifts in a problem's representation depend on experience gained in attempts to solve it in a given representation. This experience allows us to recognize the occurrence of simplifying notions such as symmetries or useful sequences of operators that ought to be combined into *macro-operators*.

An extremely important representation idea involves the use of variables in state descriptions. An expression containing variables then can be used to describe a whole set of states rather than just one; substituting (constant) instances for the variables in the expression yields a particular state description. An expression containing variables that is used to describe a set of states in this manner is called a *state-description schema*. We shall illustrate the use of state-description schemas by an example.

The monkey-and-bananas problem is often used in the artificial-intelligence literature to demonstrate the operation of automatic problem solvers designed to perform commonsense reasoning. The problem can be stated as follows: A monkey is in a room containing a box and a bunch of bananas. The bananas are hanging from the ceiling out of reach of the monkey. What sequence of actions will allow the monkey to get the bananas? (The monkey is supposed to go to the box, push it under the bananas, climb on top of it and grasp the bananas.)

How should this problem be given a state-space representation? Elements that certainly should appear in the state description are: the monkey's position in the room (both horizontally and vertically), the box's position in the room, and whether or not the monkey has the bananas. These elements can conveniently be represented by a four-element list $(\mathbf{w},x,\mathbf{y},z)$ where:

$\mathbf{w}$ = horizontal position of monkey (a two-dimensional vector)

x = 1 or 0, depending on whether the monkey is on top of the box or not, respectively

$\mathbf{y}$ = horizontal position of the box (a two-dimensional vector)

z = 1 or 0, depending on whether the monkey has the bananas or not, respectively

If we thought of each different value of the list $(\mathbf{w},x,\mathbf{y},z)$ as describing a unique state, we would have an infinite number of states and state descriptions since there are an infinite number of locations in the room. We could make the state space finite by admitting only locations at a finite number of points (say the points of a grid), but still an adequate number of points would result in an extremely large state-space. An alternative is to use state-description schemas. The schema variables will have instances (constants or other variables) substituted for them either when operators are applied or in order to satisfy a goal test.

The operators in this problem correspond to four possible actions that can be performed by the monkey:

1. goto($\mathbf{u}$) monkey goes to horizontal position $\mathbf{u}$ (a variable)
2. pushbox($\mathbf{v}$) monkey pushes box to horizontal position $\mathbf{v}$ (a variable)
3. climbbox monkey climbs on top of the box
4. grasp monkey grasps the bananas

Because of the occurrence of variables in goto and pushbox, these operators are actually operator schemas. The applicability and the effects of the operators are given by the following rewriting rules:

$$(\mathbf{w},0,\mathbf{y},z) \xrightarrow{\text{goto}(\mathbf{u})} (\mathbf{u},0,\mathbf{y},z)$$

$$(\mathbf{w},0,\mathbf{w},z) \xrightarrow{\text{pushbox}(\mathbf{v})} (\mathbf{v},0,\mathbf{v},z)$$

$$(\mathbf{w},0,\mathbf{w},z) \xrightarrow{\text{climbbox}} (\mathbf{w},1,\mathbf{w},z)$$

$$(\mathbf{c},1,\mathbf{c},0) \xrightarrow{\text{grasp}} (\mathbf{c},1,\mathbf{c},1)$$

where $\mathbf{c}$ is the location on the floor directly under the bananas. The application of some of the operators, for example, pushbox, constrains the variables representing the positions of the monkey and of the box to be the same. We shall take two state-description schemas to be identical when they differ only in the names of variables.

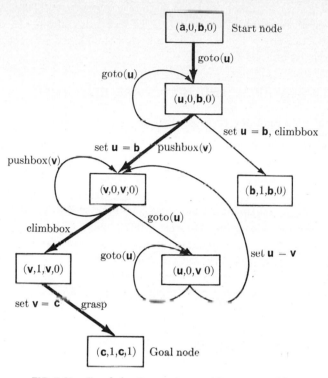

FIG. 2-10 *Graph for the monkey-and-bananas problem.*

In this formulation the set of goal states is described by any list whose last element is equal to 1.

Suppose initially the monkey is on the floor at position **a** and the box is at position **b**. Then the initial state is described by (**a**,0,**b**,0). The only operator that is applicable in this state is goto(**u**), resulting in the schema (**u**,0,**b**,0). Now three operators are applicable. If **u** = **b**, the monkey can either climb the box or push it. Regardless of the value of **u**, the monkey could go somewhere else. Climbing the box yields the state described by (**b**,1,**b**,0); pushing the box to **v** yields the schema (**v**,0,**v**,0), and going to some place described by a new variable does not change the description. If we continue to apply all operators applicable at every state-description schema, we produce the state space illustrated by the graph of Fig. 2-10. We note that this graph is quite small and a solution path (the dark branch) is easily obtained. When variables are instantiated as indicated along the solution path we obtain the operator sequence: goto(**b**), pushbox(**c**), climbbox, grasp.

We shall now leave the subject of state-space representations. The examples presented in this chapter have touched on several aspects of the representation problem, even though a satisfactory theory of representations and representation shifts is as yet unavailable. In the next chapter we shall cover the much more highly developed subject of state-space search techniques.

2-8 BIBLIOGRAPHICAL AND HISTORICAL REMARKS

Elements of a state-space representation

The three elements of a state-space representation—state descriptions, operators, and goal tests—have long been recognized as basic in automatic problem solving. These notions are discussed in the book on the general problem solving (GPS) program by Ernst and Newell (1969). A more abstract treatment of the problem of description of states and operators may be found in Amarel (1967, 1969). An example of the use of rewriting rules to represent operators can be found in the problem-solving system of Quinlan and Hunt (1968).

The basic vocabulary of graph theory (arcs, nodes, paths, and so on) is often used to describe problem-solving processes. Classic books on graph theory are those of Berge (1962) and Ore (1962). Ore (1963) has also written a popular, elementary book illustrating applications of graph theory to various combinatorial problems.

Nondeterministic programs

The phrase *nondeterministic algorithm* was proposed by Floyd (1967a). In these algorithms, Floyd allowed the use of a "choice" function to simplify the description of exhaustive search strategies. Later, Manna (1970) described a class of programs that allowed nondeterministic assignment statements (similar to the choice function) as well as nondeterministic branching operations. He described techniques for proving the correctness of programs containing these new elements. [In an earlier paper, Manna (1969) considered the problem of proving the correctness of ordinary (deterministic) programs.] Fikes (1970) describes a complete problem-solving system in which problems are stated in a procedural language that allows the use of nondeterministic choice functions.

Background literature on the example problems

The example problems that we have used to illustrate state-space techniques come from diverse fields, each with its own individual tradition of specialized problem-solving methods. Many of these methods can be viewed as an application of the state-space approach. It would be instructive for the reader to carry out the exercise of translating some of the descriptions of these specialized methods into the common language of the state-space approach.

The traveling-salesman problem has occupied an important place in operations research. For a review see Bellmore and Nemhauser (1968).

Problems of syntax analysis are common in language processing. Feldman and Gries (1968) give a thorough survey of syntax-analysis techniques as used by translating systems for the formal languages of computation. Amarel (1965) discusses syntax analysis from the point of view of automatic problem solving and proposes a problem-reduction procedure. For a highly readable treatment of the use of symbol strings and production systems as models of computation see the final chapters in a book on computation by Minsky (1967).

Many problems involving distribution, flow, and queuing can be solved by state-space methods. A discussion of these can be found in a book by Ford and Fulkerson (1962).

Control theory is a large and specialized field with a variety of problem-solution methods. A book by De Russo, Roy, and Close (1965) is a good introduction to modern control theory.

The problem of finding a good representation

The problem of finding good representations for problems has been treated by only a few researchers, notably by Amarel. Amarel (1968) has written a classic paper on the subject; it takes the reader through a series of progressively better representations for the missionaries-and-cannibals problem. An interesting puzzle that emphasizes the importance of good representations is mentioned by McCarthy (1964). The monkey-and-bananas problem is a standard example problem of commonsense reasoning. It is thoroughly discussed in some notes by Amarel (1966).

The use of state-description schemas has been mentioned as a powerful representational technique. Later versions of GPS allowed the use of object schemas with variables as did Fikes' (1970) problem-solving system. A paper by Newell (1965) examines some possible approaches (and their limitations) toward making progress on the representation problem.

PROBLEMS

Exercises marked with a † may require several hours of effort. Some of these might be suitable as term projects.

2-1   The order (from left to right) in which the locomotive L and cars stand on the track shown below can be represented by the string $LABCD$.

Assume that one can couple and decouple locomotive and individual cars arbitrarily, that the switches can be set arbitrarily, and that the locomotive can either push or pull the cars to which it is coupled. List a set of rewriting rules for strings that can be used to generate representations for all possible rearrangements of cars and locomotive on the straight track.

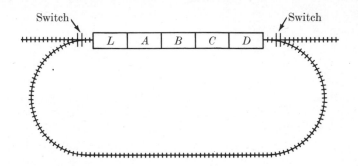

2-2 The arc between a node n_i and its successor node n_j is called *irrevocable* if n_i is not accessible from n_j. Give two examples of problems having state-space graphs containing irrevocable arcs.

2-3 Show by means of a path in a state-space graph that the string $(((),()),(),((),()))$ is a sentence S in the grammar defined by the following rewriting rules:

a. $S \leftarrow ()$

b. $A \leftarrow S$

c. $A \leftarrow A,A$

d. $S \leftarrow (A)$

In these rewriting rules we assume the convention that the symbol at the left of the arrow may replace the substring of symbols at the right of the arrow at any place in the string at which the substring occurs.

2-4 Select a state-description form, operators, and a goal test for the following water-jug problem:

Given a 5-gal jug filled with water and an empty 2-gal jug, how can one obtain precisely 1 gal in the 2-gal jug? Water may either be discarded or poured from one jug into another; however, no more water than the initial 5 gal is available.

Draw that part of the search tree corresponding to the moves you tried in finding a solution.

2-5   Select a state-description form, operators, and a goal test for the 8-queens problem:

Place 8 queens on a standard chess board such that each row, column, and diagonal contains no more than 1 queen.

Draw a part of the state-space graph and label the nodes and arcs with the appropriate descriptions.

2-6   Write a program that produces the set of strings that can be obtained by replacing the substring S_2 for any occurrence of the substring S_1 in a given string S.

2-7   † Read the article by Amarel on representations (Amarel, 1968). Note that Amarel starts with quite a primitive representation, experiments with it a bit, and then progressively refines it. Conduct a similar study for the following problem, mentioned in McCarthy (1964):

Deform a $2n$ by $2n$ square board by removing a 1 by 1 cell from each of two opposite corners:

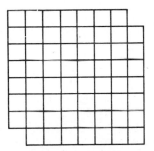

Demonstrate that it is now impossible to completely cover this mutilated board with 1 by 2 tiles in such a way that the tiles neither overlap nor stick out over the edge of the board.

At some stage in your study you might want to experiment with a 2 by 2 board, then a 4 by 4 board, etc., to identify concepts useful in a representation for the general case. Write a paper describing your work on this problem and conclude it with any observations you might have on the difficulty of the representation problem.

REFERENCES

Amarel, S. (1965): Problem Solving Procedures for Efficient Syntactic Analysis, *ACM 20th Natl. Conf.* [Also printed as *Sci. Rept.* no. 1, AFOSR Contr. no. AF49(638)-1184, 1968.]

——— (1966): More on Representations of the Monkey Problem, *Carnegie Institute of Technology Lecture Notes,* March 1, 1966.

―――― (1967): An Approach to Heuristic Problem-Solving and Theorem Proving in the Propositional Calculus, in J. Hart and S. Takasu (eds.), "Systems and Computer Science," University of Toronto Press, Toronto, 1967.

―――― (1968): On Representations of Problems of Reasoning about Actions, in D. Michie (ed.), "Machine Intelligence 3," pp. 131–171, American Elsevier Publishing Company, Inc., New York, 1968.

―――― (1969): On the Representation of Problems and Goal Directed Procedures for Computers, *Commun. Am. Soc. Cybernetics,* vol. 1, no. 2, 1969.

Bellmore, M. and G. Nemhauser (1968): The Traveling Salesman Problem: A Survey, *Operations Res.,* vol. 16, no. 3, pp. 538–558, May-June 1968.

Berge, C. (1962): "The Theory of Graphs and Its Applications," Dunod, Paris, 1958 (in French); English translation, Alison Doig, John Wiley & Sons, Inc., New York, 1962.

De Russo, P., R. Roy, and C. Close (1965): "State Variables for Engineers," John Wiley & Sons, Inc., New York, 1965.

Ernst, G. and A. Newell (1969): "GPS: A Case Study in Generality and Problem Solving," ACM Monograph Series, Academic Press, Inc., New York, 1969.

Feldman, J. and D. Gries (1968): Translator Writing Systems, *Commun. ACM,* vol. 11, no. 2, pp. 77–113, February 1968.

Fikes, R. (1970): Ref-Arf: A System for Solving Problems Stated as Procedures, *Artificial Intelligence,* vol. 1, no. 1, 1970.

Floyd, R. (1967*a*): Nondeterministic Algorithms, *J. ACM,* vol. 14, no. 4, pp. 636–644, October 1967.

Ford, L., Jr., and D. Fulkerson (1962): "Flows in Networks," Princeton University Press, Princeton, N.J., 1962.

Manna, Z. (1969): The Correctness of Programs," *J. Computer and Sys. Sci.,* vol. 3, May 1969.

―――― (1970): The Correctness of Non-Deterministic Programs, *Artificial Intelligence,* vol. 1, no. 1, 1970.

Minsky, M. (1967): "Computation: Finite and Infinite Machines," Prentice-Hall, Inc., Englewood Cliffs, N.J., 1967.

McCarthy, J. (1964): A Tough Nut for Proof Procedures, *Stanford University Artificial Intelligence Project Memo* no. 16, 1964.

Newell, A. (1965): Limitations of the Current Stock of Ideas about Problem Solving, in A. Kent and O. Taulbee (eds.), "Electronic Information Handling," Spartan Books, Washington, D.C., 1965.

Ore, O. (1962): Theory of Graphs, *Am. Math. Soc. Colloq. Publ.,* vol. XXXVIII, Providence, Rhode Island, 1962.

―――― (1963): "Graphs and Their Uses," Random House, Inc., New York, 1963.

Quinlan, J. and E. Hunt (1968): A Formal Deductive Problem-Solving System, *J. ACM,* vol. 15, no. 4, pp. 625–646, October 1968.

CHAPTER THREE

STATE-SPACE SEARCH METHODS

3-1 GRAPH-SEARCHING PROCESSES

In our state-space formulation of problems, a solution is obtained by applying operators to state descriptions until an expression describing the goal state is obtained. In the examples of the last chapter we saw how graphs can be used to illustrate state spaces. The language of graphs is extremely useful for describing efficient state-space search strategies. All of the state-space search methods that we shall discuss can be modeled by the following graph-theoretic process:

A *start node* is associated with the initial state description.

The successors of a node are calculated using the operators that are applicable to the state description associated with the node. Let Γ be a special operator that calculates *all* of the successors of a node. We shall call the process of applying Γ to a node *expanding* a node.

Pointers are set up from each successor back to its parent node. These pointers indicate a path back to the start node when a goal node is finally found.

The successor nodes are checked to see if they are goal nodes. (That is, the associated state descriptions are checked to see if they describe goal states.) If a goal node has not yet been found, the process of expanding nodes (and setting up pointers) continues. When a goal node is found, the pointers are traced back to the start to produce a solution path. The state-description operators associated with the arcs of this path are then assembled into a solution sequence.

The steps listed above merely describe the major elements of the search process in a manner similar to the description provided by the flow chart of a nondeterministic program. A complete specification of a search process must describe the order in which the nodes are to be expanded. If we expand the nodes in the order in which they are generated, we have what is called a *breadth-first* process. If we expand the most recently generated nodes first, we have what is called a *depth-first* process. Breadth-first and depth-first methods can be called *blind-search procedures* since the order in which nodes are expanded is unaffected by the location of the goal.

It is possible though that some heuristic information about the global nature of the graph and the general direction of the goal is available. (The word *heuristic* means serving to discover.) Such information can often be used to help "pull" the search toward the goal by causing the most promising nodes to be expanded first. In this chapter we shall discuss several heuristic search methods in graph-theoretic terms. First though, we shall introduce some of the fundamental ideas of search by a more thorough treatment of blind-search methods.

The explanation of these methods is made somewhat clearer if we limit our discussion at first to trees rather than graphs. A tree is a graph each of whose nodes has a unique parent except for a distinguished node, called the *root node,* that has no parent. The root node is thus the start node. Trees are simpler to search than graphs primarily because when a new node is generated we can be sure that it has never been generated before nor will it be generated again. Thus a path from the root node to any given node is unique. After describing some blind-search methods for trees we shall indicate how they must be modified for graphs.

3-2 BREADTH-FIRST METHODS

The breadth-first search method expands nodes in the order in which they are generated. A simple algorithm for searching trees breadth-first consists of the following sequence of steps:

(1) Put the start node on a list called OPEN.
(2) If OPEN is empty, exit with failure; otherwise continue.
(3) Remove the first node on OPEN and put it on a list called CLOSED; call this node n.
(4) Expand node n, generating all of its successors. If there are no successors, go immediately to (2). Put the successors at the end of OPEN and provide pointers from these successors back to n.
(5) If any of the successors are goal nodes, exit with the solution obtained by tracing back through the pointers; otherwise go to (2).

This algorithm assumes that the start node is not itself a goal node, although a test for this possibility could easily be added. A flow chart of the algorithm is shown in Fig. 3-1. The nodes and pointers generated by the search process form a subtree of the entire implicitly defined state-space tree. We shall call such a subtree a *search tree*.

It is easy to show that this breadth-first method is guaranteed to find a shortest-length path to a goal node in the tree, providing a path exists at all. (If no path exists, the method as stated will exit with failure for finite graphs or won't ever terminate for infinite graphs.)

In Fig. 3-2 we show the search tree generated by a breadth-first search applied to an 8-puzzle. (The state-space graph of an 8-puzzle is actually not a tree, but this fact is unimportant so long as the search process never generates the same node from more than one parent.) The problem is to transform the configuration

2	8	3
1	6	4
7	■	5

into

1	2	3
8	■	4
7	6	5

The nodes are labeled by their corresponding state descriptions and are numbered in the order in which they were expanded.[1] The dark branch

---

[1] We generate successors in the order obtained by trying first to move the blank to the left, then up, then right, and then down.

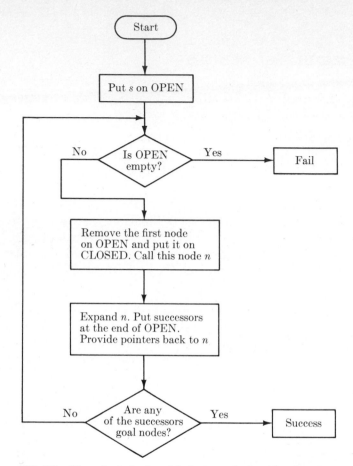

FIG. 3-1 *Flow chart of a breadth-first search algorithm for trees.*

shows a solution of five moves. (Arrowheads are omitted from the arcs since the parent-successor relationship is unambiguous in a search tree.) Note that a total of 26 nodes were expanded and 46 nodes were generated before this solution was found. Also, direct inspection of this graph indicates that no solution exists having a shorter sequence of moves.

There may be problems for which we desire a solution having some property other than the shortest sequence of operator applications. Associating costs with arcs in the tree (and then finding a solution path having minimal cost) accommodates many of these generalized criteria, as we saw in some of the examples of the last chapter. A more general version of the breadth-first method, called the *uniform-cost method*, is guaranteed to find a path of minimal cost from the start node to

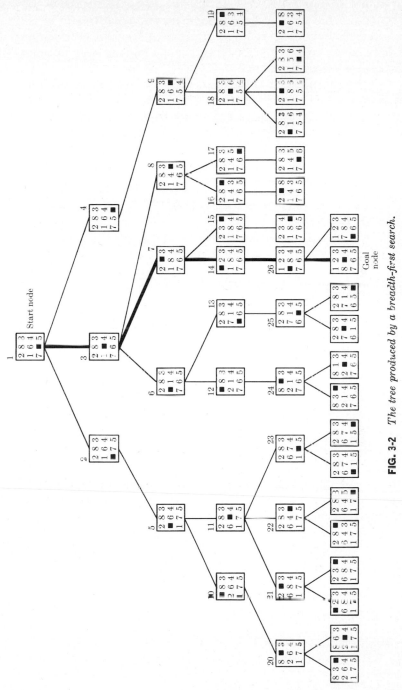

FIG. 3-2 *The tree produced by a breadth-first search.*

47

a goal node. Whereas the algorithm just described spreads out along contours of equal path length, the more general algorithm to be described next spreads out along contours of equal path cost. We assume that we have given a cost function $c(n_i,n_j)$ giving the cost of going from node n_i to a successor node n_j.

In the uniform-cost method we must, for each node n in the search tree, keep track of the cost of the path generated from the start node s to node n. We shall denote the cost of a path from s to a node n in the search tree by $\hat{g}(n)$. In searching trees we are assured that $\hat{g}(n)$ is also the cost of a *minimal* cost path from s to n (since it is the only path). The uniform-cost method expands nodes in order of increasing $\hat{g}(n)$. It is defined by the following sequence of steps:

(1) Put the start node s on a list called OPEN. Set $\hat{g}(s) = 0$.
(2) If OPEN is empty, exit with failure; otherwise continue.
(3) Remove that node from OPEN whose $\hat{g}$ value is smallest and put it on a list called CLOSED. Call this node n. (Resolve ties for minimal $\hat{g}$ values arbitrarily but always in favor of any goal node.)
(4) If n is a goal node, exit with the solution path obtained by tracing back through the pointers; otherwise continue.
(5) Expand node n, generating all of its successors. [If there are no successors, go immediately to (2).] For each successor n_i, compute $\hat{g}(n_i)$ by $\hat{g}(n_i) = \hat{g}(n) + c(n,n_i)$. Put these successors on OPEN, associating with them the $\hat{g}$ values just computed, and provide pointers back to n.
(6) Go to (2).

A flow chart of this algorithm is shown in Fig. 3-3. Note that the test for a goal node is in a location that guarantees finding minimal cost paths.

We note that the uniform-cost algorithm can also be used to find paths of minimum length merely by assuming a *unit* arc cost between nodes and their successors. If there are several start nodes, the algorithms are simply modified by putting *all* of the start nodes on OPEN in step (1). If the goal states can be explicitly described, the search process can also be worked backward by letting the nodes in the goal set be the start nodes and vice versa, using a Γ inverse.

3-3 A DEPTH-FIRST METHOD

In depth-first methods we expand the most recently generated nodes first. We define the *depth* of a node in a tree as follows:

The depth of the root node is zero

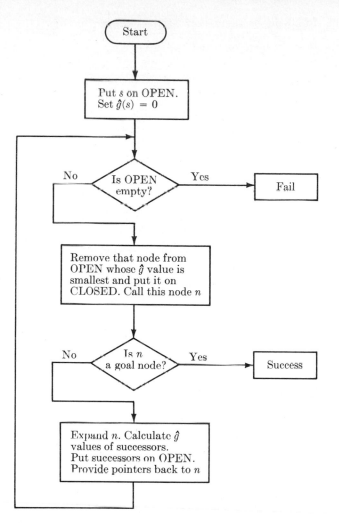

FIG. 3-3 *Flow chart of the uniform-cost algorithm for trees.*

The depth of any node that is a descendant of the root is one plus the depth of its parent

Thus the currently deepest node in the search tree is the one selected for expansion. Such a policy might result in the process running away along some fruitless path so we must provide for a backtracking procedure. After the process generates a node exceeding some *depth bound* we expand the deepest node not exceeding this bound, and so forth.

The following sequence of steps defines the depth-first method:

(1)   Put the start node on a list called OPEN.

(2)   If OPEN is empty, exit with failure; otherwise continue.

(3)   Remove the *first* node from OPEN and put it on a list called CLOSED. Call this node n.

(4)   If the depth of n equals the depth bound, go to (2); otherwise continue.

(5)   Expand node n, generating all successors of n. Put these (in arbitrary order) at the *beginning* of OPEN and provide pointers back to n.

(6)   If any of the successors are goal nodes, exit with the solution obtained by tracing back through the pointers; otherwise go to (2).

We show a flow chart for the depth-first method in Fig. 3-4. The tree generated by a depth-first search applied to the same 8-puzzle as before is illustrated in Fig. 3-5. Again we want a sequence of moves for transforming

The nodes are numbered in the order in which they were expanded and we assume a depth bound of five (so we are looking for paths to the goal of length five or less).

We see that the depth-first algorithm pushes along one path until it reaches maximum depth, then it begins to consider alternative paths of the same or less depth that differ only in the last step, then those that differ in the last two steps, etc.

3-4 MODIFICATIONS NEEDED WHEN SEARCHING GRAPHS

When searching graphs rather than trees, some obvious modifications must be made to the above algorithms. The simple breadth-first method need not be modified except to provide means for recognizing whether a newly generated node is already on either OPEN or CLOSED as a result of a previous node expansion. If it is, it need not be put on OPEN again.

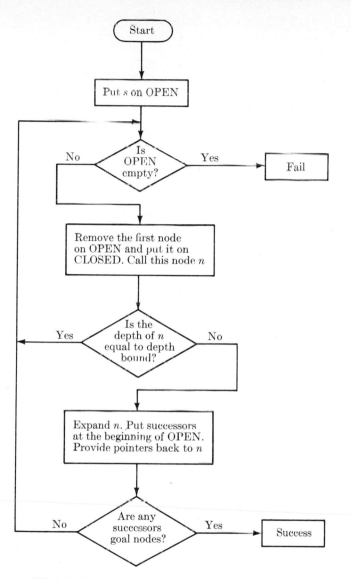

FIG. 3-4 *Flow chart of a depth-first algorithm for trees.*

Some rather more complex modifications are needed in the uniform-cost algorithm:

(1) If a newly generated successor is already on OPEN, it need not be added to OPEN again, but its $\hat{g}$ value may now be smaller. (A less costly path may have been found.) One always associates with those nodes on OPEN the smallest $\hat{g}$ values found so far. Also the pointer

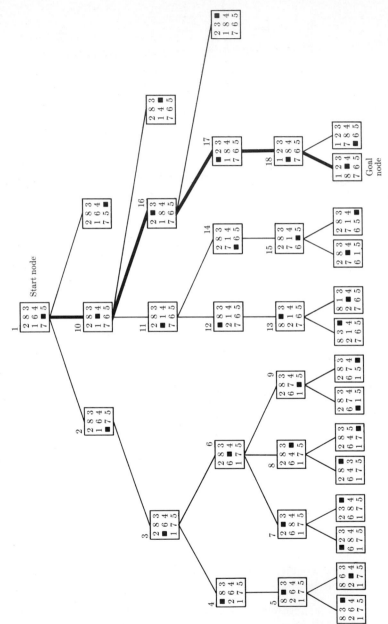

FIG. 3-5 *The tree produced by a depth-first search.*

from a node must be directed to that parent on the least costly path found so far to the node.

(2) If a newly generated successor is already on CLOSED, one might at first suppose that its g value might now be smaller than before so that its pointer ought to be redirected, but such is not the case. Later we will prove that when the uniform-cost algorithm places a node on CLOSED, the smallest g value (and thus the minimal cost path to that node) has already been found.

Before changes can be made to the depth-first algorithm, one must decide what is meant by the *depth* of a node in a graph. A common definition makes the depth of a node equal to one plus the depth of its shallowest parent with the start node having zero depth. One could then achieve a depth-first search by selecting for expansion the deepest node on OPEN (subject to the depth bound). When successors are generated that are already on either OPEN or CLOSED, recomputations of depth may be necessary.

Even when searching a general graph, the set of nodes and pointers generated by the search process still forms a search *tree*. (Pointers still point to only one parent.) For the remainder of this chapter we will be treating the general case of graph-searching, and therefore the algorithms we will be discussing will deal explicitly with these added complications.

3-5   DISCUSSION OF HEURISTIC INFORMATION

The blind-search methods, whether breadth-first or depth-first, are exhaustive methods for finding paths to a goal node. In principle, these methods provide a solution to the path-finding problem, but it is often infeasible to use these methods because the search will expand too many nodes before a path is found. Since there are always practical limits on the amount of time and storage available to expend on the search, we must look for more efficient alternatives to blind search.

For many tasks it is possible to state principles or rules of thumb to help reduce the search. Any such technique used to speed up the search depends on special information about the problem being represented by the graph. Let us call information of this sort *heuristic information* (serving to aid discovery) and call search procedures using it *heuristic search methods*. One way to reduce the search is to provide a more "informed" Γ that doesn't generate so many extraneous successors. Such a technique would be applicable to both breadth-first and depth-first methods. Another way to use heuristic information involves modifying step (5) of the depth-first algorithm. Instead of placing newly generated successors in arbitrary order at the beginning of OPEN, these successors are placed there in some definite order determined by the heuristic information. In this way, depth-first search expands next that successor thought to be best.

A more flexible (and costly) way to use heuristic information is to use some criterion to reorder all of the nodes on OPEN at every step. Then search could expand outward along those sectors of the frontier thought to be most promising. In order to apply such an ordering procedure we need some measure by which to evaluate the "promise" of a node. Such measures are called *evaluation functions*.

As we shall see, it is often possible to specify heuristics that reduce search effort (below that expended by, say, uniform-cost search) without sacrificing the guarantee of finding a minimal cost path. More frequently the heuristics that are used greatly reduce search effort at the expense of giving up the guarantee of finding a minimal cost path on some or all problems. But in most practical problems we are interested in minimizing some *combination* of the cost of the path and the cost of the search required to obtain the path. Furthermore, we are usually interested in search methods that minimize this combination *averaged* over all problems likely to be encountered. (In computing this average cost, of course, we should use weights proportional to the frequency of occurrence of each problem, so that we tolerate larger costs on infrequently encountered problems if they are offset by smaller costs on frequently encountered problems.) If the averaged combination cost of search method 1 is lower than the averaged combination cost of search method 2, then we say that search method 1 has more *heuristic power* than search method 2. Note that according to our definition it is not necessary (though it is a common misconception) that a search method having more heuristic power than another give up any guarantees about finding minimal cost paths that the other might have enjoyed.

Averaged combination costs are never actually computed, both because it is difficult to decide on the way to combine path cost and search-effort cost and because it would be difficult to define a probability distribution over the set of problems to be encountered. Therefore, the matter of deciding whether one search method has more heuristic power than another is usually left up to informed intuition gained by actual experience with the methods.

3-6 USE OF EVALUATION FUNCTIONS

As already mentioned, one common use of heuristic information involves an *evaluation function* to be used in ordering the search. The purpose of an evaluation function is to provide a means for ranking those nodes that are candidates for expansion to determine which one is most likely to be on the best path to the goal. Evaluation functions have been based on a variety of ideas. Attempts have been made to define a *probability* that a node is on the best path. *Distance* or *difference* metrics between an arbitrary node and the goal set have been suggested. In board games or puzzles, a configuration is often scored points on the basis of those features that it possesses that are thought to be related to its promise as a step toward the goal.

Suppose we had some function $\hat{f}$ that could be used to order nodes for expansion. Then by $\hat{f}(n)$ we denote the value of this function at node n. Although for the moment $\hat{f}$ can be any arbitrary function, later we shall propose that it be an estimate of the cost of a minimal cost path from the start node to a goal node constrained to go through node n.

By convention, we shall order nodes for expansion in *increasing* order of their $\hat{f}$ values. An algorithm (like the uniform-cost algorithm) can then be used in which that node on OPEN having the smallest $\hat{f}$ value is selected for expansion next. We shall call such a procedure the *ordered-search algorithm*.

In order that the ordered-search algorithm be applicable to searching general graphs (rather than just trees), we must include provisions for dealing with the generation of nodes that are already on either OPEN or CLOSED. When using some arbitrary $\hat{f}$ function we must note that the $\hat{f}$ value of a node on CLOSED might be lowered if a new path to it is found [$\hat{f}(n)$ may depend on the path from s to n even for nodes on CLOSED]. Therefore we must put such nodes back on OPEN, and we must provide for redirecting their pointers.

With these needed provisions, the ordered-search algorithm then consists of the following sequence of steps:

(1) Put the start node s on a list called OPEN and compute $\hat{f}(s)$.

(2) If OPEN is empty, exit with failure; otherwise continue.

(3) Remove from OPEN that node whose $\hat{f}$ value is smallest and put it on a list called CLOSED. Call this node n. (Resolve ties for minimal $\hat{f}$ values arbitrarily, but always in favor of any goal node.)

(4) If n is a goal node, exit with the solution path obtained by tracing back through the pointers; otherwise continue.

(5) Expand node n, generating all of its successors. [If there are no successors, go immediately to (2).] For each successor n_i, compute $\hat{f}(n_i)$.

(6) Associate with the successors not already on either OPEN or CLOSED the $\hat{f}$ values just computed. Put these nodes on OPEN and direct pointers from them back to n.

(7) Associate with those successors that were already on OPEN or CLOSED the smaller of the $\hat{f}$ values just computed and their previous

$\hat{f}$ values. Put on OPEN those successors on CLOSED whose $\hat{f}$ values were thus lowered, and redirect to n the pointers from all nodes whose $\hat{f}$ values were lowered.

(8)   Go to (2).

The general structure of the algorithm is identical to that of the uniform-cost method (Fig. 3-3) so we shall omit an illustration of its flow chart. We note that the set of nodes and pointers generated by the algorithm forms a tree (the search tree) with the nodes on OPEN at the tips of the tree.

The way in which the algorithm works can easily be illustrated by considering again the same 8-puzzle example. We shall use the simple evaluation function

$$\hat{f}(n) = \hat{g}(n) + W(n)$$

where $\hat{g}(n)$ is the length of the path in the search tree from the start node to node n, and $W(n)$ counts the number of misplaced tiles in the state description associated with node n.

Thus the start node

2	8	3
1	6	4
7	■	5

has an $\hat{f}$ value equal to $0 + 4 = 4$. Supposedly, the node having the lowest evaluation is the most likely to be on the optimal path.

The results of applying the ordered-search algorithm to the 8-puzzle and using this evaluation function are summarized in Fig. 3-6. The value of $\hat{f}$ for each node is circled; the uncircled numbers show the order in which nodes are expanded. We see that the same solution path is found here as was found by the other search methods, although the use of the evaluation function has resulted in substantially fewer nodes being expanded.

The choice of the evaluation function critically determines the search results. The use of an evaluation function that ignores the true promise of some nodes can result in nonminimal cost paths. On the other hand, the use of an evaluation function that over-generously acknowledges the possible promise of all nodes (such as the uniform-cost algorithm) will result in the expansion of too many nodes. In the next few sections we shall develop some theoretical results about a par-

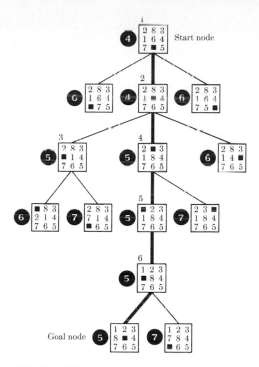

FIG. 3-6 *The tree produced by an ordered search.*

ticular evaluation function whose use expands the fewest number of nodes consistent with the guarantee of finding a minimal cost path.

3-7 AN OPTIMAL SEARCH ALGORITHM

We shall now describe a specific evaluation function and then show that its use maximizes one measure of search efficiency while still guaranteeing a minimal cost path to a goal. We define the evaluation function $\hat{f}$ so that its value $\hat{f}(n)$ at any node n is an *estimate* of the cost of a minimal cost path from the start node s to node n plus an estimate of the cost of a minimal cost path from node n to a goal node. That is, $\hat{f}(n)$ is an estimate of the cost of a minimal cost path *constrained to go through node n*. That node on OPEN having the smallest value of $\hat{f}$ is then the node estimated to be on a minimal cost path; hence, it should be expanded next.

In order to demonstrate some of the properties of this evaluation function, we shall first introduce some notation. Let the function $k(n_i, n_j)$ give the *actual* cost of a minimal cost path between two arbitrary nodes n_i and n_j. (The function k is undefined for nodes having no path between them.) If T is a set of goal nodes, then we denote the cost of a minimal cost path from node n_i to a goal by

$$h(n_i) = \min_{n_j \epsilon T} k(n_i, n_j)$$

(The function h is undefined for any node n from which no goal node is accessible.) We shall say that any path from node n_i to a goal node that achieves $h(n_i)$ is an *optimal* path from n_i to a goal.

Often we shall be interested in knowing the cost $k(s,n)$ of an optimal path from a given start node s to some arbitrary node n. It will simplify our notation somewhat to introduce a new function g for this purpose and to define g as follows:

$$g(n) = k(s,n)$$

for all n accessible from s.

We next define the function f so that its value $f(n)$ at any node n is the actual cost of an optimal path from node s to node n plus the cost of an optimal path from node n to a goal node. That is,

$$f(n) = g(n) + h(n)$$

The value of $f(n)$ is then the cost of an optimal path constrained to go through node n. [Note that $f(s) = h(s)$ is the actual cost of an unconstrained optimal path from s to a goal.]

We desire our evaluation function $\hat{f}$ to be an estimate of f. We shall take our estimate to be given by

$$\hat{f}(n) = \hat{g}(n) + \hat{h}(n)$$

where $\hat{g}$ is an estimate of g, and $\hat{h}$ is an estimate of h.

An obvious choice for $\hat{g}(n)$ is the cost of the path in the *search tree* from s to n given by summing the arc costs encountered while following the pointers from n back to s. (This path is the lowest cost path from s to n found so far by the algorithm.) Notice that this definition implies $\hat{g}(n) \geq g(n)$.

A simple example will illustrate that this estimate is easy to calculate as the algorithm proceeds. Consider the subgraph shown in Fig. 3-7. It consists of a start node s and three other nodes n_1, n_2, and n_3. The arcs are shown with arrowheads and costs. Let us trace how the algorithm works in searching this subgraph. Starting with s we obtain successors n_1 and n_2. The estimates $\hat{g}(n_1)$ and $\hat{g}(n_2)$ are then 3 and 7, respectively. Suppose the algorithm expands n_1 next with successors n_2 and n_3. At this stage $\hat{g}(n_3) = 3 + 2 = 5$, and $\hat{g}(n_2)$ is lowered (because a less costly path to it has been found) to $3 + 3 = 6$. The value of $\hat{g}(n_1)$ remains equal to 3.

Next we must have an estimate $\hat{h}(n)$ of $h(n)$. *Here we rely on any heuristic information available from the problem domain.* Such information

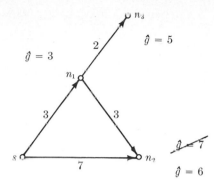

FIG. 3-7 *Example calculation of $\hat{g}$.*

might be similar to that used in deciding on the function $W(n)$ in the 8-puzzle example. We shall call $\hat{h}$ the *heuristic function* and will discuss it in more detail later.

Suppose we now use as an evaluation function

$$\hat{f}(n) = \hat{g}(n) + \hat{h}(n)$$

We shall call the ordered-search algorithm that uses this evaluation function algorithm A^*. Note that when $\hat{h} \equiv 0$, algorithm A^* is identical to the uniform-cost algorithm previously described.

We have stated earlier (without proof) that the uniform-cost algorithm is guaranteed to find a minimal cost path to a goal. We shall now show that if $\hat{h}$ is a lower bound on h, then algorithm A^* will also find an optimal path to a goal. (Since $\hat{h} \equiv 0$ is certainly a lower bound on h, the fact that the uniform-cost algorithm finds optimal paths will follow as a special case of this more general result for A^*.)

3-8 THE ADMISSIBILITY OF A^*

Let us say in general that a search algorithm is *admissible* if for any graph it always terminates in an optimal path to a goal whenever a path exists. In this section we shall prove that if $\hat{h}$ is a lower bound on h, then A^* is admissible. Our strategy for proving this result will be first to show (with this restriction on $\hat{h}$) that before termination of A^* there will always be some node on OPEN and on an optimal path whose $\hat{f}$ value is no greater than the actual cost $f(s)$ of an optimal path. Using this result, we see that the admissibility of A^* follows from the fact that the node on OPEN having a minimum value of $\hat{f}$ can never be a goal node (terminating the algorithm) until a goal node having an $\hat{f}$ value equal to $f(s)$ is found.

Thus we shall first prove a lemma that states that if the heuristic function $\hat{h}$ is a lower bound on h, then before termination of A^*, any optimal path has on it an open[1] node having an $\hat{f}$ value no greater than the actual cost $f(s)$ of an optimal path.

Lemma 3-1   If $\hat{h}(n) \leq h(n)$ for all n, then at any time before A^* terminates and for any optimal path P from node s to a goal, there exists an open node n' on P with $\hat{f}(n') \leq f(s)$.

Proof   Suppose an optimal path P is represented by the ordered sequence $(s = n_0, n_1, n_2, \ldots, n_k)$, where n_k is a goal node. Let n' be the first open node in the sequence. (There must be at least one, since if n_k is closed, A^* has terminated.) By the definition of $\hat{f}$ we have

$$\hat{f}(n') = \hat{g}(n') + \hat{h}(n')$$

We know that A^* has found an optimal path to n' since n' is on P and all of its antecedents on P are closed. Therefore $\hat{g}(n') = g(n')$ and

$$\hat{f}(n') = g(n') + \hat{h}(n')$$

Since we are assuming $\hat{h}(n') \leq h(n')$ we can write

$$\hat{f}(n') \leq g(n') + h(n') = f(n')$$

But the f value of any node on an optimal path is just equal to $f(s)$, the minimal cost, and therefore we have $\hat{f}(n') \leq f(s)$, as claimed by the lemma.

We now prove that if $\hat{h}$ is a lower bound on h, then A^* is admissible.

Theorem 3-1   If $\hat{h}(n) \leq h(n)$ for all nodes n, and if all arc costs are greater than some small positive number δ, then algorithm A^* is admissible.

Proof   We prove this theorem by assuming the contrary, namely that A^* does not always terminate by finding an optimal path from a start node s to a goal. There are three cases to consider: Either the algorithm terminates without finding a goal node, fails to terminate at all, or terminates at a goal node without achieving minimal cost.

Case 1: Termination without finding a goal node   Because of step 4 of the algorithm (p. 55), a successful termination cannot occur unless a goal node is found. The only other kind of termination,

---

[1] Any node on OPEN we shall say is open, and any node on CLOSED we shall say is closed. A nonclosed node is a node that is either on OPEN or one not yet produced by the search process.

a failure termination (step 2), can occur only if OPEN is empty. But from Lemma 3-1, we know that OPEN cannot be empty before termination if a path from s to a goal exists.

Case 2: No termination   Let t be a goal node attainable from the start in a finite number of steps, with associated minimum cost $f(s)$. Since the cost on any arc is at least δ, then for any node n farther than $M = f(s)/\delta$ steps from s we have $\hat{f}(n) \geq \hat{g}(n) \geq g(n) > M\delta = f(s)$. Clearly, no node n further than M steps from s is ever expanded, for by Lemma 3-1, there will be some open node n' on an optimal path such that $\hat{f}(n') \leq f(s) < \hat{f}(n)$, so by step 3 of the algorithm, A^* will select n' instead of n. Failure of A^* to terminate could then only be caused by continued reopening (in step 7) of nodes within M steps of s. Let $\chi(M)$ be the set of nodes accessible within M steps from s, and let $\nu(M)$ be the number of nodes in $\chi(M)$. Now, any node n in $\chi(M)$ can be reopened at most a finite number of times, say $\bar{\rho}(n,M)$, since there are only a finite number of paths from s to n passing only through nodes within M steps of s. Let

$$\rho(M) = \max_{n \in \chi(M)} \bar{\rho}(n,M)$$

the maximum number of times any one node can be reopened. Hence, after at most $\nu(M)\rho(M)$ expansions, all nodes in $\chi(M)$ must be forever closed. Since no nodes outside $\chi(M)$ can be expanded, A^* must terminate.

Case 3: Termination at a goal node without achieving minimal cost   Suppose A^* terminates at some goal node t with $\hat{f}(t) = \hat{g}(t) > f(s)$. But by Lemma 3-1 there existed just before termination an open node n' on an optimal path with $\hat{f}(n') \leq f(s) < \hat{f}(t)$. Thus at this stage, n' would have been selected for expansion rather than t, contradicting the assumption that A^* terminated.

The proof of Theorem 3-1 is now complete. In the next section we shall show that given another reasonable limitation on the function $\hat{h}(n)$, A^* is not only admissible but optimal in the sense that no other comparable admissible algorithm expands fewer nodes.

3-9   THE OPTIMALITY OF A^*

The precision of our heuristic function $\hat{h}$ depends on the amount of heuristic knowledge possessed about the problem domain modeled by the graph. Clearly, using $\hat{h}(n) = 0$ reflects complete absence of any heuristic information about the problem even though such an estimate is a lower bound on $h(n)$ and therefore leads to an admissible algorithm (the uniform-cost algorithm previously discussed). We shall say that algorithm A is *more informed* than algorithm B if the heuristic information used by A permits computing a lower bound on $h(n)$ that is everywhere *strictly* larger (for all nongoal nodes n) than that permitted by the heuristic information used by B. As an example, consider the 8-puzzle solved in Fig. 3-6. There we used the evaluation function $\hat{f}(n) = \hat{g}(n) + W(n)$. We can interpret the ordered-search process of that example as an application of A^* with $\hat{h}(n) = W(n)$. Since $W(n)$ is a lower bound on the number of steps remaining to the goal, algorithm A^* is admissible in this case. Furthermore, A^* with $\hat{h}(n) = W(n)$ is obviously more informed than the uniform-cost algorithm, which uses $\hat{h}(n) \equiv 0$.

We would expect intuitively that the more informed algorithm typically would need to expand fewer nodes in finding a minimal cost path. In the case of the 8-puzzle this observation is supported by comparing Figs. 3-2 and 3-6. Of course, merely because one algorithm expands fewer nodes than another does not imply that it is more efficient. The more informed algorithm may indeed have to make costly computations that destroy efficiency. Nevertheless, the number of nodes expanded by an algorithm is one of the factors that determines efficiency, and it is a factor that permits simple comparisons.

If we make one more mild restriction on the heuristic function $\hat{f}$, we can demonstrate that algorithm A^* is optimal in the following sense: Algorithm A^* never expands more nodes than does any other admissible algorithm A such that A^* is more informed than A. We shall precede a formal proof of the optimality of A^* by a brief description of the plan of the argument.

Consider any admissible algorithm A, such that A^* is more informed than A. We shall show that any node n expanded by A^* must also be expanded by A. To do this, we shall first need to demonstrate that the class of nodes expanded by A^* obeys the following restrictions:

When A^* expands any node n, it has already found an optimal path to n; that is, $\hat{g}(n) = g(n)$, and

When A^* expands a node n, the evaluation $\hat{f}(n)$ is no greater than the optimal cost $f(s)$.

Given these restrictions we will show that if A fails to expand a node n expanded by A^*, then A must have known that any path to the goal constrained to go through node n is nonoptimal. In short, algorithm A^* could not be more informed than algorithm A, if A can avoid expanding nodes that A^* expands.

Our first task, then, is to establish the two preliminary results stated above. It is obvious that for trees, $\hat{g}(n) = g(n)$ for all nodes n since there is only *one* path from the start node s to any node n in the tree. But, in general, we need to place one more restriction on $\hat{h}$ in order to show that whenever A^* expands a node in a *graph*, an optimal path to that node has already been found. We shall assume that for any two nodes m and n for which $k(m,n)$ exists,

$$\hat{h}(m) - \hat{h}(n) \le k(m,n)$$

That is, the difference between the estimated costs to the goal from any pair of nodes m and n must be a lower bound on the true cost of an optimal path from m to n. (Note that if $\hat{h} \equiv 0$ for goal nodes, then this restriction includes the previous one about $\hat{h}$ being a lower bound on h as can be seen by letting n be a goal node.) This new restriction will typically not be violated if the heuristic information used to calculate $\hat{h}$ is applied *consistently* at all nodes. Thus we shall call this assumption the *consistency assumption*. [It is easily verified, for example, that using $\hat{h} = W(n)$ in the 8-puzzle does satisfy the consistency assumption.] If the function $\hat{h}$ is changed in any manner *during* the search process, then the consistency assumption might not be satisfied.

With the consistency assumption, we can now prove in general that when A^* expands a node, an optimal path to that node has been found. This fact is important for two reasons: first, it is used in the proof of the theorem about the optimality of A^* to follow; and second it states that A^* need never redirect a pointer from a closed node since the optimal path to that node has already been found. Thus, the reopening provision in step (7) of the ordered-search algorithm (p. 55) is vacuous and may be eliminated when the consistency assumption is satisfied.

Lemma 3-2 Suppose the consistency assumption is satisfied, and suppose that node n is closed by A^*. Then $\hat{g}(n) = g(n)$.

Proof Consider the search tree of nodes generated by A^* just before closing n, and suppose the contrary, i.e., suppose $\hat{g}(n) > g(n)$. Now, there exists some optimal path P from s to n. Since $\hat{g}(n) > g(n)$, A^* did not find P. But by the reasoning of Lemma 3-1 there exists an open node n' on P with $\hat{g}(n') = g(n')$. If $n' = n$, we have proved the lemma. Otherwise,

$$g(n) = g(n') + k(n',n)$$
$$= \hat{g}(n') + k(n',n)$$

Thus, if we assume that $\hat{g}(n) > g(n)$, then

$$\hat{g}(n) > \hat{g}(n') + k(n',n)$$

Adding $\hat{h}(n)$ to both sides yields

$$\hat{g}(n) + \hat{h}(n) > \hat{g}(n') + k(n',n) + \hat{h}(n)$$

We can apply the consistency assumption to the right-hand side of the above inequality to yield

$$\hat{g}(n) + \hat{h}(n) > \hat{g}(n') + \hat{h}(n')$$

or

$$\hat{f}(n) > \hat{f}(n')$$

contradicting the fact that A^* selected n for expansion when n' was available and thus proving the lemma.

Next we must demonstrate that if $\hat{h}$ is a lower bound on h, then the $\hat{f}$ value of a node closed by A^* is never greater than the cost of an optimal path from s to a goal.

Lemma 3-3 For any node n closed by A^*, if $\hat{h}$ is a lower bound on h, then $\hat{f}(n) \leq f(s)$.

Proof This proof follows easily from Lemma 3-1. Let n be any node closed by A^*. If n is a goal node, we have $\hat{f}(n) = f(s)$ trivially; so suppose n is not a goal node. Now A^* closed n before termination, so at this time (by Lemma 3-1) we know that there existed some open node n' on an optimal path from s to a goal with $\hat{f}(n') \leq f(s)$. If $n = n'$, our proof is finished. Otherwise we know that A^* chose to expand n rather than n' so that it must have been the case that

$$\hat{f}(n) \leq \hat{f}(n') \leq f(s)$$

After having established these two lemmas, we can now prove the optimality of algorithm A^*.

Theorem 3-2 Let A and A^* be admissible algorithms such that A^* is more informed than A, and let the consistency assumption be satisfied by the $\hat{h}$ used in A^*. Then for any graph, if node n was expanded by A^*, it was also expanded by A.

Proof Suppose the contrary. Then there exists some node n expanded by A^* but not by A. (Because A^* expanded node n we know that n is not a goal node.) If algorithm A never expanded node n it must have been because algorithm A used information that any path to a goal through node n would have had a cost larger than or equal to $f(s)$, the true cost of an optimal path to a goal. (If there were a less costly path to a goal through node n, algorithm

A would certainly have missed it and thus would be inadmissible, contrary to our assumption. Thus, we must assume that algorithm A "knew" that there was no less costly path through node n.) The actual cost of an optimal path constrained to go through node n is

$$f(n) = g(n) + h(n)$$

from which we can state that

$$h(n) = f(n) - g(n)$$

Now, as argued above, algorithm A knows that $f(n) \geq f(s)$ and therefore it knows that

$$h(n) \geq f(s) - g(n)$$

Such information available to algorithm A would permit a lower bound estimate of

$$\hat{h}(n) = f(s) - g(n)$$

On the other hand, algorithm A^* used the evaluation function

$$\hat{f}(n) = \hat{g}(n) + \hat{h}(n)$$

We know from Lemma 3-3 that

$$\hat{f}(n) \leq f(s)$$

Thus we know

$$\hat{g}(n) + \hat{h}(n) \leq f(s)$$

Therefore, whatever the $\hat{h}$ function used by A^* it must have satisfied the inequality

$$\hat{h}(n) \leq f(s) - \hat{g}(n)$$

Now, at the time A^* expanded node n, $\hat{g}(n) = g(n)$ by Lemma 3-2 and thus

$$\hat{h}(n) \leq f(s) - g(n)$$

But now we see that, at least for node n, algorithm A used information permitting a lower bound on h at least as large as the lower bound used by algorithm A^*. Thus A^* could not be more informed than A, contradicting our assumption and proving the theorem.

3-10 THE HEURISTIC POWER OF $\hat{h}$

The selection of $\hat{h}$ is crucial in determining the heuristic power of the ordered-search algorithm. Using $\hat{h} \equiv 0$ assures admissibility but results in blind search and is thus usually inefficient. Setting $\hat{h}$ equal to the highest possible lower bound on h expands the fewest nodes consistent with maintaining admissibility.

Often heuristic power can be gained at the expense of giving up admissibility by using for $\hat{h}$ some function that is not a lower bound on h. This added heuristic power then allows us to solve much harder problems. In the 8-puzzle, the function $\hat{h}(n) = W(n)$ (where $W(n)$ is the number of tiles in the wrong place) is a lower bound on $h(n)$, but it does not provide a very good estimate of the difficulty (in terms of number of steps to the goal) of a tile configuration. A better estimate is the function $\hat{h}(n) = P(n)$, where $P(n)$ is the sum of the distances that each tile is from "home" (ignoring intervening pieces). Even this estimate is too gross, however, in that it does not accurately appraise the difficulty of exchanging the positions of two adjacent tiles.

An estimate that works quite well for the 8-puzzle is

$$\hat{h}(n) = P(n) + 3\,S(n)$$

The quantity $S(n)$ is a *sequence score* obtained by checking around the noncentral squares in turn, allotting 2 for every tile not followed by its proper successor and 0 for every other tile, except that a piece in the center scores 1. We note that this $\hat{h}$ function does not provide a lower bound for h.

With this $\hat{h}$ used in the evaluation function $\hat{f}(n) = \hat{g}(n) + \hat{h}(n)$, we can easily solve much more difficult 8-puzzles than the one we solved earlier. In Fig. 3-8 we show the tree resulting from applying the ordered-search algorithm with this evaluation function to the problem of transforming

Again the $\hat{f}$ value of each node is circled, and the uncircled numbers show the order in which nodes are expanded.

The solution path found happens to be of minimal length (18 steps), although since the $\hat{h}$ function is not a lower bound for h, we were not guaranteed finding an optimal path. Note that this $\hat{h}$ function results in a focusing of search rather directly toward the goal; only a very limited amount of spreading occurred, and that was near the start.

Another factor that determines the heuristic power of the ordered-

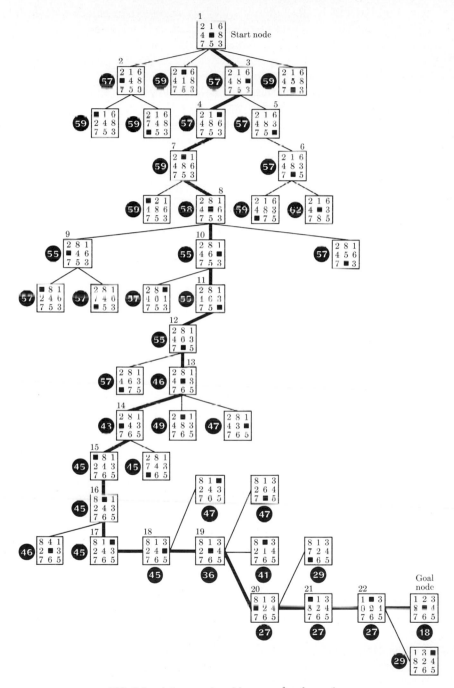

FIG. 3-8 *A tree produced by an ordered search.*

search algorithm is the amount of effort involved in calculating $\hat{h}$. The best $\hat{h}$ would be a function identically equal to h, resulting in an absolute minimum number of node expansions. Such an $\hat{h}$ could, for example, be determined as a result of a separate complete search at every node, but this obviously would not reduce the total computational effort.

Sometimes an $\hat{h}$ function that is not a lower bound on h is easier to compute than one that is. In these cases the heuristic power might be doubly improved—because the total number of nodes expanded may be reduced (at the expense of admissibility) *and* the computational effort is reduced. In certain cases the heuristic power of a given $\hat{h}$ can be increased simply by multiplying it by some positive constant greater than unity. If this factor is *very* large, the situation is as if $\hat{g}(n) \equiv 0$. Such a selection, of course, leads to an inadmissible algorithm but one that might nevertheless perform satisfactorily. In fact, one might intuitively suppose that setting $\hat{g}(n) \equiv 0$ would increase search efficiency in those cases in which *any* path (not necessarily the least costly) to the goal is desired. In the next section we shall present some results counter to such intuition.

To summarize, there are three important factors influencing the heuristic power of an ordered-search algorithm:

1. The cost of the path
2. The number of nodes expanded in finding the path
3. The computational effort required to compute $\hat{h}$

The selection of a suitable $\hat{h}$ then permits one to choose for each problem a desirable compromise among these factors to maximize heuristic power.

3-11 THE IMPORTANCE OF $\hat{g}$

In many problems, we merely desire to find *some* path to a goal node and are unconcerned about the cost of the resulting path. (We are, of course, concerned about the amount of search effort required to find a path.) In such situations, intuitive arguments can be given both for including $\hat{g}$ in the evaluation function and for ignoring it.

Intuitive argument for ignoring $\hat{g}$

When merely any path to a goal is desired, $\hat{g}$ can be ignored since, at any stage during the search, we don't care about the costs of the paths developed thus far. We care only about the remaining search effort required to find a goal node, and this search effort, while possibly dependent on the $\hat{h}$ values of the open nodes, is certainly independent of the $\hat{g}$ values of the open nodes. Therefore, for such problems we should use as the evaluation function $\hat{f} \equiv \hat{h}$.

Intuitive argument for including $\hat{g}$

Even when it is not essential to find a path of minimal cost, $\hat{g}$ should be included in $\hat{f}$ to be sure that *some* path will eventually be found. Such insurance is necessary whenever $\hat{h}$ is not a perfect estimator, for if that node with minimum $\hat{h}$ were always expanded, the search process might forever expand deceptive nodes without ever reaching a goal node. Including $\hat{g}$ tends to add a breadth-first component to the search and thus ensures that no part of the graph will go permanently unsearched.

Both of these arguments seem reasonable, although we believe the second to be the sounder of the two. In certain special cases the second argument can even be supported by analysis.

We shall consider the case of an infinite graph *in the shape of* (but not actually) an infinite m-ary tree. (An infinite m-ary tree is a tree in which every node has precisely m successors.) The graph has a unique goal node at the kth level; note that the goal is accessible from *every* node in this particular graph. An illustration of such a graph is given in Fig. 3-9. We assume arc costs of unity.

FIG. 3-9   *A graph in the shape of an infinite m-ary tree.*

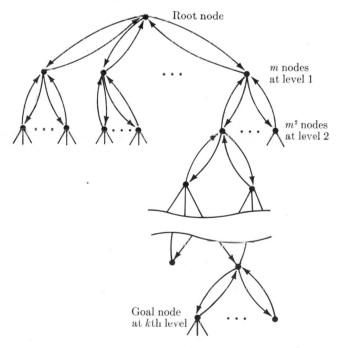

Root node

m nodes at level 1

m^2 nodes at level 2

Goal node at kth level

Suppose that in searching this graph we use the following $\hat{h}$ function:

$$\hat{h}(n) = h(n) + E \qquad \text{for nodes } n \text{ on the shortest path}$$
$$= h(n) - E \qquad \text{for nodes } n \text{ off the shortest path}$$

where E is some *integer error*. That is, our $\hat{h}$ function is always in error by an amount equal to some integer E.[1]

Furthermore, the sign of the error has been chosen to be the most harmful. We shall show, using a worst-case analysis, that for such an $\hat{h}$ function, a search with $\hat{f} = \hat{g} + \hat{h}$ is more efficient than a search with $\hat{f} = \hat{h}$ whenever $E > 1$.

We have two cases to compare:

Case 1: $\hat{f} = \hat{g} + \hat{h}$ Let $N_{g+h} =$ number of nodes expanded before reaching the goal. Here we must expand a node if it lies within E units from a node on the shortest path. (In the spirit of our worst-case analysis, we shall always resolve ties in the least favorable way.) We see then that

$$N_{g+h} = k\{1 + (m-1) \text{ [number of nodes in an } m\text{-ary tree of}$$
$$\text{depth } E - 1]\}$$

$$= k\left\{1 + (m-1)\left[\frac{m^E - 1}{m-1}\right]\right\}$$

$$= km^E$$

Case 2: $\hat{f} = \hat{h}$ Let $N_h =$ number of nodes expanded before reaching the goal. Here we must expand a node if it lies within $2E - 1$ units from a node on the shortest path. (Deceptively promising nodes in this case cause the search to wander farther from the shortest path to the goal.) So now for $E \geq 1$ we have

$$N_h = k\{1 + (m-1) \text{ [number of nodes in an } m\text{-ary tree of}$$
$$\text{depth } 2E - 2]\}$$

$$= k\left\{1 + (m-1)\left[\frac{m^{2E-1} - 1}{m-1}\right]\right\}$$

$$= km^{2E-1}$$

(Another analysis produces $N_h = k$ for $E = 0$.)

We see that N_h is larger than N_{g+h} for $E > 1$, demonstrating that (for this graph) efficient search demands including $\hat{g}$ in the evaluation function. The ratio N_{g+h}/N_h is independent of k and is simply given by

$$\frac{N_{g+h}}{N_h} = \frac{1}{m^{E-1}} \qquad \text{for } E \geq 1$$

---

[1] Note that our $\hat{h}$ function in this case does not provide a lower bound on h.

Although this contrast in efficiency might be softened somewhat in actual problems, this worst-case analysis illustrates in extreme form the substance of the intuitive argument for the importance of including $\hat{g}$.

3-12 USE OF OTHER HEURISTICS

Staged search

The use of heuristic information as discussed so far in this chapter can substantially reduce the amount of search effort required to find acceptable paths. Its use, therefore, also allows much larger graphs to be searched than otherwise. Even so, there may arise occasions when available storage is exhausted before a satisfactory path is found. Rather than abandon the search process completely in such cases, it may be desirable to "prune" the tree so far generated by the search, thus freeing needed storage space to be used in pressing the search deeper.

The search process can then continue in stages punctuated by pruning operations to obtain storage space. At the end of each stage some subset of the open nodes, e.g., those having the smallest values of $\hat{f}$, are marked for retention. The best paths to these nodes are remembered, and the rest of the tree thrown away. Search then begins again, starting with these "best" open nodes. This process continues until either a goal node is found or resources are exhausted. Of course, even if A^* is used in each stage and the whole process does terminate in a path, there is now no guarantee that it is an optimal path.

Limitation of successors

It was mentioned earlier in this chapter that another way to reduce search is to provide a more informed Γ that doesn't generate so many extraneous successors. In the limit, a "fully informed" Γ would generate only that successor on an optimal path, obviating entirely the need for search.

One technique that may save search effort is to throw away immediately after expansion all successors except a few having the smallest values of $\hat{f}$. Of course the nodes thrown away may be on the best (or the only!) paths, so the value of any such pruning method for particular problems can be determined only by experience.

There are also search problems for which the successors of a node can be enumerated and their $\hat{h}$'s computed before the corresponding state descriptions themselves are explicitly calculated. Furthermore, it may pay to delay calculating the state description associated with a node until it itself is expanded. Then the process never calculates any extraneous successors that are never expanded by the algorithm.

Generation of one successor at a time

When the successors of a node are calculated by using state-space operators, then successors obviously can be calculated individually and independently of each other. Furthermore, there are cases in which the application of *all* applicable operators would be very costly computationally. As mentioned above, a more informed Γ would single out the few most promising operators and calculate only the successors resulting from applying these. A more flexible policy would allow the application of *the* most promising operator first (resulting in a single successor) while allowing the possibility later in the search of generating more successors. Appropriate modifications would have to be made to the ordered-search algorithm in order to use this idea in conjunction with the use of evaluation functions for node ordering.

3-13   MEASURES OF PERFORMANCE

The heuristic power of a searching technique depends heavily on the particular factors specific to a given problem, and its determination is a judgment usually based on experience rather than on calculation. Certain measures of performance can be calculated, however, and though they do not completely determine heuristic power, they are nevertheless useful in comparing various searching techniques.

One such measure is called *penetrance*. The penetrance P of a search measures the extent to which the search has focused toward a goal rather than wandered off in irrelevant directions. It is simply defined as

$$P = \frac{L}{T}$$

where L is the length of the path found to the goal and T is the total number of nodes generated during the search (including the goal node but not including the start node). For example, if the successor operator Γ is so precise that the only nodes generated are those on a path toward the goal, P will attain its maximum value of 1. Blind search is characterized by small values of P. Thus, penetrance measures the extent to which the tree generated by the search is elongated rather than bushy.

TABLE 3-1 *Penetrance and Effective Branching Factor for Various Examples*

	8-PUZZLE 1 BREADTH FIRST	8-PUZZLE 1 $\hat{f} = \hat{g} + W(n)$	8-PUZZLE 2 $\hat{f} = \hat{g} +$ $P(n) + 3S(n)$
Penetrance P	5/46	5/13	18/43
	0.108	0.385	0.419
Effective branching factor B	1.86	1.34	1.08

The penetrance values of some of the search examples used in this chapter are given in Table 3-1.

The penetrance value of a search depends on the difficulty of the problem being searched as well as on the efficiency of the search method. A *given* search method might have a high penetrance value when the optimal solution path is short and a much lower one when it is long. (Increasing the length of the solution path L usually causes T to increase even faster.)

Another measure, the effective branching factor B, is more nearly independent of the length of the optimal solution path. Its definition is based on imagining a tree having a depth equal to the path length and a total number of nodes equal to the number generated during the search. Then B is the constant number of successors that would be possessed by each node in such a tree. Therefore, B is related to path length L, and total number of nodes generated T, by the expressions

$$B + B^2 + \cdots + B^L = T$$

and

$$\frac{B}{B - 1} (B^L - 1) = T$$

Although B cannot be written explicitly as a function of L and T, a plot of it versus T for various values of L is given in Fig. 3-10. A value of B near unity corresponds to a search that is highly focused toward the goal with very little branching in other directions. On the other hand, a bushy search graph would have a high value of B.

The B values for our example searches have been obtained using Fig. 3-10 and are given along with the penetrance measures in Table 3-1. Penetrance can be related to B and path length by the expression $P = L(B - 1)/B(B^L - 1)$. In Fig. 3-11 we illustrate how penetrance varies with path length for various values of B.

To the extent that B is reasonably independent of path length, it can be used to give a prediction of how many nodes might be generated in

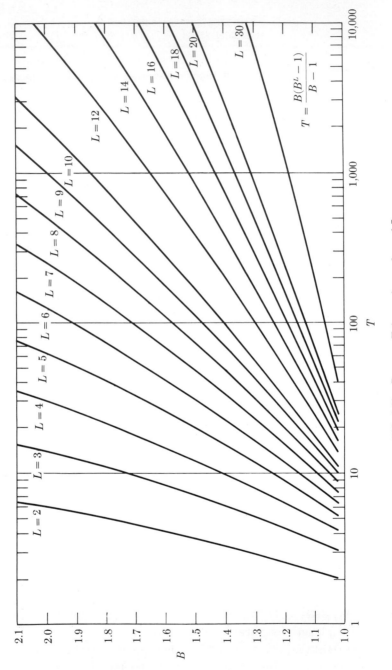

FIG. 3-10 B versus T for various values of L.

$$T = \frac{B(B^L - 1)}{B - 1}$$

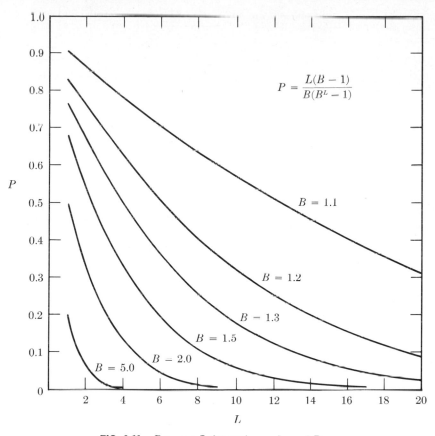

FIG. 3-11 *P versus L for various values of B.*

searches of various lengths. For example, we note from Table 3-1 that
$\hat{f} = \hat{g} + P + 3S$ resulted in a value of B equal to 1.08 for an 8-puzzle
problem. Suppose we wanted to estimate how many nodes would be
generated using this same $\hat{f}$ function in solving a more difficult 8-puzzle
problem, say one requiring 30 steps. From Fig. 3-10 we note that the
30-step puzzle would involve the generation of about 120 nodes, assuming
that the branching factor remained constant. [This estimate incidentally
is not inconsistent with the experimental results of Doran and Michie
(1966) on a wide variety of 8-puzzle problems.]

3-14 BIBLIOGRAPHICAL AND HISTORICAL REMARKS

Shortest-path algorithms

Efficient methods for finding the shortest (or least costly) path between
two nodes in a graph are of great interest in a variety of disciplines.

The procedure that we have called the uniform-cost method was first described by Dijkstra (1959). A similar breadth-first search technique was also proposed by Moore (1959). Also, the dynamic programming algorithms of Bellman are essentially breadth-first search methods. For a thorough discussion of dynamic programming see the book by Bellman and Dreyfus (1962). A depth-first search procedure, often called *backtrack programming* in computer science, is described by Golomb and Baumert (1965). Stuart Dreyfus (1969) presents a detailed survey of these and other graph searching methods.

Heuristic search techniques

The use of heuristic information to increase search efficiency has been studied both in artificial intelligence and in operations research. Probably the most well-known use of heuristic evaluation functions has been in game-playing programs, notably the checker-playing program of Samuel (1959, 1967). The use of evaluation functions to direct the search of state-space graphs has been proposed by Doran and Michie (1966) and further discussed by Doran (1968) and by Michie and Ross (1970). Our examples using the 8-puzzle are based on those of Doran and Michie. A general theory of the use of evaluation functions to guide search was presented in a paper by Hart, Nilsson, and Raphael (1968); our description of the ordered-search algorithm and its properties is based on that paper.

In the branch-and-bound methods of operations research we also see the use of evaluation functions to guide search. For a description of these see the survey article by Lawler and Wood (1966). The branch-and-bound technique proposed by Shapiro (1966) for the traveling-salesman problem can also be interpreted as a direct application of algorithm A^*.

Our analysis supporting the importance of including $\hat{g}$ (as well as $\hat{h}$) is taken from a dissertation by Pohl (1969). [See also Pohl (1970).] Pohl (1969) considers also the problem of searching outward from both start and goal nodes. Particularly interesting here is his thorough discussion of the more complex termination criterion needed for bidirectional search.

Punctuating the search process by occasional tree pruning (to reclaim needed storage space) was investigated by Doran and Michie (1966) and by Doran (1967).

Measures of performance

Doran and Michie (1966) proposed the penetrance measure for judging the efficiency of a given search. Slagle and Dixon (1969) propose another measure which they call the "depth ratio." Our "effective branching factor" was motivated by these earlier measures.

PROBLEMS

3-1 Consider the state-space representation of the traveling-salesman problem presented in Sec. 2-6. Propose at least two $\hat{h}$ functions ($\hat{h} \neq 0$) that give lower bounds on h. In your opinion, which of these would result in more efficient search? Apply A^* with these $\hat{h}$ functions to the five-city problem shown in Fig. 2-4.

3-2 Using the map of Fig. 2-4 plan, by a state-space method, a *maximal* mileage trip that starts at A, visits no other city more than once, and returns to A. Select a state representation and show part of the resulting state-space graph with the nodes and arc costs appropriately labeled and indicate the optimal path from start to goal in the graph.

3-3 Discuss the possible advantages of the following state-space search strategy: Obtain by any convenient method *some* path to a goal node and its associated cost C. This cost is not necessarily minimal but does give an upper bound on the minimal cost. Now use algorithm A^* with an $\hat{h}$ function that guarantees admissibility and discard immediately any open nodes reached whose $\hat{f}$ values are greater than C. Is this modified strategy admissible? Does the fact that the algorithm might discard some of the open nodes mean that fewer nodes might be expanded? Does it reduce the total storage requirements?

3-4 Suppose $\hat{h}$ is a lower bound on h. Prove that if A^* ever expands a node n with $\hat{f}(n) = f(s)$, then either n was on an optimal path, or just before expansion there was a node m on OPEN and on an optimal path such that $\hat{f}(n) = \hat{f}(m) = f(s)$.

3-5 Let $n_1, n_2, \ldots, n_k$ be the sequence of nodes expanded by A^*. Prove that if $\hat{h}$ satisfies the consistency assumption (see Sec. 3-9), then $\hat{f}(n_i) \leq \hat{f}(n_{i+1})$ for any $1 \leq i < k - 1$.

3-6 † Using the most advanced of the representations for the missionaries-and-cannibals problem given in Amarel (1968), write a program that produces a minimal move solution for any number n of missionaries and cannibals and any boat capacity k.

3-7 † Write a computer program that uses algorithm A^* to solve the problem of transforming an arbitrary configuration of the *sliding block puzzle* into the configuration

when such a transformation is possible.

REFERENCES

Amarel, S. (1968) : On Representations of Problems of Reasoning about Actions, in D. Michie (ed.), "Machine Intelligence 3," pp. 131–171, American Elsevier Publishing Company, Inc., New York, 1968.

Bellman, R. and S. Dreyfus (1962) : "Applied Dynamic Programming," Princeton University Press, Princeton, N.J., 1962.

Dijkstra, E. (1959) : A Note on Two Problems in Connection with Graphs, *Numerische Math.*, vol. 1, 269–271, 1959.

Doran, J. (1967) : An Approach to Automatic Problem-Solving, in N. Collins and D. Michie (eds.), "Machine Intelligence 1," pp. 105–123, American Elsevier Publishing Company, Inc., New York, 1967.

———— (1968) : New Developments of the Graph Traverser, in E. Dale and D. Michie (eds.), "Machine Intelligence 2," pp. 119–135, American Elsevier Publishing Company, Inc., New York, 1968.

———— and D. Michie (1966) : Experiments with the Graph Traverser Program, *Proc. Roy. Soc.*, A, vol. 294, pp. 235–259, 1966.

Dreyfus, S. (1969) : An Appraisal of Some Shortest Path Algorithms, *Operations Res.*, vol. 17, no. 3, pp. 395–412, May–June 1969.

Golomb, S. and L. Baumert (1965) : Backtrack Programming, *J. ACM*, vol. 12, no. 4, pp. 516–524, 1965.

Hart, P., N. Nilsson, and B. Raphael (1968) : A Formal Basis for the Heuristic Determination of Minimum Cost Paths, *IEEE Trans. Sys. Sci. Cybernetics*, vol. SSC-4, no. 2, pp. 100–107, July 1968.

Lawler, E. and D. Wood (1966) : Branch and Bound Methods: A Survey, *Operations Res.*, vol. 14, no. 4, pp. 699–719, July–August 1966.

Michie, D. and R. Ross (1970) : Experiments with the Adaptive Graph Traverser, in B. Meltzer and D. Michie (eds.), "Machine Intelligence 5," pp. 301–318, American Elsevier Publishing Company, Inc., New York, 1970.

Moore, E. (1959) : The Shortest Path Through a Maze, *Proc. Intern. Symp. Theory Switching, Part II*, April 2–5, 1957, The Annals of the Computation Laboratory of Harvard University 30, Harvard University Press, Cambridge, Mass., 1959.

Pohl, I. (1969): "Bi-Directional and Heuristic Search in Path Problems," doctoral dissertation, Computer Science Dept., Stanford University Press, Stanford, Calif., 1969. Also printed as *Stanford Linear Accelerator Center Report* no. 104, May 1969.

———— (1970): First Results on the Effect of Error in Heuristic Search, in B. Meltzer and D. Michie (eds.), "Machine Intelligence 5," American Elsevier Publishing Company, Inc., New York, 1970.

Samuel, A. (1959): Some Studies in Machine Learning Using the Game of Checkers, *IBM J. Res. Develop.*, vol. 3, no. 3, pp. 211–229, 1959. Reprinted in E. Feigenbaum and J. Feldman (eds.), "Computers and Thought," pp. 71–105, McGraw-Hill Book Company, New York, 1963.

———— (1967): Some Studies in Machine Learning Using the Game of Checkers II. Recent Progress, *IBM J. Res. Develop.*, vol. 11, no. 6, pp. 601–617, November 1967.

Shapiro, D. (1966): Algorithms for the Solution of the Optimal Cost Traveling Salesman Problem, Sc.D. thesis, Washington University, St. Louis, Mo., 1966.

Slagle, J. and J. Dixon (1969): "Experiments with Some Programs That Search Game Trees," *J. ACM*, vol. 16, no. 2, pp. 189–207, April 1969.

CHAPTER FOUR

PROBLEM-REDUCTION REPRESENTATIONS

4-1 AN EXAMPLE OF A PROBLEM-REDUCTION REPRESENTATION

In this chapter we shall explore another approach to problem solving, that of *problem reduction*. The theme of this approach is to "reason backward" from the problem to be solved, establishing subproblems and sub-subproblems until, finally, the original problem is reduced to a set of trivial *primitive* problems.

We shall consider another puzzle in order to illustrate how a problem might be solved by the problem-reduction approach. A version of the *Tower-of-Hanoi puzzle* can be stated as follows:

There are three pegs—1, 2, and 3—and three disks of differing

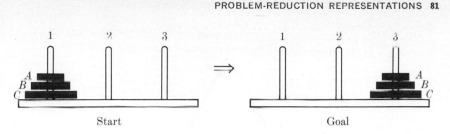

Start   Goal

FIG. 4-1 *The Tower-of-Hanoi puzzle.*

sizes *A*, *B*, and *C*. The disks have holes in their centers so that they can be stacked on the pegs. Initially the disks are all on peg 1; the largest, disk *C*, is on the bottom, and the smallest, disk *A*, is on top. It is desired to transfer all of the disks to peg 3 by moving disks one at a time. Only the top disk on a peg can be moved, but it can never be placed on top of a smaller disk. The initial and goal configurations are shown in Fig. 4-1.

This problem can, of course, be solved by a state-space approach. In fact, the graph of Fig. 4-2 illustrates the complete state space.[1] The graph has 27 nodes, each representing one of the legal configurations of disks on pegs. The notation (*ijk*) labeling each node describes a state in which disk *C* (the largest) is on peg *i*, disk *B* on *j*, and disk *A* (the smallest) on *k*. If more than one disk is on the same peg, it is assumed that the largest is on the bottom, etc. The arcs connecting pairs of nodes mean that a disk can be transferred such that the configuration represented by one node in the pair is changed to that represented by the other. For example, the arc pointing from (113) to (123) means that (113) can be changed into (123) by the action of moving disk *B* from peg 1 to peg 2. This action is represented by the label "Move (*B*,1,2)" on the arc. (The path indicated by heavy lines in the graph represents a solution.)

The Tower-of-Hanoi puzzle can also be solved by a simple problem-reduction approach. One way of reducing the original Tower-of Hanoi problem illustrated in Fig. 4-1 to a set of simpler problems involves the following chain of reasoning:

1. In order to move all of the disks to peg 3, we must certainly move disk *C* there, and peg 3 must be empty just prior to moving disk *C* to it.
2. Now looking at the initial configuration, we cannot move disk *C* anywhere until disks *A* and *B* are first removed. Furthermore, disks *A* and *B* had better not be moved to peg 3 since then we would not

[1] This graph was suggested by Professor John McCarthy (personal communication).

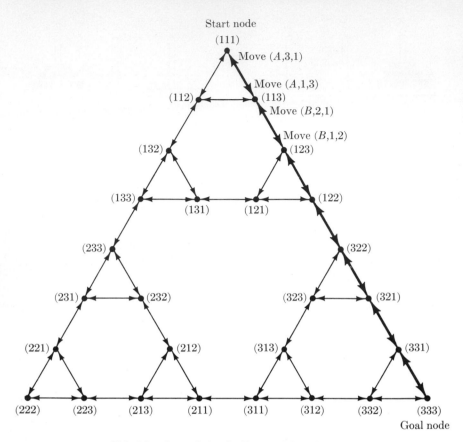

FIG. 4-2 *A graph for the Tower-of-Hanoi puzzle.*

be able to move disk *C* there. Therefore we should first move disks *A* and *B* to peg **2**.
3. Then we can complete the key step of moving disk *C* from peg 1 to peg 3 and go on to solve the rest of the puzzle.

We see that this argument allows us to reduce the original puzzle to the following three puzzles:

1. The two-disk puzzle of moving disks *A* and *B* to peg **2**:

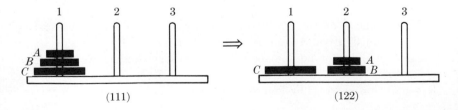

2. The one-disk puzzle of moving disk C to peg 3:

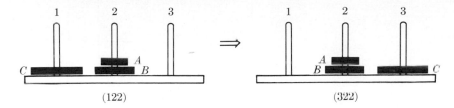

(122)   (322)

3. The two-disk puzzle of moving disks A and B to peg 3:

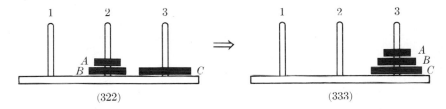

(322)   (333)

Since each of these three reduced puzzles is a smaller one, each ought to be easier to solve than the original puzzle. In fact, puzzle number **2** can be considered primitive, since its solution involves just one move. By using a similar chain of reasoning, puzzles 1 and 3 can be reduced to primitive ones also, as is shown schematically in Fig. 4-3. (This same reduction scheme can be applied to an initial configuration with an arbitrary number of disks.)

The graph structure of Fig. 4-3 is called an AND/OR graph (or subproblem graph) and is useful for illustrating solutions obtained by the problem-reduction approach. In this and the next chapter we shall consider in detail the topic of applying the reduction approach to problem solving. Reduction methods have been applied to a variety of problems including the problem of producing an expression that is the integral of a mathematical function and the problem of proving theorems in plane geometry. We shall also see that reduction methods are quite similar to those involved in calculating the best next move in a game such as checkers or chess.

4-2 PROBLEM DESCRIPTIONS

The problem-reduction approach employs operators that transform *problem descriptions* into subproblem descriptions. Problem descriptions can be of a variety of forms. Again, lists, trees, strings, vectors, arrays, and other forms have been used. In the Tower-of-Hanoi puzzle, the subproblems can be described by a list of two lists. Thus the problem

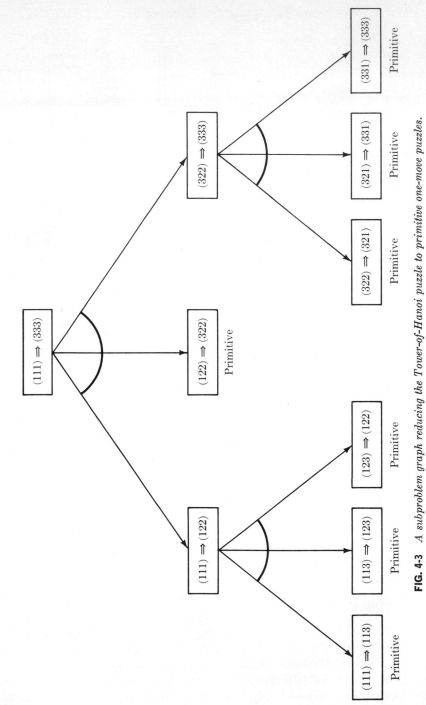

FIG. 4-3 A subproblem graph reducing the Tower-of-Hanoi puzzle to primitive one-move puzzles.

description [(113), (333)], means: "Change configuration (113) into configuration (333)."

Often it is convenient to describe a problem in terms of the elements of a state-space representation. We have seen that any state-space search problem can be represented by three entities:

1. The set S of starting states
2. The set F of operators that map state descriptions into state descriptions
3. The set G of goal states

The triple (S,F,G) then defines a problem and can be used as a problem description. In the Tower-of-Hanoi puzzle, we used essentially this notation although the set F of state-space operators was assumed to be the same for all problems and thus was not explicitly mentioned in the problem descriptions.

When problems and subproblems are described by (S,F,G) triples, the subproblems are easily recognized as problems of finding paths between certain *stepping-stone* states in the state space. For example, in the Tower-of-Hanoi problem, the subproblems [(111) $\Rightarrow$ (122)], [(122) $\Rightarrow$ (322)], and [(322) $\Rightarrow$ (333)] define the stepping-stone states (122) and (322) that the final solution path will go through.

Merely because the problem-reduction approach might use the notions of states, operators, and goals in describing problems does not mean that the problem-reduction and the state-space approaches are fundamentally identical. Actually, as we have already pointed out, the incremental state-space search employs a trivial type of problem reduction, and thus the problem-reduction approach might be viewed as a more general solution method than the incremental state-space approach. One could think of the problem-reduction approach simply as providing the means for enumerating the separate searches for subpaths between proposed stepping stones in the state space, and for monitoring the progress toward assembling subpaths into complete solutions.

4-3 PROBLEM-REDUCTION OPERATORS

A problem-reduction operator transforms a problem description into a set of *reduced* or *successor* problem descriptions. The transformation is such that solutions to *all* of the successor problems imply a solution to the parent problem. When the set of successor problems contains a single member, we have the simple case in which one problem is replaced by another equivalent problem.

For any given problem description there may be many reduction operators that are applicable. Each of these produces an alternative set of subproblems. Some of the subproblems may not be solvable, however, so we may have to try several operators in order to produce a set whose members are *all* solvable. Thus the problem of search appears again.

One class of problems involves proving[1] that certain statements are true. Let S stand for a statement that we want to prove true and let T stand for a set of premise statements assumed to be true. Then we shall let $S|T$ (read "S given T") describe the problem of proving S, given the premises in T. A common scheme for reducing problems of this sort is to introduce new premises into the original problem and then set up the additional problems of proving the new premises. Thus in reducing the problem $S|T$ we add, say, N premises to obtain the set of reduced problems:

$$S|T, X_1, X_2, \ldots , X_N$$
$$X_1|T, X_2, \ldots , X_N$$
.
.
.
$$X_N|T$$

where $X_1, X_2, \ldots , X_N$ are n extra premises. Often this reduction operator is applied by adding just one premise at a time. Then $S|T$ is reduced to the set $S|X,T$ and $X|T$.

We might think of the premise symbols $X_1, \ldots , X_N$ as variables that range over some set of premises. Each possible instantiation then corresponds to the application of a different problem-reduction operator. The variables can be instantiated immediately by specific premises (possibly containing new variables) or instead can be left as variables to be instantiated at later reductions. Later we shall consider some suggested approaches for premise instantiation. Often we will want to instantiate with more than one set of specific premises so that our proof can reason backward along alternative lines.

4-4 PRIMITIVE PROBLEM DESCRIPTIONS

The object of all problem reductions, of course, is to produce eventually primitive problems whose solutions are obvious. These problems may be ones that can be solved by one move in a state-space search or they may be other more complex problems having known solutions. Besides playing an obvious role in terminating the search process, the primi-

---

[1] Our discussion of proofs in this chapter will be quite informal. In subsequent chapters we shall treat more formally the subject of proof and its role in problem solving.

tive problems are sometimes used to restrict the generation of alternative sets of successor problems during the reduction process. This restriction comes about by insisting that one or more of the successors belong to a specified subclass of the primitive problems.

4-5 AND/OR GRAPHS

We can conveniently diagram the reduction of a problem to alternative sets of successor problems by a graph-like structure. Thus, suppose problem A can be solved either by solving problems B and C or by solving problems D and E, or by solving problem F. This relationship is shown by the structure in Fig. 4-4. The nodes of this structure are labeled by the problems they represent.

Problems B and C constitute one set of successor problems, problems D and E another, and problem F, a third. The nodes corresponding to a given set are indicated by a special mark linking their incoming arcs.

It is usual to introduce some extra nodes into the structure so that each set containing more than one successor problem is grouped below its own parent node. With this convention the structure of Fig. 4-4 becomes as shown in Fig. 4-5. There, the added nodes labeled N and M serve as exclusive parents for sets $\{B,C\}$ and $\{D,E\}$, respectively. If one thinks of N and M as playing the role of problem descriptions, then we see that problem A is reduced to single *alternative* subproblems N, M, or F. For this reason the nodes labeled N, M, and F are called OR nodes. Problem N, however, is reduced to a single set of subproblems B and C, *all* of which must be solved to solve N. For this reason the nodes labeled B and C are called AND nodes. AND nodes are indicated by marks on their incoming arcs.

Structures like that shown in Fig. 4-5 are called AND/OR graphs.

FIG. 4-4 *A structure showing the alternative sets of subproblems for A.*

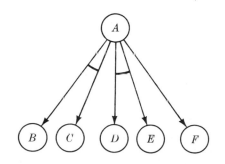

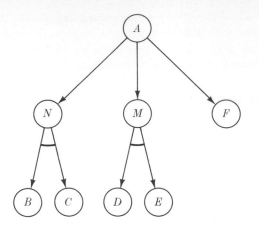

FIG. 4-5 *An AND/OR graph.*

In AND/OR graphs, if a node has any successors at all they are either all OR nodes, or all AND nodes. (When a node has a single successor, then, of course, this successor can be viewed either as an OR node or an AND node.)

We note that in the special case in which no AND nodes occur at all, we have an ordinary graph of the type occurring in the state-space searches. Because of the presence of AND nodes in AND/OR graphs, however, these structures are quite different from ordinary graph structures. They call for their own specialized search techniques, and this is the primary reason for distinguishing between the two problem-solving approaches.

In describing AND/OR graphs we shall continue to use terms like *parent* nodes, *successor* nodes, and an *arc* connecting two nodes, giving them the obvious meanings.

In terms of AND/OR graphs, the typical application of a single problem-reduction operator to a problem description produces one intermediate OR node and its AND node successors in turn. (The exception is when the set of subproblems contains a single member, in which case just the OR node is produced.)

Thus, the relevant structure modeling the problem-reduction method is an AND/OR graph. One of the nodes in this graph, called the *start node*, corresponds to the original problem description. Those nodes in the graph corresponding to primitive problem descriptions are called *terminal* nodes.

The object of the search process carried out on an AND/OR graph is to show that the start node is *solved*. The general definition of a *solved* node in an AND/OR graph can be given recursively as follows:

The terminal nodes are solved nodes (since they are associated with primitive problems)

If a nonterminal node has OR successors, then it is a solved node if and only if at least *one* of its successors is solved

If a nonterminal node has AND successors, then it is a solved node if and only if *all* of its successors are solved

A *solution graph* is then defined to be that subgraph of solved nodes that demonstrates (according to the above definition) that the start node is solved.

We show in Fig. 4-6 some examples of AND/OR graphs. The terminal nodes are indicated by a letter *t*, the solved nodes are solid, and solution graphs are indicated by darkened branches.

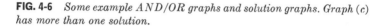

FIG. 4-6 *Some example AND/OR graphs and solution graphs. Graph (c) has more than one solution.*

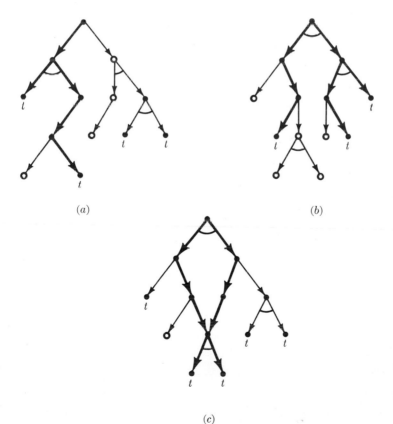

When a nonterminal node in an AND/OR graph has no successors at all we say it is *unsolvable*. The occurrence of such unsolvable nodes may imply that other nodes in the graph (even the start node) are also unsolvable. The general definition of an unsolvable node is given recursively as follows:

Nonterminal nodes with no successors are unsolvable nodes

If a nonterminal node has OR successors, then it is unsolvable if and only if *all* of its successors are unsolvable

If a nonterminal node has AND successors, then it is unsolvable if and only if at least *one* of its successors is unsolvable

The unsolvable nodes in Fig. 4-6 are indicated by double circles.

The AND/OR graphs shown in Fig. 4-6 are explicit graphs. Just as with state-space problem solving, we seldom have explicit graphs to search, but instead the graph is defined implicitly by an initial problem description and reduction operators. It is convenient to introduce the notion of a *successor operator* Γ that when applied to a problem description produces all of the sets of successor problem descriptions. (The successor operator Γ is applied by applying all of the applicable reduction operators.) Thus in Fig. 4-5 the application of Γ to A produces the entire AND/OR graph structure shown.

The process of problem solving is then accomplished by generating a sufficient portion of the AND/OR graph to demonstrate that the start node is solved. We shall take up the subject of efficient search methods in the next chapter.

4-6 REPRESENTATION OF AND/OR GRAPHS BY NONDETERMINISTIC PROGRAMS[1]

We can include some additional nondeterministic program elements so that these programs can be used to represent the process of AND/OR graph generation. Analogous to the SELECT assignment statement (in which a program variable is set equal to *any* member of a set), we can define an ALL assignment statement. In an ALL assignment statement, a program variable is set equal to *all* the members of a set. (Imagine that the computation after an ALL statement branches to a set of fictitious parallel processors, each assuming a different value for the program variable.)

---

[1] This section may be omitted in a first reading.

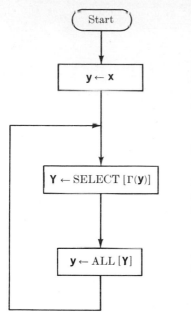

INITIALIZATION   A program variable **y** (ranging over problem descriptions) is set equal to an input data structure **x** describing the initial problem

SELECT   The value of a program variable **Y** (ranging over *sets* of problem descriptions) is set equal to some member of the set $\Gamma(\mathbf{y})$ of *sets* of successors of the old value of **y**

ALL   The new value of **y** is set equal to all members of the set **Y**

FIG. 4-7   *A nondeterministic program defining an AND/OR graph.*

A flow chart of a nondeterministic program defining an AND/OR graph is shown in Fig. 4-7. Termination conditions have been omitted for simplicity, but they would involve the obvious tests for solved nodes and unsolvable nodes.

In general, an ALL assignment is represented in flow charts by the notation

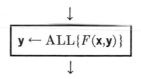

The data structure **x** is the input to the program, the data structure **y** is a program variable, and the function F is a total function mapping the cross domain of **x** and **y** into a subset of the domain of **y**. Again, we use the notation $\{F\}$ to denote this subset; the operation $\mathbf{y} \leftarrow \text{ALL}\{F\}$ sets the new values of the program variable **y** equal to all the members of $\{F\}$.

We also introduce the notion of a $\wedge$-branch. It is an n-way branch using the n predicates $p_1(\mathbf{x},\mathbf{y}), \ldots, p_n(\mathbf{x},\mathbf{y})$. These predicates have the values T (true) or F (false) over the cross domain of **x** and **y**. (**x** is

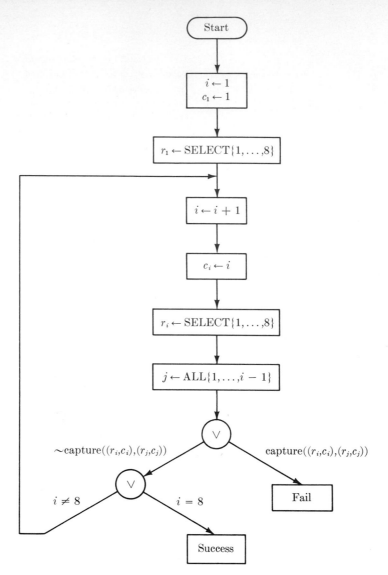

FIG. 4-8   *A nondeterministic program for the 8-queens problem.*

again an input data structure, and **y** is a program variable.) The value of at least one of the predicates must be T. Each predicate corresponds to a branch, and *all* branches for which the corresponding predicate has value T are selected. (Again imagine fictitious parallel processors starting up to handle each branch selected.) The notation for $\wedge$-branches in flow charts is

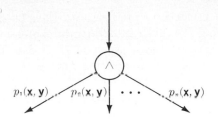

Again, ordinary deterministic branches are special cases of $\wedge$-branches. Also, when the value of $F(\mathbf{x,y})$ is a singleton, SELECT statements, ALL statements, and ordinary deterministic assignments are all identical.

A particular execution of a nondeterministic program makes one specific selection at $\vee$-branches and at SELECT statements and makes all possible selections at $\wedge$-branches and at ALL statements. The set of all possible executions defines an AND/OR tree. A given execution contains many paths (branching at $\wedge$-branches and ALL statements). It terminates only if each of its paths terminates. If for any input there exists at least one execution that terminates, then the program is said to be well defined.

Use of all of the nondeterministic (and deterministic) elements allows us to describe problems by nondeterministic program flow charts. As an example consider the so-called *8-queens problem*. In this problem we must place eight queens on an ordinary chess board so that none of the queens can capture any of the others. A nondeterministic program flow chart for this problem is shown in Fig. 4-8. In this flow chart, r_i and c_i represent the row and column locations (respectively) of the ith queen. The predicate, capture $[(r_i,c_i), (r_j,c_j)]$, has value T only if the ith queen, at (r_i,c_i), can capture the jth queen, at (r_j,c_j).

4-7 EXAMPLES OF PROBLEM-REDUCTION REPRESENTATIONS

The problem of symbolic integration

In the problem of symbolic integration we want an automatic process that will accept any indefinite integral as input, say $\int x \sin 3x \, dx$, and deliver the answer, $1/9 \sin 3x - 1/3x \cos 3x$, as output. We shall allow a table containing such simple integral forms as:

$$\int u \, du = \frac{u^2}{2}$$
$$\int \sin u \, du = - \cos u$$
$$\int a^u \, du = a^u \log_a e$$
etc.

Any symbolic integration problem can then be represented as the problem of converting the given integral into expressions involving only instances of those integral forms given in the table. For simplicity, we shall describe the problem of integrating $I(x)$ with respect to x by the expression $\int I(x)\, dx$.

The primitive problem descriptions are simply given by the integral forms in the table. We note that each form actually is a schema defining an infinite set of primitive problems. The members of a set are obtained by substituting expressions for the variables in the form. In order to determine whether or not a given integral is an instance of a primitive form, we need to employ a matching operation that looks for substitutions that will make integral and form match.

Problem-reduction operators can be based on the integration-by-parts rule, the decomposition-of-an-integral-of-a-sum rule, and other transformation rules such as those involving algebraic and trigonometric substitutions. The integration-by-parts rule states that

$$\int u\, dv = u\!\int dv - \int v\, du$$

We can use this rule to justify the following problem reduction:

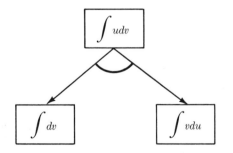

Note that the reduction merely claims that the problem $\int u\, dv$ can be solved if we can solve the problems $\int dv$ and $\int v\, du$. The equivalence $\int u\, dv = u\!\int dv - \int v\, du$ must be employed later to construct the actual solution. If there are alternatives about which part of the original integrand is to be u and which is to be dv, then a separate reduction operator covers each alternative.

The *decomposition rule* states that

$$\int \sum_{i=1}^{n} f_i(x)\, dx = \sum_{i=1}^{n} \int f_i(x)\, dx$$

This rule justifies the following problem reduction:

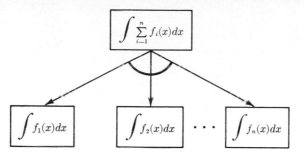

Another rule, called the *factoring rule*, allows us to replace the problem $\int k f(x)\ dx$ by the problem $\int f(x)\ dx$. Thus we have the reduction

Other operators merely substitute one integral expression for another and thus create OR nodes. These operators are based on the following processes:

Algebraic substitutions

Example

$$\int \frac{x^2\ dx}{(2 + 3x)^{\frac{2}{3}}} \rightarrow \int \frac{1}{9}\ (z^6 - 4z^3 + 4)\ dz \qquad \text{using } z^2 = (2 + 3x)^{\frac{2}{3}}$$

Trigonometric substitutions

Example

$$\int \frac{dx}{x^2 \sqrt{25x^2 + 16}} \rightarrow \int \frac{5}{16} \cot \theta \csc \theta\ d\theta \qquad \text{using } x = \frac{4}{5} \tan \theta$$

Division of numerator by denominator

Example

$$\int \frac{z^4\ dz}{z^2 + 1} \rightarrow \int \left(z^2 - 1 + \frac{1}{1 + z^2}\right) dz$$

Completing the square

Example

$$\int \frac{dx}{(x^2 - 4x + 13)^2} \rightarrow \int \frac{dx}{[(x-2)^2 + 9]^2}$$

At any given stage in the process we have many alternative reduction operators that may be applicable. If we used all applicable alternatives on every problem, the resulting search task would rapidly become unmanageable. In problems such as these it is important to use heuristic guides to limit successor generation.

FIG. 4-9 *AND/OR search graph for an integration problem.*

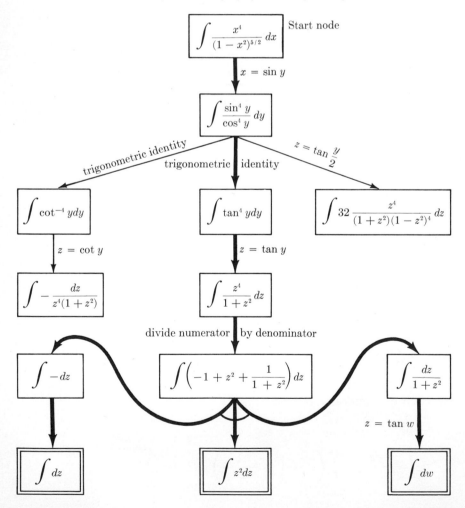

In the integration problem some of the reduction operators are so useful that they (and they exclusively) should be applied whenever they are applicable. Thus the reductions corresponding to decomposition and factoring are used exclusively whenever possible.

The utility of other rules and operators, such as trigonometric substitutions, depends strongly on the form of the integrand. In a symbolic integration system actually programmed (Slagle, 1963a), the integrands were classified according to various features that they possessed. For each class of integrand the various operators were selected according to their heuristic applicability.

An example solution In Fig. 4-9 we show an AND/OR search graph produced by a process like that we have just described.[1] The problem is to integrate

$$\int \frac{x^4}{(1 - x^2)^{5/2}}\, dx$$

The nodes of the graph represent problem descriptions and are labeled by integrals. The terminal nodes (corresponding to integrals in the table) are shown by double boxes. The darkened arcs indicate a solution graph for this problem. From this solution graph and the integrals obtained from the integral table we determine that

$$\int \frac{x^4}{(1 - x^2)^{5/2}}\, dx = \arcsin x + \frac{1}{3} \tan^3 (\arcsin x) - \tan (\arcsin x)^3$$

So far, of course, we have not said anything about the order in which problems are reduced. This topic will be covered in the next chapter, which deals with problem-reduction search methods.

Proving theorems in plane geometry

Another problem that can be attacked by the problem-reduction approach is the problem of proving theorems in plane geometry. For example, suppose we wished to prove the theorem: A point on the bisector of an angle is equidistant from the sides of the angle. We shall assume that this problem is stated in the form:

Given: $\angle DBA = \angle DBC$
$AD \perp BA$
$CD \perp BC$
DB is a segment
$\triangle BCD$ is a triangle
$\triangle BAD$ is a triangle

To prove: $AD = CD$

[1] Figure 4-9 is based on an integration problem solved by Slagle's (1963a) program.

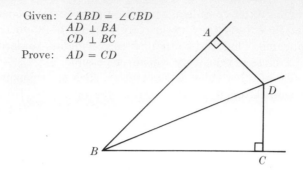

Given: $\angle ABD = \angle CBD$
$AD \perp BA$
$CD \perp BC$

Prove: $AD = CD$

FIG. 4-10 *Diagram for example geometry theorem.*

The reader (but not our problem-solving system) may refer to Fig. 4-10 for a diagrammatic interpretation of the problem. (Later we shall discuss how the problem-solving system also can be guided by referring to a "diagram.")

We shall represent a problem of proof, such as this one is, by an expression of the form $S|T$, where S is the statement to be proved and T is a set of premises. Our example problem is then described by the expression

$$AD = CD \ \Big| \ \begin{array}{l} \angle DBA = \angle DBC, \ AD \perp BA, \ CD \perp BC, \ DB, \\ \triangle BCD, \ \triangle BAD \end{array}$$

The primitive problems correspond to proving any statements that we are willing to assume as true. These can be axioms or previously proved theorems. For example, we may want to include such problems as the following among our list of primitive problems:[1]

P1 $\angle X_1 = \angle X_2 | X_1 =$ right angle, $X_2 =$ right angle
(all right angles are equal)

P2 $X_1 X_2 = X_1 X_2$
(a segment is equal to itself)

P3 $\angle X_1 = \angle X_1$
(an angle is equal to itself)

P4 $\triangle X_1 X_2 X_3 \cong \triangle Y_1 Y_2 Y_3 \ \Big| \ \begin{array}{l} X_3 X_1 = Y_3 Y_1, \angle X_3 X_1 X_2 = \angle Y_3 Y_1 Y_2, \\ \angle X_1 X_2 X_3 = \angle Y_1 Y_2 Y_3 \end{array}$
(side, angle, angle = side, angle, angle)

---

[1] As in the integration example, the primitive problem expressions are defined by forms.

P5 $\angle X_1 X_2 X_3 = $ right angle $| X_1 X_2 \perp X_2 X_3$
(two intersecting perpendicular segments define a right angle)

P6 $X_2 X_3 = Y_2 Y_3 | \triangle X_1 X_2 X_3 \cong \triangle Y_1 Y_2 Y_3$
(corresponding sides of congruent triangles are equal)

A powerful geometry theorem-proving program would, of course, employ many more primitive forms. Those above will be sufficient to illustrate the process of proving our example theorem.

To reduce a problem to subproblems we shall introduce a sufficient number of new premises to make the given problem an instance of some true statement. The set of true statements allowed for this purpose may be some subset of the primitive problems. The subproblems thus created will be those of proving the new premises (still given the old ones, of course). In order to cut down on the number of different sets of subproblems, we will insist that the added premises name only entities already named in the original premises. Since usually there will be many different new premises that meet these conditions, we shall still have a large number of different sets of subproblems. Each corresponds to the application of a different problem-reduction operator.

Let us describe how a simple geometry theorem-proving system might prove the example theorem stated at the beginning of this section. In this example we shall use as primitives only the set $\{P1, \ldots, P6\}$ mentioned above. We shall also allow just the members of this set to correspond to the true statements when adding premises to make a statement true.

We first reduce the main problem $AD = CD|T$ (where, for simplicity, we let T stand for the set of premises). The only primitive problem that can be matched by adding premises to T is P6:

$$X_2 X_3 = Y_2 Y_3 | \triangle X_1 X_2 X_3 \cong \triangle Y_1 Y_2 Y_3$$

To match we must have

$$X_2 = A \qquad X_3 = D \qquad Y_2 = C \qquad Y_3 = D$$

so we need the premise $\triangle X_1 AD \cong \triangle Y_1 CD$. Since the only triangles named in T are $\triangle BCD$ and $\triangle BAD$, we set $X_1 = B$ and $Y_1 = B$. Thus we reduce our original problem to the problem

$$\triangle BAD \cong \triangle BCD | T$$

Reduction of this problem (by adding premises to match P4) produces the set of subproblems

$$DB = DB|T, \ \angle BAD = \angle BCD \qquad \angle BAD = \angle BCD|T$$

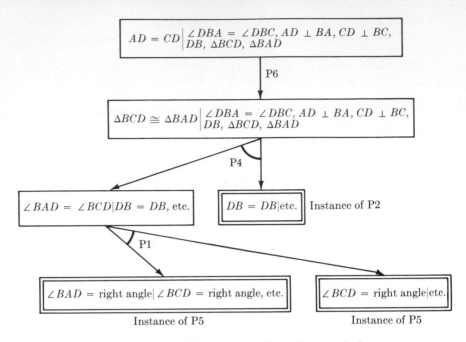

FIG. 4-11 *An AND/OR solution graph for the example theorem.*

Continuing this process in a straightforward manner results in the AND/OR solution graph shown in Fig. 4-11. Because of the small set of primitive problem forms (well chosen for this example but inadequate in general), the search process never generated any extraneous sets of AND nodes. The reader might experiment with the effects of adding a few more primitive forms such as

$$\triangle X_1 X_2 X_3 \cong \triangle Y_1 Y_2 Y_3 \left| \begin{array}{l} X_1 X_2 = Y_1 Y_2, \angle X_1 X_2 X_3 \\ = \angle Y_1 Y_2 Y_3, X_2 X_3 = Y_2 Y_3 \end{array} \right.$$

(side-angle-side)

An important way to control the number of successor nodes in AND/OR graphs involves the use of *models*. By a model here we mean a particular interpretation of a general logical statement. Statements to be proved are very often general statements that cover a variety of special cases. Any one of the special cases could be used as a model for the statement. If the general statement is in fact provable, any special case is *a fortiori* observably true in the appropriate model.

For example, consider the geometry theorem we have just proved:

$$AD = CD \left| \begin{array}{l} \angle DBA = \angle DBC, AD \perp BA, CD \perp BC, \\ DB, \triangle BCD, \triangle BAD \end{array} \right.$$

This problem can be thought of as involving a statement that is formally provable by an abstract symbol-manipulating process using purely syntactic reduction rules. Alternatively we may interpret it as a meaningful statement about actual points and segments etc., in a plane. Semantically the statement asserts that regardless of the actual positions of these points in the plane, as long as the premises hold, segment AD will be equal in length to segment CD. That is, we can actually measure both segments and find them equal. Of course, before we can measure anything we must set up an *instance* of the premises; we must decide on actual positions for points and segments as we did in constructing Fig. 4-10. Such an instance is a *model* for the statement.

Certainly if the statement is provable in general, its interpretation in the model must also be true. *Conversely, if we find that an interpretation in a model is not true, then obviously the statement cannot be proved.* The use of a model to "measure" the nonprovability of candidate statements can often be used to eliminate a large number of futile successors.

Let us illustrate the use of a model for the problem

$$AB = BC \ \bigg| \ \begin{array}{l} BD = AB, \angle BDC = \angle DCB, BC \\ DC, CD, AD, \triangle DAB, \triangle DBC \end{array}$$

We assume that the theorem-proving program has access to the diagram of Fig. 4-12. The problem would be solved in a straightforward manner by introducing the premise $BC = BD$ and setting up the subproblem of proving it. Before reaching a solution, however, the simple theorem prover would also introduce the premise $\triangle DAB \cong \triangle DBC$ and set up the problem of proving it. Obviously $\triangle DAB \cong \triangle DBC$ is not provable from the premises. By performing simple calculations on the diagram

FIG. 4-12 *Diagram for a geometry problem.*

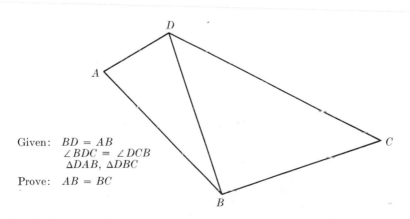

Given: $BD = AB$
        $\angle BDC = \angle DCB$
        $\triangle DAB, \triangle DBC$

Prove: $AB = BC$

(Fig. 4-12), the theorem prover could readily determine that the model triangles $\triangle DAB$ and $\triangle DBC$ were not congruent, and thus learn that the subproblem $\triangle DAB \cong \triangle DBC|$etc. is not solvable. This subproblem would then be eliminated from the list of viable successors.

A model can usually be readily supplied to a theorem-proving program. In the case of geometry, the model would be a diagram created from the premises and suitably represented by lists of coordinates, lines, segments, etc., from which measurements may be calculated using, say, analytic geometry. Care should be taken to ensure that points are selected to be in the most general position so that coincidental equalities, collinearities, etc., do not occur. Notice that if coincidences did occur, or if measurements made in the diagram were inaccurate, a theorem prover using the diagram could even so never prove an unprovable statement. (Diagrammatic errors may lead to *attempts* to prove unprovable statements; these obviously will be unsuccessful.) Errors may also cause key provable statements to be discarded, resulting in perhaps a longer proof or no proof at all.

Usually these difficulties can be protected against with the net result that the use of a diagram greatly increases search efficiency. Gelernter et al. (1960) estimate that the use of a diagram in the geometry theorem-proving program cut the average number of successors down from around 1000 per node to around 5 per node.

Gelernter's program also had the ability to add certain types of *construction lines* to the diagram. Consider for example the following problem:

$$AB = CD \ \Big| \ \begin{array}{l} ABCD \text{ is a quadrilateral, segment } BC \text{ is parallel to} \\ \text{segment } AD,\ BC = AD,\ AB,\ CD \end{array}$$

The theorem prover has access to the diagram of Fig. 4-13.

In attempting to generate successors to the start node by adding premises, the theorem prover unfortunately cannot attempt to match such primitive problems as $AB = CD|\triangle ABD \cong \triangle BDC$ because $\triangle ABD$

FIG. 4-13 *Example requiring a construction line.*

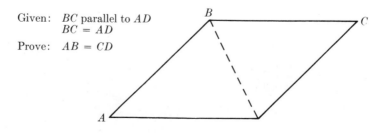

Given: BC parallel to AD
         $BC = AD$
Prove: $AB = CD$

and $\triangle BDC$ are not named in the premises. Suppose no successors can be found at all. Then, there being no alternative subproblems to work on in this case, the theorem prover reconsiders the primitive problems that were previously thought inapplicable for a match because they contained items not named in the premises. In the case of using $AB = CD|\triangle ABD \cong \triangle BDC$, the theorem prover generates the following AND/OR graph structure below the start node:

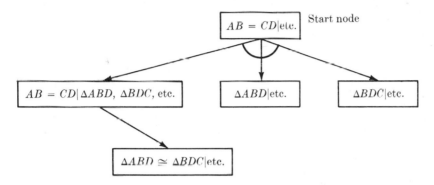

The problems $\triangle ABD|$etc., and $\triangle BDC|$etc., are taken to be primitive (three points determine a triangle). The result of this operation is as if a segment BD creating the two triangles were constructed in the diagram. After this construction the proof can proceed in a straightforward manner.

4-8 PLANNING MECHANISMS IN PROBLEM REDUCTION

In this section we shall describe a problem-reduction technique that successively reduces state-space search problems to simpler and simpler search problems until all can be solved trivially. In addition, the reduction process is guided by a type of planning mechanism that is of great importance in artificial intelligence.

Suppose we wanted to reduce the state-space search problem specified by the triple (S,F,G) to simpler state-space search problems. If we could identify a sequence of appropriate "milestone" states $g_1, g_2, \ldots, g_N$, then we could reduce the initial problem to the set of problems specified by the triples $(S,F,\{g_1\})$, $(\{g_1\},F,\{g_2\})$, $\ldots$, $(\{g_N\},F,G)$. Solving all of these problems is equivalent to solving the initial problem.

When the milestone states $g_1, g_2, \ldots, g_N$ are explicitly specified, it makes no difference in which order the successor problems are solved. Sometimes, however, we may specify a set G_1 of states any one of which could serve as the first milestone, a set G_2 for the second milestone, etc. The problem described by the triple (S,F,G_1) must then be solved first to establish a specific $g_1 \in G_1$ before the next problem $(\{g_1\}, F, G_2)$ can be set up, etc. In the next section we shall describe an interesting technique for specifying these milestone sets.

4-9 KEY OPERATORS

In many state-space search problems it is not too difficult to guess the identity of at least one of the state-space operators that will occur somewhere in a solution sequence of operators. That is, although the problem of finding the entire sequence of operators in a solution is difficult, the problem of specifying one of them is often easy. The possibility of finding one such operator is enhanced when the problem is such that the application of one of the operators is regarded as a crucial step in the problem solution. (In terms of the state-space graph, the application of such an operator corresponds to an arc linking otherwise almost separate parts of the graph.) For example, in the Tower-of-Hanoi problem that we considered previously, the operator "move disk C to peg 3" can be singled out as a crucial step in the problem solution. (See Fig. 4-2.) We shall call operators of this sort *key operators*.

When a key operator can be determined, it can be used to identify a milestone in the problem-reduction process. Suppose some f in F is a key operator for the problem given by the triple (S, F, G). Since we suspect that f must be applied, the first successor to (S, F, G) is one representing the problem of finding a path to some state to which f is applicable. Let G_f be the set of states to which f is applicable. Then we have the subproblem described by (S, F, G_f). Once this subproblem is solved, thus naming a state $g \in G_f$, we can set up the primitive problem represented by $(\{g\}, F, \{f(g)\})$, where $f(g)$ represents the state attained by applying f to g. This problem is primitive since it is solved merely by applying the key operator f. We are then left with the problem described by the triple $(\{f(g)\}, F, G)$.

Thus when a key state-space operator f can be specified we can use the following problem reduction:

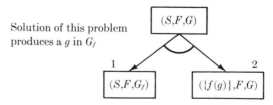

Solution of this problem produces a g in G_f

[We have simplified this diagram by not showing the primitive subproblem $(\{g\}, F, \{f(g)\})$.] The two successor problems can then be solved either by direct state-space search techniques or by further problem reductions. If the strategy is to employ further reductions, we must be able to identify some key operator for the problem (S,F,G_f), etc.

In many problems we cannot always identify a single key operator known a priori to be crucial in a problem solution. Instead we might only be able to guess some subset of operators such that one of them has some high likelihood of being crucial. Each operator in the subset creates a pair of successor problems. A search process employing this idea would thus build up an AND/OR graph while searching for a solution among the various alternatives.

Before this method can be applied we must have some way of calculating a set of candidate key operators for any state-space search problem. In the next section we shall describe one specific method based on *differences*.

4-10 DIFFERENCES

One method for finding candidate key operators involves calculating the *difference* for a problem (S,F,G). Loosely speaking, a difference for (S,F,G) is a partial list of reasons why the goal test (defining the set G) is failed by the members of S. (If some member of S is in G, the problem is solved and there is no difference.) For example, if the goal set G is defined by some set of conditions on states, and if some $s \in S$ satisfies some but not all of these conditions, then the difference might consist of a partial list of the conditions not satisfied by s. If these conditions can be ranked in importance, we might use just the most important unsatisfied condition as the difference.

Next we associate some state-space operator or set of operators with each possible difference. These are the candidate key operators. An operator is associated with a difference only if its application is relevant to removing that difference. Let us illustrate the process by applying it to the monkey-and-bananas problem.

The monkey-and-bananas problem was discussed in Chapter 2 in connection with the use of state-description schemas. Recall that these schemas were of the form $(\mathbf{w},x,\mathbf{y},z)$, where

$\mathbf{w}$ — horizontal position of monkey (a two-dimensional vector)

$x = 1$ or 0, depending on whether the monkey is on top of the box or not, respectively

$\mathbf{y}$ = horizontal position of box (a two-dimensional vector)

$z = 1$ or 0, depending on whether the monkey has the bananas or not, respectively

There were four operators whose effects and applicability are given by the following rewriting rules:

$$f_1 \quad (\mathbf{w},0,\mathbf{y},z) \xrightarrow{\text{goto}(\mathbf{u})} (\mathbf{u},0,\mathbf{y},z)$$

$$f_2 \quad (\mathbf{w},0,\mathbf{w},z) \xrightarrow{\text{pushbox}(\mathbf{v})} (\mathbf{v},0,\mathbf{v},z)$$

$$f_3 \quad (\mathbf{w},0,\mathbf{w},z) \xrightarrow{\text{climbbox}} (\mathbf{w},1,\mathbf{w},z)$$

$$f_4 \quad (\mathbf{c},1,\mathbf{c},0) \xrightarrow{\text{grasp}} (\mathbf{c},1,\mathbf{c},1)$$

where $\mathbf{c}$ is the location on the floor directly under the bananas.

The goal condition on state descriptions is satisfied just when the last element of the state-description schema is equal to 1. The initial state is described by the list $(\mathbf{a},0,\mathbf{b},0)$.

If $F = \{f_1,f_2,f_3,f_4\}$ is the set of four operators and G is the set of states satisfying the goal condition, we then have as our initial problem

$$(\{(\mathbf{a},0,\mathbf{b},0)\},F,G)$$

Since the operator set does not change in this problem, we can suppress the symbol F from the notation and denote the problem simply by $(\{(\mathbf{a},0,\mathbf{b},0)\},G)$.

The reduction procedure using the notions of key operators and differences can then be explained as follows:

First we calculate the difference for the initial problem. The reason that the list $(\mathbf{a},0,\mathbf{b},0)$ fails to satisfy the goal test is that the last element is not a one. The key operator (relevant to reducing this difference) is operator f_4, grasp.

(We assume that the association between the possible differences and their key operators has previously been given to the problem solver.)

Using f_4 to reduce the initial problem, we obtain the following pair of subproblems:

$$(\{(\mathbf{a},0,\mathbf{b},0)\},G_{f_4})$$

and

$$(\{f_4(s_1)\},G)$$

where G_{f_4} is the set of state descriptions to which the operator f_4 is applicable (the state descriptions in the domain of f_4), and s_1 is that state in G_{f_4} obtained as a consequence of solving $(\{\mathbf{a},0,\mathbf{b},0)\}, G_{f_4})$.

Since we need to solve the first member of the pair first, we apply the same procedure to it. First we calculate its difference. The state described by $(\mathbf{a},0,\mathbf{b},0)$ is not in G_{f_4} because

The box is not at $\mathbf{c}$

The monkey is not at $\mathbf{c}$

The monkey is not on the box

Taking this list of statements as the difference in this case, we identify the following key operators:

f_2 pushbox(c)
f_1 goto(c)
f_3 climbbox

We then employ each of these key operators in turn to produce alternative pairs of reduced problems. The first of these key operators is used to reduce the problem $(\{(a,0,b,0)\}, G_{f_4})$ to the pair

(1-1) $(\{(a,0,b,0)\}, G_{f_2})$
(1-2) $(\{f_2(s_{11})\}, G_{f_4})$

where $s_{11} \in G_{f_2}$ is obtained as a consequence of solving 1-1.

Since 1-1 must be solved first, we calculate its difference:

The monkey is not at **b**

This difference gives us the key operator

f_1 goto(**b**)

This key operator is then used to reduce $(\{(a,0,b,0)\}, G_{f_2})$ to the pair

(1-11) $(\{(a,0,b,0)\}, G_{f_1})$
(1-12) $(\{f_1(s_{111})\}, G_{f_2})$

Now the first of these problems is primitive; its difference is zero since $(a,0,b,0)$ is in the domain of f_1. Therefore we can begin working on the problem 1-12. We shall carry our description of the procedure ahead just one more step. We see now that $f_1(s_{111})$ is $(b,0,b,0)$ so 1-12 becomes

$(\{(b,0,b,0)\}, G_{f_2})$

This problem is also primitive since $(b,0,b,0)$ is in the domain of f_2. This process of completing the solution of problems generated earlier is continued until the initial problem is finally solved.

In Fig. 4-14 we show an AND/OR graph giving the solution tree for this problem. The numbers above the nodes show the order in which the problems were examined by our search process described. Our ordering happened to result in a solution before the unnumbered problems were examined, but in general, additional searching might have been required. The solution graph of Fig. 4-14 can easily be analyzed to produce the solution sequence of operators

(goto(**b**),pushbox(**c**),climbbox,grasp)

The method of using key operators splits a problem into parts with a consequent reduction in search effort. (The monkey-and-bananas

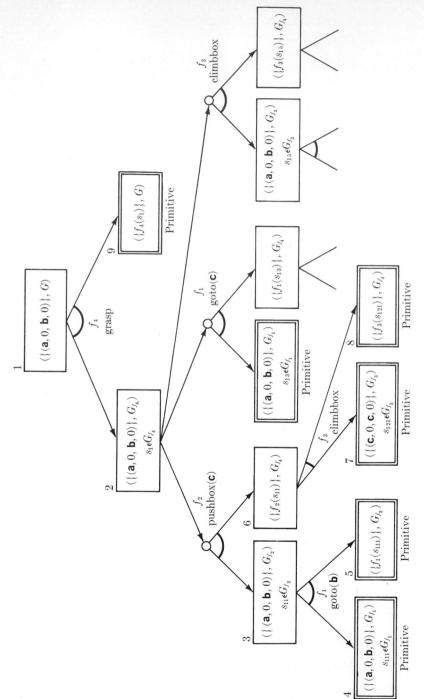

FIG. 4-14 *AND/OR graph for monkey-and-bananas problem.*

problem had such a small search space anyway that the use of key operators didn't noticeably increase efficiency in this case.) In order to use key operators, however, the problem solver must be given a procedure for calculating differences and associating key operators with them. A good difference-operator association depends greatly on the problem domain.

4-11 HIGHER-LEVEL STATE SPACES

A problem reduction based on a key operator f and applied to a problem (S,F,G) produces two AND subproblems (S,F,G_f) and $(\{f(g)\},F,G)$, where G_f is the set of states to which f is applicable and g is a member of G_f.

It is often the case that one *must* solve the first successor problem (S,F,G_f) first before the second can be posed and solved; then it may be more convenient to represent this entire problem-reduction problem-solving process by a *higher-level* state space. In the higher-level state space, a state description consists of an ordered list of problem descriptions. (The individual problems in the list must be solved in the order in which they appear on the list.) The higher-level successor operator uses differences and key operators to generate two subproblems to replace the first problem on the list. (Unless the first problem on the list is a primitive problem, in which case it is simply removed from the list. Usually the removal of a primitive problem from the list corresponds to the application of a key operator; this application must be noted for inclusion in the solution sequence.) The goal state in the higher-level state space is any state description with an empty problem list. The reader will find it instructive to trace through the solution of the monkey-and-bananas problem using such a higher-level state space.

4-12 GAMES

The problem-reduction approach can also be used to find playing strategies for certain kinds of games. The games that we shall consider are those called two-person, perfect-information games. These are played by two players who move in turn. They each know completely what both players have done and can do. Specifically we shall be interested in those games for which one of the two players *wins* (and the other *loses*) or the result is a *draw*. Some example games from this class are checkers, tic-tac-toe, chess, go, and nim. We are not going to consider here any games in which the results are determined even partially by chance; thus dice games and most card games are ruled out. (Our treatment could be generalized to include certain chance games though.)

The problem-reduction approach finds a winning strategy through the process of *proving* that the game can be *won*. The problem description, then, must describe the state or configuration of the game from which it is asserted that a win is guaranteed. For example, in chess a configuration is a complete representation of the positions of all the pieces on the board and a statement of whose turn it is to move next.

Suppose we name the two players PLUS and MINUS. Consider the problem of finding a playing strategy for player PLUS starting with some configuration represented by X^t. The superscript t stands for either $+$ or $-$; X^+ represents a configuration in which it is PLUS's turn to move next, and X^- represents a configuration in which it is MINUS's turn to move next. We would like to be able to prove that PLUS can win from X^t; failing to find such a proof we would at least like to be able to prove that PLUS can draw from X^t. Let us describe the problem of proving that PLUS can win from configuration X^t by the expression $W(X^t)$.

The legal moves of the game provide the scheme for reducing game problems to subproblems. Suppose it is PLUS's turn to move in configuration X^+, and suppose there are N legal moves resulting in configurations $X_1^{t_1}, X_2^{t_2}, \ldots, X_N^{t_N}$. Then to prove $W(X^+)$, we must be able to prove one or another of the $W(X_i^{t_i})$. On the other hand, if it is MINUS's turn to move in configuration X^-, and if there are M legal moves resulting in configurations $Y_1^{s_1}, Y_2^{s_2}, \ldots, Y_M^{s_M}$, then to prove $W(X^-)$ we must be able to prove *all* of the $W(Y_i^{s_i})$. Of course, similar reductions apply when we are attempting only to prove that draws are possible.

Applying these problem-reduction operators generates what is often called a *game tree*. The primitive problems are given by the termination rules of the game, and the proof process continues until a solution tree is found terminating in primitive problems. (For most games of interest, such as chess, go, and checkers, it is unfeasible to generate complete solution trees. In the next chapter we shall discuss some specialized game tree-search methods that generate partial trees.)

We shall illustrate these ideas using a simple game called "Grundy's game," and employ problem-reduction techniques to find a strategy for player PLUS.

The rules of Grundy's game are as follows: Two players have in front of them a single pile of objects, say a stack of pennies. The first player divides the original stack into two stacks that must be unequal. Each player alternately thereafter does the same to some single stack when it is his turn to play. The game proceeds until finally every stack has either just one penny or two, at which point continuation becomes impossible. The player who first cannot play is the loser.

Let us start with seven pennies in the stack and let MINUS play first. A configuration for this game is a sequence of numbers representing the number of pennies in the various stacks plus an indication of who is to move next. Thus 7⁻ is the starting configuration.

From 7⁻, MINUS has three alternative moves creating the configurations $6,1^+$, $5,2^+$, or $4,3^+$. There are just three configurations where the player next to move loses:

$$2,1,1,1,1,1^+ \qquad 2,2,1,1,1^- \qquad 2,2,2,1^+$$

The only primitive problem (indicating a win for PLUS) is thus $W(2,2,1,1,1^-)$.

If we apply our problem-reduction process starting with $W(7^-)$, we obtain the AND/OR graph shown in Fig. 4-15. A solution tree for this graph is indicated by darkened arcs, and primitive problems are indicated by double boxes.

If we changed the game to let PLUS start first (starting configuration 7^+), then it happens that we cannot prove $W(7^+)$. (The second

FIG. 4-15 *An AND/OR graph for Grundy's game.*

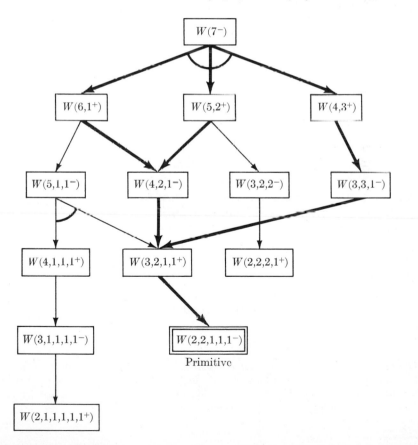

player can always win.) In attempting to prove $W(7^+)$, eventually we would be unable to generate new nodes, and the start node could then be determined to be unsolvable. (For example, configuration $2,2,1,1,1^+$ has no next configurations by definition of the rules.)

4-13 BIBLIOGRAPHICAL AND HISTORICAL REMARKS

Problem-reduction methods and AND/OR graphs

Some of the very earliest work in artificial intelligence used the problem-reduction technique (also called "reasoning backwards") to solve problems. Newell, Shaw, and Simon (1957) programmed a logic-theory machine (LT) that proved theorems in the propositional calculus by working backward from the theorem to be proved. In the LT program, use was made of a tree of subproblems to keep track of alternative chains of reasoning.

Another early program in which problem-reduction methods and subproblem trees were used was the symbolic integration (SAINT) program of Slagle (1963a). Slagle first called these trees AND/OR trees; in a later paper Slagle and Bursky (1968) used the term proposition tree. Amarel (1967) also used special graph structures in discussing problem-reduction methods. Rigney and Towne (1969) propose the use of AND/OR-like graphs for analyzing the structure of serial action schedules in industry. Manna (1970) gives some examples of representing implicit AND/OR trees by nondeterministic programs.

Example programs using the problem-reduction approach

Our example symbolic integration system is based on the SAINT program of Slagle (1963a). This program is described in detail in Slagle's Ph.D. dissertation [Slagle (1961)]. A much more elaborate integration system (called SIN) was later programmed by Moses (1967). Moses' system embodied so many special criteria for applying the various operators that most integrations are carried out with little or no search.[1] Risch (1969) has recently developed algorithmic procedures for integrating many types of expressions (see Problem 4-5).

The geometry theorem-proving examples were based on the program by Gelernter et al. (1959, 1960). Several features of this program represented important and original innovations.

The notion of key operators and differences and their use in prob-

---

[1] One might speculate that most of the search effort that might have been needed to perform integrations was carried out once and for all by Moses himself in designing the program. The results of this design search were the special rules about which operators to apply in all cases.

lcm solving is due largely to Newell and his coworkers on GPS. [See Ernst and Newell (1969).] It might be mentioned that our explanation of these ideas differs somewhat from that of Newell et al. Newell has used the phrase "means-ends analysis" to refer to the process of extracting differences and matching these differences with relevant operators. He also distinguishes among three kinds of goals in the GPS system: the transform-object goal, the reduce-difference goal, and the apply-operator goal. Our description does not acknowledge the utility of these distinctions. Our interest in GPS is solely in its ability as an automatic problem-solving system, whereas many of the GPS workers were also interested in it as a psychological model of human thought processes. This difference in purpose undoubtedly contributed to part of the difference in its description.

Stressing the problem-solving ability of GPS, Ernst (1969) inquired about conditions under which GPS is guaranteed to find a solution. Ernst's study resulted in formalizing the notions of differences and ordering of differences.

Games and the problem-reduction approach

Slagle and his coworkers have stressed the essential similarities between AND/OR trees and game trees [Slagle (1970), Slagle and Bursky (1968)]. This similarity is particularly apparent in simple games that can be searched to termination or in the "end-games" of more complex games such as chess. Indeed, one often thinks of chess end-game puzzles as problems of proof rather than as games. Our Grundy's-game example is taken from an article by O'Beirne (1961).

PROBLEMS

4-1   (For electrical engineers) Show how an AND/OR solution tree can be used to represent the calculation of the impedance of the electrical network shown below. Use as primitives the facts that the impedance of a *single* R, L, or C can be calculated (to be, respectively, R, $j\omega L$, or $1/j\omega C$). The successor operators should be based on the rules for combining impedances in parallel and in series.

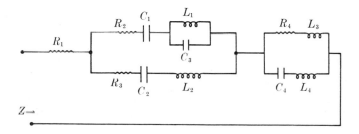

4-2   Imagine that you are a high school geometry student and find a proof for the theorem: The diagonals of a parallelogram bisect each other. Use an AND/OR tree to chart the steps in your search for a proof. Label the nodes of this tree with the propositions you considered in searching for a proof. Were any of these eliminated by referring to a model? Indicate the solution subtree that constitutes a proof of the theorem.

4-3   (For LISP programmers) Write a LISP predicate SOLVED(TREE) that has value T if the node at the root of TREE (an AND/OR tree) is solved and has value F otherwise. Use any convenient data structure for TREE.

4-4   Explain how you would design a problem-reduction problem-solving system to break down any English word into its component syllables. Assume that each problem reduction splits a symbol string into precisely two strings.

4-5   The history of progress in the development of systems for automatic symbolic integration poses an interesting question about the definition of artificial intelligence. Few would argue that Slagle's SAINT program was a product of artificial-intelligence research. Moses' SIN program for symbolic integration seldom needed to resort to search, and for this reason some people consider it much more powerful (intelligent?) than SAINT. Now, Risch (1969) has developed an algorithm for integrating many types of expressions. Risch considers himself a mathematician, not an artificial-intelligence researcher. In your opinion, should Risch's algorithm be considered part of the subject matter of artificial intelligence? Answer with an essay about the criteria for what constitutes artificial intelligence. If you would exclude Risch from artificial intelligence, how would you respond to the statement that every artificial-intelligence program might eventually be dominated by a (more intelligent?) non-artificial-intelligence algorithm? If you would include Risch, would you also include the long-division algorithm?

4-6   A game called "Last One Loses" is played as follows: Two players alternate in removing one, two, or three pennies from a stack initially containing nine pennies. The player who picks up the last penny loses. Show the AND/OR solution tree that proves that the player who plays second can always win.

REFERENCES

Amarel, S. (1967): An Approach to Heuristic Problem-Solving and Theorem Proving in the Propositional Calculus, in J. Hart and S. Takasu (eds.), "Systems and Computer Science," University of Toronto Press, Toronto, 1967.

Ernst, G. (1969): Sufficient Conditions for the Success of GPS, *J. ACM*, vol. 16, no. 4, pp. 517–533, October 1969.

——— and A. Newell (1969): "GPS: A Case Study in Generality and Problem Solving," ACM Monograph Series, Academic Press, Inc., New York, 1969.

Gelernter, H. (1959): Realization of a Geometry Theorem-Proving Machine, *Proc. Intern. Conf. Info. Proc.*, pp. 273–282, UNESCO House, Paris, 1959. Reprinted in E. Feigenbaum and J. Feldman (eds.), "Computers and Thought," pp. 134–152, McGraw-Hill Book Company, New York, 1963.

———, J. Hansen, and D. Loveland (1960): Empirical Explorations of the Geometry Theorem Proving Machine, *Proc. West. Joint Computer Conf.*, vol. 17, pp. 143–147, 1960. Reprinted in E. Feigenbaum and J. Feldman (eds.), "Computers and Thought," pp. 153–167, McGraw-Hill Book Company, New York, 1963.

Manna, Z. (1970): The Correctness of Non-Deterministic Programs, *Artificial Intelligence*, vol. 1, no. 1, 1970.

Moses, J. (1967): "Symbolic Integration," thesis, Project MAC, Report MAC-TR-47, Massachusetts Institute of Technology, December 1967.

Newell, A., J. Shaw, and H. Simon (1957): Empirical Explorations of the Logic Theory Machine, *Proc. West. Joint Computer Conf.*, vol. 15, pp. 218–239, 1957. Reprinted in E. Feigenbaum and J. Feldman (eds.), "Computers and Thought," pp. 109–133, McGraw-Hill Book Company, New York, 1963.

O'Beirne, T. H. (1961): Puzzles and Paradoxes, *New Scientist*, no. 245, July 27, 1961, and no. 246, August 3, 1961.

Rigney, J. W. and D. M. Towne (1969): Computer Techniques for Analyzing the Microstructure of Serial-Action Work in Industry, *Human Factors*, vol. 11, no. 2, pp. 113–122, 1969.

Risch, R. H. (1969): The Problem of Integration in Finite Terms, *Trans. Am. Math. Soc.*, vol. 139, pp. 167–189, 1969.

Slagle, J. (1961): "A Computer Program for Solving Problems in Freshman Calculus (SAINT)," doctoral dissertation, Massachusetts Institute of Technology, Cambridge, Mass., 1961. Also printed as *Lincoln Laboratory Report* 5G-0001, May 10, 1961.

——— (1963a): A Heuristic Program That Solves Symbolic Integration Problems in Freshman Calculus, *JACM*, vol. 10, no. 4, pp. 507–520, October 1963. Also in E. Feigenbaum and J. Feldman (eds.), "Computers and Thought," pp. 191–203, McGraw-Hill Book Company, New York, 1963.

——— (1970): Heuristic Search Programs, in R. Banerji and M. Mesarovic (eds.), "Theoretical Approaches to Non-Numerical Problem Solving," pp. 246–273, Springer-Verlag New York, Inc., New York, 1970.

——— and P. Bursky (1968): Experiments with a Multipurpose, Theorem-Proving Heuristic Program, *J. ACM*, vol. 15, no. 1, pp. 85–99, January 1968.

CHAPTER FIVE

PROBLEM-REDUCTION SEARCH METHODS

5-1   AND/OR GRAPH-SEARCHING PROCESSES

After specifying problem descriptions and problem-reduction operators, an AND/OR graph may be generated to solve the initial problem or to show that it is unsolvable (under the representation chosen). The generation of this graph comprises a search process that terminates successfully when a solution graph is found. In this chapter we shall describe the major techniques for conducting efficient searches for solution graphs.

Finding a solution graph is accomplished by generating a sufficient part of the AND/OR graph to demonstrate that the start node is *solved*. We shall repeat here the definitions for *solved* and *unsolvable* nodes that were given in the last chapter.

Solved nodes

The terminal nodes (those corresponding to primitive problems) are solved.

A nonterminal node with OR successors is solved if and only if at least one of its successors is solved.

A nonterminal node with AND successors is solved if and only if all of its successors are solved.

Unsolvable nodes

Nonterminal nodes with no successors are unsolvable.

A nonterminal node with OR successors is unsolvable if and only if all of its successors are unsolvable.

A nonterminal node with AND successors is unsolvable if and only if at least one of its successors is unsolvable.

We note that the definitions of solved and unsolvable nodes are recursive. These definitions can be used in simple recursive or iterative procedures that operate on an AND/OR graph to label all of the solved and unsolvable nodes. We shall call these procedures the *solve-labeling* and *unsolvable-labeling* procedures; they are used in termination checks in the search algorithms we shall be discussing. Search terminates successfully as soon as the start node can be labeled *solved*. It terminates unsuccessfully as soon as the start node can be labeled *unsolvable*.

When the start node can finally be labeled *solved* and search terminates, the solution graph is that subgraph (containing only solved nodes) that demonstrates, according to our definition, that the start node is solved.

The search processes that we shall discuss all involve the following steps:

(1) A start node is associated with the initial problem description.
(2) Sets of successors of the start node are calculated by applying the applicable problem-reduction operators. Let Γ be the combined operator that calculates all the successors of a node. Again we shall call the process of applying Γ to a node *expanding* a node. (Recall that if more than one set of AND successors are generated, each nonsingleton set is grouped below an intermediate OR node.)
(3) *Pointers* are set up from each successor back to parent nodes. These pointers are used when attempting to label solved and un-

solvable nodes, and they also indicate a solution graph upon termination.

(4) The process of expanding nodes and setting up pointers continues until the start node can be labeled either solved or unsolvable.

The structure of nodes and pointers generated by the search process forms an AND/OR graph that is a subgraph of the entire implicitly defined graph. We shall call it the *search graph*.

We shall be concerned in this chapter with various AND/OR graph-searching processes that efficiently order the expansion of nodes.[1] These processes differ in several ways from those for searching state-space graphs. The major differences arise because the termination checks and the node-ordering techniques must now be more complex. Instead of searching for a goal node, we are now searching for a solution graph. Thus we must test at appropriate times to see if the start node is solved. There is no point, however, in applying this test except after generating successor nodes that are solved (e.g., terminal nodes). To apply it, we must first apply the solve-labeling procedure to the AND/OR search graph developed so far. If the start node is labeled solved, we are through; otherwise we continue expanding nodes (possibly remembering which of the previously expanded nodes were labeled solved to save computation during the next termination check).

Whenever a node selected for expansion is not terminal and has no successors, it is unsolvable; it is then appropriate to apply the unsolvable-labeling procedure to the search graph to see whether or not the start node is unsolvable. If the start node is unsolvable, we fail; otherwise we continue expanding nodes (again remembering which of the previously expanded nodes were labeled unsolvable).

The presence of solved and unsolvable nodes leads to another interesting aspect of AND/OR graph searching. Since there is no reason to solve a problem in more than one way, we can prune from the search graph any unsolved descendants of solved nodes. Similarly, we can prune away descendants of unsolvable nodes. Searching below any of the pruned nodes would be pointless.

The search methods for AND/OR graphs differ from each other mainly in the way in which nodes are ordered for expansion. Again, *breadth-first* methods expand nodes in the order in which they are generated, and *depth-first* methods expand the most recently generated nodes first. Although our primary interest is in *ordered-search methods* (which

---

[1] As we observed in the example of Sec. 4-10, one successor subproblem may have to be solved first before we can begin to solve the others. Our ordering methods of this chapter will apply only so far as there is a choice about which node should be expanded next.

use heuristic evaluation functions to order node expansions), we shall begin by discussing breadth-first and depth-first methods since they are simple and help to introduce some important ideas.

Again the search methods are considerably simplified when applied to trees (rather than general graphs). We shall describe the tree versions of these methods and then later mention some of the problems involved in the extensions needed for searching graphs. An AND/OR tree is a special case of an AND/OR graph in which all nodes have precisely one parent (except the *root* node, which has no parents). As with ordinary trees, we are assured that when a successor node is generated it has never been generated before in the search, nor will it ever be generated again. Searching an AND/OR tree produces a subtree called the *search tree*.

5-2 BREADTH-FIRST SEARCH

The breadth-first method expands nodes in the order in which they are generated. The sequence of steps defining it appears long but most of the steps are concerned with the termination checks. The structure of the procedure is quite simple as can be seen by the flow chart of Fig. 5-1. The sequence of steps for breadth-first search of AND/OR trees is as follows:

(1) Put the start node s on a list called OPEN.
(2) Remove the first node on OPEN and put it on a list called CLOSED; call this node n.
(3) Expand node n, generating all of its successors. Put these successors at the *end* of OPEN and provide pointers back to n. If there are no successors, label n unsolvable and continue; otherwise go to (8).
(4) Apply the unsolvable-labeling procedure to the search tree.
(5) If the start node is labeled unsolvable, exit with failure; otherwise continue.
(6) Remove from OPEN any nodes having ancestors that are unsolvable. (This step allows us to avoid the unnecessary effort that would be expended in attempting to solve unsolvable problems.)
(7) Go to (2).
(8) If any of the successors are terminal nodes, label them solved and continue; otherwise go to (2).
(9) Apply the solve-labeling procedure to the search tree.
(10) If the start node is labeled solved, exit with the solution tree that verifies that the start node is solved; otherwise continue.
(11) Remove from OPEN any nodes that are solved or that have an-

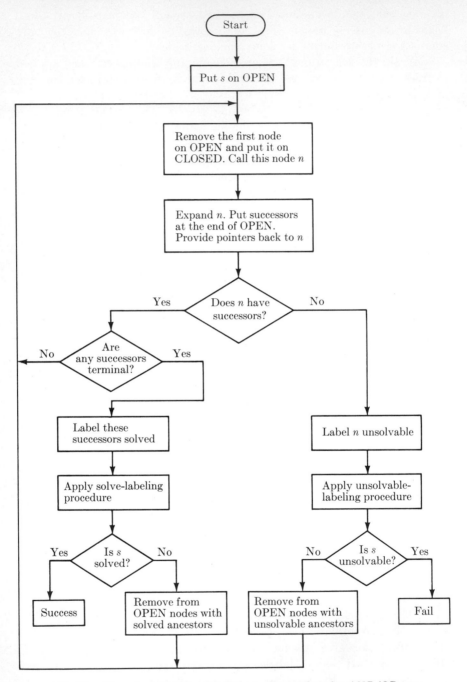

FIG. 5-1 *Flow chart for a breadth-first search procedure for AND/OR trees.*

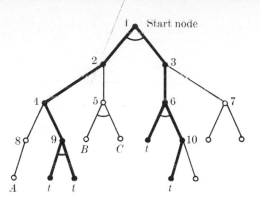

FIG. 5-2 *An AND/OR tree showing the order of node expansions in a breadth-first search.*

cestors that are solved. (This step allows us to avoid the unnecessary effort that would be expended in solving a problem in more than one way.)

(12) Go to (2).

Just as in ordinary trees, the *depth* of a node in an AND/OR tree is defined as follows:

The depth of the start node is 0

The depth of any other node is 1 plus the depth of its parent

A special consequence of a theorem to be proved later is that the breadth-first procedure we have just described is guaranteed to find that solution tree whose deepest node (a terminal node) is of minimal depth (provided, of course, that a solution tree exists at all).

An example of the order in which the breadth-first procedure expands nodes is illustrated in Fig. 5-2. The numbers adjacent to the nodes indicate the order of node expansions; solved nodes are shown solid, and the solution tree found is indicated by the dark branches. Note that when the ninth node is expanded and its successors are recognized as terminal, the nodes marked *A, B,* and *C* are removed from OPEN.

5-3 DEPTH-FIRST SEARCH

A depth-first search attempts to find a solution tree within a certain depth bound and expands the most recently generated nodes first. No nodes deeper than the depth bound are ever expanded, hence nonterminal nodes right at the depth bound are labeled unsolvable. Just as in state-

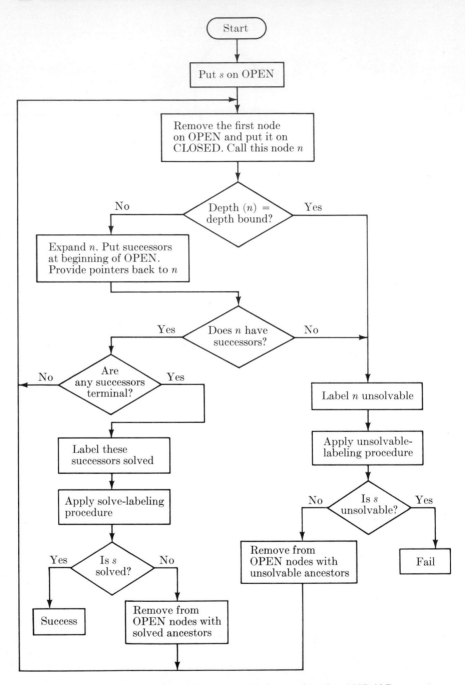

FIG. 5-3 *Flow chart for a depth-first search procedure for AND/OR trees.*

space searches, a depth bound may preclude finding a solution, but the process will find any solution within the bound. The structure of the procedure is similar to that of the breadth-first method. It is illustrated by the flow chart of Fig. 5-3. The sequence of steps for the depth-first procedure is as follows:

(1) Put the start node s on a list called OPEN.
(2) Remove the first node on OPEN and put it on a list called CLOSED; call this node n.
(3) If the depth of n is equal to the depth bound, label n unsolvable and go to (5); otherwise continue.
(4) Expand node n, generating all of its successors. Put these successors (in arbitrary order) at the *beginning* of OPEN and provide pointers back to n. If there are no successors, label n unsolvable and continue; otherwise go to (9).
(5) Apply the unsolvable-labeling procedure to the search tree.
(6) If the start node is labeled unsolvable, exit with failure; otherwise continue.
(7) Remove from OPEN any nodes having ancestors that are unsolvable.
(8) Go to (2).
(9) If any of the successors are terminal nodes, label them solved and continue; otherwise go to (2).
(10) Apply the solved-labeling procedure to the search tree.
(11) If the start node is labeled solved, exit with the solution tree that verifies that the start node is solved; otherwise continue.
(12) Remove from OPEN any nodes that are solved or that have ancestors that are solved.
(13) Go to (2).

An example showing the order in which the depth-first method expands nodes is illustrated in Fig. 5-4. In this example the depth bound is set at 4. Solved nodes are shown solid, unsolvable nodes are indicated by double circles, and the solution tree is indicated by the dark branches.

5-4 SEARCHING AND/OR GRAPHS

Whenever a problem reduction produces a successor that is equivalent to some problem description produced earlier in the search process, the resulting structure can more efficiently be represented by an AND/OR graph having nodes with multiple parents than it can by a tree. If we are able to recognize problem-description equivalences, search effort can generally be reduced since identical subproblems need be solved only once. Furthermore, the general graph structure reveals useless cycles

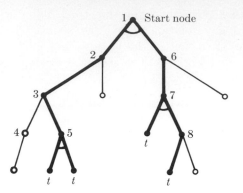

FIG. 5-4 *An AND/OR tree showing the order of node expansions in a depth-first search (depth-bound = 4).*

(circular reasoning) that could occur but would not be detectable if actually identical problem descriptions were thought to be different in the tree representation.

Some examples of AND/OR graphs whose nodes may have more than one parent are shown in Fig. 5-5. Terminal nodes are marked with a *t,* and solution graphs are indicated by dark branches. Note that the graphs in Figs. 5-5*a* and 5-5*b* have solution subgraphs, but that the graph in Fig. 5-5*c* does not, since there a cycle cannot be avoided.

One might at first suppose that cycles should be avoided simply by not generating those successors of a node that are also ancestors of that node. Actually such a rule might preclude some perfectly valid, noncircular solutions. For example, if nodes are expanded in the order shown in Fig. 5-6, we certainly want to include node 2 as one of the successors of node 6 (even though 2 is at that time also an ancestor of 6), for otherwise the solution (perhaps the only solution) indicated by the darkened branches could not be obtained.

Several complications arise when attempting to specify a search procedure for AND/OR graphs (rather than for trees). First, a reasonable definition of a breadth-first procedure would probably involve selecting for next expansion that node on OPEN having the least depth. Now, however, a good definition of depth would be slightly more complicated than it is for trees. As for ordinary graphs, a common definition is:

The depth of the start node is 0

The depth of any other node is 1 plus the depth of its *shallowest* parent

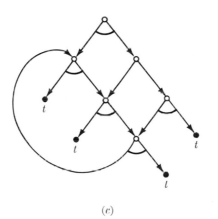

FIG. 5-5 *Some AND/OR graphs.*

A second complication involves the necessity of providing pointers from a node to more than just one of its parents. All of these pointers *may* be necessary in defining a solution graph. (For example, the ones pointing to nodes 1 and 6 from node 2 are both necessary in the solution of Fig. 5-6.) On the other hand, some of the multiple pointers may not be needed in a solution (for example the pointer from node 3 back to node 4 is not needed in the solution of Fig. 5-6). A process for searching AND/OR graphs must then be able to analyze the pointer structure of the search graph at termination in order to discard the irrelevant pointers and keep the ones that are necessary to define a solution graph.

Also, when successors are generated, we must check to see if any of them are already on CLOSED and had previously been labeled solved or unsolvable; if an already solved (or unsolvable) successor is reached by another path, a labeling procedure should be applied to see if the start node is solved (or unsolvable).

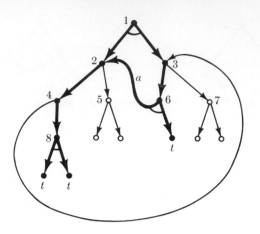

FIG. 5-6 *An example showing that node 2 can be a successor of node 6 (through arc a) even though a cycle results.*

We shall leave as an exercise the devising of algorithms for searching general AND/OR graphs. Our next task is to consider ways of efficiently ordering the node expansions using heuristic evaluation functions. Again our discussion will be considerably simplified by returning to the special case of AND/OR trees.

5-5 COSTS OF SOLUTION TREES

In state-space searches we were able to use heuristically derived *evaluation functions* to order node expansions. A key notion in defining these evaluation functions was that of a heuristic function that estimated the cost of an optimal path from a node to a goal. In AND/OR trees a corresponding notion involves an estimate of the *cost* of a solution tree rooted at a given node. Of course, before we can decide on how to estimate the cost of a solution tree below a node we must define what we mean by the cost of an AND/OR solution.

Two alternative definitions are easily given: They both involve assigning costs to the arcs of the solution tree. The first, called the *sum cost,* is simply the sum of all of the arc costs in the solution tree. The second, called the *max cost,* is based on the idea of a *path* through the solution tree. [We define a path for a tree rooted at node n to be a sequence of nodes $(n_1, n_2, \ldots, n_k)$ in the tree with $n_1 = n$, n_k terminal, and each n_j a successor of n_{j-1} for $j = 2$ to k.] The sum of the costs on the arcs connecting the nodes in a path is called the path

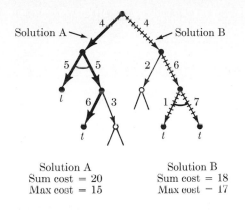

Solution A
Sum cost = 20
Max cost = 15

Solution B
Sum cost = 18
Max cost — 17

FIG. 5-7   *Two solution trees and their costs.*

cost. The max cost is now defined to be the cost of that path having maximum path cost in the solution tree.

These definitions can be illustrated using the solution trees of Fig. 5-7 where the arc costs are indicated by the numbers adjacent to the arcs. There are two solutions, one (solution A) indicated by darkened branches and the other (solution B) indicated by cross-hatched branches. Solution A has a sum cost of 20 and a max cost of 15, while solution B has a sum cost of 18 and a max cost of 17. Which solution is preferable depends, of course, on which cost one is attempting to minimize.

Often one simply uses unit arc costs. In that case the sum cost is simply a measure of the number of nodes in the solution tree (less one). Alternatively the max cost is then a measure of the longest chain of steps in the solution tree. In either case a good estimate of either of these costs can be usefully employed in an evaluation function for efficiently ordering the search.

A solution tree is itself a subtree of some implicit AND/OR tree defined by the initial problem description, the problem-reduction operators, and the set of primitive problems. We desire to find a solution tree having minimal cost within the entire implicit AND/OR tree. Such a solution tree will be called an *optimal* solution tree. Let the cost of the optimal solution tree rooted at the start node s be denoted by $h(s)$. This minimal cost $h(s)$ is defined recursively below in terms of the minimal cost $h(n)$ for a solution tree rooted at any node n. In the definition, we denote the cost of the arc between node n_i and a successor node n_j by $c(n_i, n_j)$.

1. If n is a terminal node (corresponding to a primitive problem), then

$$h(n) = 0$$

2. If n is a nonterminal node having OR successors $n_1, \ldots, n_k$, then

$$h(n) = \min_i \; [c(n,n_i) + h(n_i)]$$

3. If n is a nonterminal node having AND successors $n_1, \ldots, n_k$, then

$$h(n) = \sum_{i=1}^{k} [c(n,n_i) + h(n_i)] \qquad \text{for sum costs}$$

$$h(n) = \max_i \; [c(n,n_i) + h(n_i)] \qquad \text{for max costs}$$

Of course $h(n)$ is undefined if n is an unsolvable node.

5-6 USING COST ESTIMATES TO DIRECT SEARCH

We shall be interested in searching for solution trees achieving minimal cost (either sum cost or max cost, depending on the situation). To do so we shall make use of the idea of the *estimated cost* of a solution tree. Let $\hat{h}$ be a function such that, for any node n that is not unsolvable, $\hat{h}(n)$ is an estimate of $h(n)$, the cost of an optimal solution tree rooted at node n. We shall call $\hat{h}$ the *heuristic function* and use it to order node expansions.

The search process that we shall describe will generate a search tree. At any stage during the execution of this search process, there will be some nodes at the bottom of the search tree that are either:

1. Nodes that have been discovered to be terminal by the search process.
2. Nodes that have been discovered to be nonterminal and to possess no successors by the search process.
3. Nodes whose successors have not yet been generated by the search process.

Any such node will be called a *tip node* of the search tree.

We shall now describe how the heuristic function $\hat{h}(n)$ is to be defined for any node n in the search tree.

If n is a tip node

If n has been discovered to be terminal, $\hat{h}(n) = 0$.

If n has been discovered to be nonterminal and to possess no successors, $\hat{h}(n)$ is undefined.

If n is a node whose successors have not yet been generated, then $\hat{h}(n)$ is some heuristic estimate of the cost $h(n)$ of an optimal solution tree rooted at node n. Such an estimate would be made on the basis of heuristic information about the problem domain represented by the AND/OR tree.

If n is a nontip node having OR successors $n_1, \ldots, n_k$

$$\hat{h}(n) = \min_i [c(n,n_i) + \hat{h}(n_i)]$$

If n is a nontip node having AND successors $n_1, \ldots, n_k$

$$\hat{h}(n) = \sum_{i=1}^{k} [c(n,n_i) + \hat{h}(n_i)] \qquad \text{for sum costs}$$

$$\hat{h}(n) = \max_i [c(n,n_i) + \hat{h}(n_i)] \qquad \text{for max costs}$$

Since $\hat{h}(n) = 0$ for terminal nodes, our definition of $\hat{h}$ ensures that $\hat{h} \equiv h$ should the entire implicit AND/OR tree be included in the search tree.

Now, contained within the search tree at any stage are many subtrees rooted in s, each of which might become the top part of a complete solution tree, depending on the results of future node expansions. Let us call these subtrees *potential solution trees* for s. For each node having OR successors in the search tree, one can choose a different potential solution tree corresponding to each of the OR successors. Analogously, rooted at each node n in the search tree there are potential solution trees for n that would solve the subproblem corresponding to that node. (Unless, of course, the node has already been labeled unsolvable.)

At any stage during the search process, we can extract from the search tree that *potential* solution tree τ_o, rooted in s and estimated to be the top part of an *optimal* solution tree rooted in s. The extraction process uses the $\hat{h}$ values and is based on the following definition:

1. The start node is in τ_o.
2. If node n is in τ_o, then

   If node n has OR successors $n_1, \ldots, n_k$ in the search tree, then that successor having a minimal value of $[c(n,n_i) + \hat{h}(n_i)]$ is in τ_o (ties are resolved arbitrarily),

   If node n has AND successors in the search tree, then all of these successors are in τ_o.

The potential solution tree τ_o, estimated to be the top part of an optimal solution tree rooted in s, is a key concept in the heuristic search process to be described. The appropriate ordering technique involves asking "Which is the most promising potential solution tree to extend?" rather than asking "Which is the most promising node to expand next?" (Analogously, we observe that in state-space search, selecting that node with minimal $\hat{f} = \hat{g} + \hat{h}$ extends the most promising partial *path*.) We shall take τ_o to be the most promising potential solution tree.

Our search process must now keep track of the $\hat{h}$ values at each node in the search tree so that τ_o can be extracted. After τ_o is extracted, a tip node of τ_o that has not yet been selected for expansion is expanded, and the $\hat{h}$ values of the enlarged search tree are recomputed. Actually, only the nodes ancestral to the node just expanded need to have their $\hat{h}$ values recomputed because the $\hat{h}$ values at the other nodes will not change. (The $\hat{h}$ value of a node depends only on the $\hat{h}$ values of its descendants.)

Before we can state a precise search process based on these ideas, we must have a means for deciding which of the tip nodes of τ_o should be expanded next. Various ideas could be advanced. Perhaps a good idea would be to select that node whose expansion would be most likely to *refute* the hypothesis that τ_o will indeed turn out to be the top part of an optimal solution tree. For if τ_o is not to be the top part of an optimal solution tree even though it is momentarily estimated to be, then efficient search demands that this fact be determined as early as possible. We shall have more to say in Section 5-9 about this subject. Suppose, for the moment, that we do have some means for determining which of the tip nodes of τ_o to expand next.

5-7   AN ORDERED-SEARCH ALGORITHM FOR AND/OR TREES

We can now list the steps defining an ordered-search algorithm for AND/OR trees. The steps differ only slightly from those of the breadth-first search method:

(1)   Put the start node s on a list called OPEN and compute $\hat{h}(s)$.

(2)   Compute the potential solution tree τ_o, estimated to be the top part of the optimal solution tree rooted at s, using the $\hat{h}$ values of the nodes in the search tree.

(3)   Select some tip node of τ_o that is on OPEN and put it on CLOSED. Call this node n.

(4)   If n is a terminal node, label n solved and continue; otherwise go to (9).

(5)   Apply the solve-labeling procedure to τ_o.

(6)   If the start node is labeled solved, exit with τ_o as the solution tree; otherwise continue.

(7)   Remove from OPEN any nodes having ancestors that are solved.

(8)   Go to (2).

(9)   Apply the successor operator Γ to n, generating all the successors of n. If there are no successors, label n unsolvable and continue; otherwise go to (14).

(10)   Apply the unsolvable-labeling procedure to τ_o.

(11)   If the start node is labeled unsolvable, exit with failure; otherwise continue.

(12) Remove from OPEN any nodes having ancestors that are unsolvable.

(13) Go to (2).

(14) Put these successors on OPEN and provide pointers from them back to n. Compute the $\hat{h}$ values for these successors. Recompute the $\hat{h}$ values for n and its ancestors.

(15) Go to (2).

The flow chart for this procedure is shown in Fig. 5-8. (Note that in the special case in which no AND nodes occur, this procedure searches a tree in a manner identical to that of the state-space ordered-search method. Note also that if the arc costs are unity, if $\hat{h} \equiv 0$ for tip nodes, and if the max-cost definition is used, then this procedure achieves the same results as does a breadth-first search.)

In Fig. 5-9 we show a sequence of hypothetical search trees illustrating the operation of the ordered-search algorithm. Suppose that expansion of the start node results in the search tree of Fig. 5-9a. The numbers adjacent to the nodes are $\hat{h}$ values. For the tip nodes, these values are heuristic estimates of the *sum* costs of solutions to the corresponding problems. The $\hat{h}$ values for the other nodes in the tree are obtained using the definition of $\hat{h}(n)$ for sum costs and assuming unit arc costs. From these $\hat{h}$ values, we can calculate that potential solution tree τ_o, estimated to be the top part of an optimal solution tree. Darkened branches are used to indicate τ_o.

Next we expand some tip node in τ_o. Suppose this expansion produces the search tree of Fig. 5-9b. Because of the new $\hat{h}$ values, τ_o now shifts to another part of the search tree. Expanding a node in this τ_o produces, say, the search tree of Fig. 5-9c. Here we obtain some terminal tip nodes and thus some solved nodes. These are indicated by solid circles (●). Note that the $\hat{h}$ values of terminal nodes are 0. After another node expansion, we finally obtain the solution tree (shown by darkened branches) in Fig. 5-9d. The sum cost of this tree is 9 and is calculated using the final $\hat{h}$ values.

5-8 ADMISSIBILITY OF THE ORDERED-SEARCH ALGORITHM

As in state-space searches, we shall say that an AND/OR tree-searching algorithm is *admissible* if it always terminates in a minimal-cost solution tree whenever a solution tree exists. We now prove that if the estimate h is a lower bound on h for open nodes, then the ordered-search algorithm is admissible. To do so we first establish the following lemma:

Lemma 5-1 If a solution tree exists and if $\hat{h}(n) \leq h(n)$ for all nodes n on OPEN, then at any stage during the search process we have

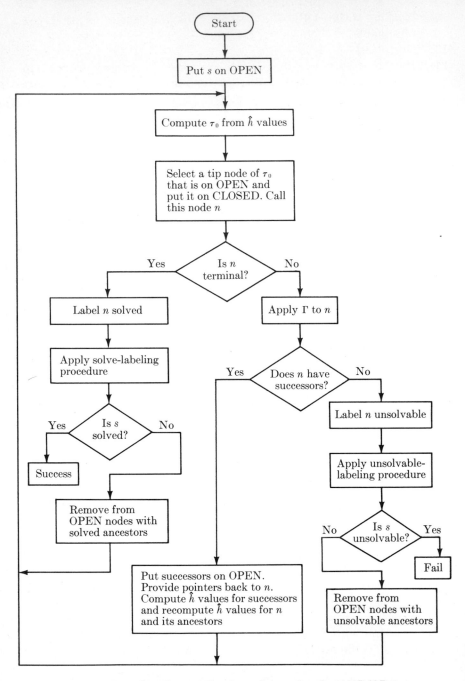

FIG. 5-8 *Flow chart for an ordered-search procedure for AND/OR trees.*

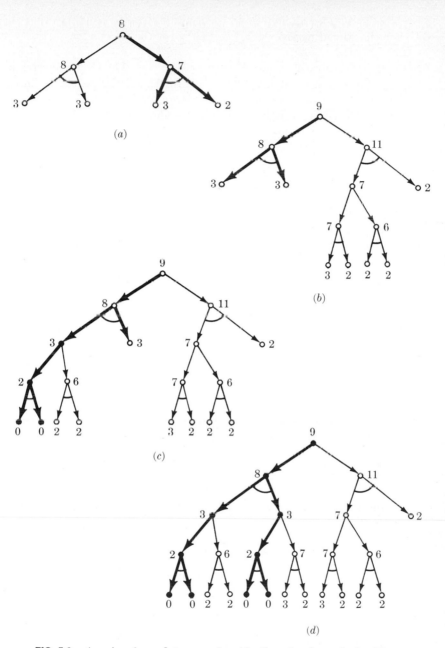

FIG. 5-9 *A series of search trees produced by the ordered-search algorithm.*

$\hat{h}(n) \leq h(n)$ for all nodes n in the search tree with equality occurring for the solved nodes.

Proof By induction on the level[1] of the search tree. The lemma is trivially true for search trees of level 0, since for these, the only node in the search tree is the start node s. If s is on OPEN, $\hat{h}(s) \leq h(s)$; if s is solved by virtue of being a terminal node, $\hat{h}(s) = h(s) = 0$.

Next we assume the lemma true for search trees of any level less than or equal to an arbitrary level ℓ ($\ell \geq 0$), and prove it true for search trees of level $\ell + 1$.

Suppose we have a search tree of level $\ell + 1$. Since $\ell \geq 0$, the start node s has immediate descendants, say, nodes $n_1, \ldots, n_k$. These nodes are the roots of subtrees of level at most ℓ, so by the induction hypothesis, the lemma is true for all of the nodes in these subtrees. That is, $\hat{h} \leq h$ for all of the nodes in these subtrees (with equality for solved nodes). We then have only to prove that $\hat{h}(s) \leq h(s)$, with equality if s is solved. Suppose first that the $n_1, \ldots, n_k$ are OR nodes. Then by the definition of $\hat{h}$ we have

$$\hat{h}(s) = \min_i [c(s,n_i) + \hat{h}(n_i)]$$

But by the induction hypothesis, we have $\hat{h}(n_i) \leq h(n_i)$ for $i = 1, \ldots, k$, so

$$\hat{h}(s) \leq \min_i [c(s,n_i) + h(n_i)]$$

The right-hand side of the above inequality is equal to $h(s)$ by definition, so we have

$$\hat{h}(s) \leq h(s)$$

Now if s is solved, the algorithm must have terminated with some solution tree τ_o in which n_{io}, say, is the successor of s. By the definition of τ_o we have

$$\hat{h}(s) = c(n,n_{io}) + \hat{h}(n_{io}) = \min_i [c(n,n_i) + \hat{h}(n_i)]$$

But for τ_o to be a solution tree for s, n_{io} must also be solved. By the induction hypothesis, $\hat{h}(n_{io}) = h(n_{io})$. Therefore

$$\hat{h}(s) = c(n,n_{io}) + h(n_{io}) = \min_i [c(n,n_i) + \hat{h}(n_i)]$$

Now, since $\hat{h}(n_i) \leq h(n_i)$ for $i = 1, \ldots, k$, certainly

$$\hat{h}(s) = c(n,n_{io}) + h(n_{io}) \leq \min_i [c(n,n_i) + h(n_i)]$$

[1] The level of a search tree is defined to be the depth of the deepest tip node.

Because n_{io} is one of the n_i, we see that

$$\hat{h}(s) = c(n,n_{io}) + h(n_{io}) = \min_i [c(n,n_i) + h(n_i)]$$

Therefore by the definition of $f(s)$, we have

$$\hat{h}(s) = h(s)$$

establishing our result in the case when s is solved.

A similar argument establishes the desired result when s has AND successors (for both sum costs and max costs), finishing the proof of the lemma.

We note that since $\hat{h}(n) = h(n)$ for all the solved nodes in the search tree, we do not preclude finding a minimal cost tree by discarding any nodes on OPEN with solved ancestors in step (7) of the algorithm; the discarded nodes could not possibly be part of a lower cost solution tree.

We can now state and prove that the ordered-search algorithm is admissible when $\hat{h}$ is a lower bound on h for any nodes on OPEN.

Theorem 5-1   If $\hat{h}(n) \leq h(n)$ for all open nodes n, and if all arc costs are larger than some small positive amount δ, then the ordered-search algorithm is admissible.

Proof   Our strategy for proving this theorem is identical to that used in proving Theorem 3-1. We assume the contrary, namely that the method does not terminate with an optimal solution tree when a solution tree does indeed exist. Again there are three cases to consider: The algorithm either terminates without finding a solution tree, fails to terminate at all, or terminates with a nonminimal cost solution tree.

Case 1: Termination without finding a solution tree   Termination can only occur at steps (6) and (11) of the algorithm (page 130). If termination occurs at step (6), the start node is solved, which can only happen if a solution tree has been found. If termination occurs at step (11) we have demonstrated that the start node is unsolvable; but we have assumed that a solution tree does exist, so we can reject this case.

Case 2: No termination   In this case eventually a node will be expanded with depth $d > h(s)/\delta$. But by the definition of $\hat{h}$ (with either sum cost or max cost), we will then have $\hat{h}(s) \geq d\delta > h(s)$, contradicting Lemma 5-1.

Case 3: Termination with a solution tree having nonminimal cost At termination, s must be solved and therefore $\hat{h}(s) = h(s)$ by Lemma 5-1. But $\hat{h}(s)$ at termination is just equal to the cost of τ_o, the solution tree found, and therefore this solution tree has minimal cost.

5-9 SELECTING A NODE IN τ_o TO EXPAND NEXT

Clearly, the admissibility of the ordered-search algorithm with $\hat{h}$ a lower bound on h for open nodes does not depend on which tip node of τ_o on OPEN is selected for expansion. We stated earlier that perhaps it would be efficient to select that tip node of τ_o most likely[1] to refute the hypothesis that τ_o is the top part of a minimal cost solution tree. If τ_o is in fact part of a minimal cost tree, then it doesn't make any difference which of the open nodes in τ_o is expanded first; in that case they all eventually have to be selected for expansion anyway. However, if τ_o is not part of a minimal cost solution tree, there is no point in wasting search effort on it; we ought next to expand that node in τ_o that is most likely to reveal our error in selecting τ_o.

When using sum costs, perhaps that open node in τ_o most likely to spoil τ_o is the open node having the largest value of $\hat{h}$. Since it is thought to be the tip node with the highest cost solution, perhaps expanding it will raise the estimated (sum) cost of τ_o the most.

When using max costs, a possibly useful method of selecting an open node in τ_o involves starting at s and traveling down through τ_o to an open tip node by selecting a specific arc below each node. Whenever we encounter a node n in τ_o having multiple (AND) successors n_1, n_2, . . . , n_k we proceed down to that nonsolved successor that *maximizes* $[c(n, n_i) + \hat{h}(n_i)]$. The open tip node reached by this process ought to be the node whose expansion is most likely to affect adversely the estimated max cost of τ_o.

In any case, we cannot prove the optimality of any of these methods for selecting open nodes. There seems to be no result for AND/OR trees analogous to the one for state-space searches about expanding the *fewest* number of nodes. It seems intuitively plausible, however, that whatever method is used for selecting an open node within τ_o, search efficiency is higher for those $\hat{h}$ functions that more closely approximate the true value of h. The better the lower bound on h that is used for $\hat{h}$, the more directly the search will be focused toward obtaining the minimal cost solution tree.

5-10 MODIFICATIONS

As in state-space searches, the basic ordered-search algorithm may be modified in a variety of ways to render it more practical in special

---

[1] We use the words *most likely* here in an informal manner. No attempt will be made to define probabilities and to perform a statistical analysis.

situations. First, rather than recompute a new potential solution tree τ_0 after every node expansion, one might instead expand one or more nodes on τ_0 and some number of their descendants in a burst and then recompute τ_0. This strategy reduces the overhead expense of frequent τ_0 computations while incurring the risk that some node expansions may not be on the best potential solution tree.

The staged-search strategy described in Chapter 3 may also be used for AND/OR trees. To employ it, one periodically reclaims needed storage space by discarding some of the AND/OR search tree. One can, for example, determine that potential solution tree within the search tree having the *largest* estimated cost. Some number of the more costly potential solution trees can then be discarded periodically (with the risk, of course, of discarding one that might turn out to be the top part of the true minimal cost tree).

Major modifications must be made if the method is to be applied to searching AND/OR graphs (rather than AND/OR trees). The considerations mentioned in Section 5-4 must then be taken into account.

5-11 THE MINIMAX PROCEDURE FOR SEARCHING GAME TREES

In the last chapter we saw that game trees can be thought of as AND/OR trees. Given that we are attempting to prove that PLUS can win from some initial position, then those positions resulting from a move by PLUS are represented by OR nodes, and those positions resulting from a move by MINUS are represented by AND nodes. We shall arbitrarily assume that PLUS moves first and that thereafter the moves of MINUS and PLUS alternate. Therefore, the successors of AND nodes are OR nodes and vice versa. Consistent with this convention, we shall consider the start node to be an AND node. A terminal node corresponds to any position defined to be a win for PLUS. (The definition of a terminal node would be altered if the object of the search was to prove that PLUS could draw from a given position or that PLUS could not be beaten from a given position.)

Many simple games (as well as the ending sequences of more complex games) can be handled by an AND/OR tree search because then a proof of a win (or draw) can be found without having to generate a deep search tree. The solution tree proving the win (or draw) then provides a complete playing strategy for PLUS. Grundy's game of the last chapter, tic-tac-toe (naughts and crosses), various versions of nim, and some chess and checker end-games, are examples of simple games in which AND/OR search to termination is feasible. A gross estimate of the size of the tic-tac-toe game tree, for example, can be obtained by noting that the start node has nine successors, these in turn have eight, etc., yielding $9! = 362,880$ nodes at the bottom of the tree. Many of the paths end in terminal nodes at shallower levels, however, and further reductions in the size of the tree result if symmetries are acknowledged.

For more complex games, such as complete chess and checker games, AND/OR tree search to termination is wholly out of the question. It has been estimated that the complete game tree for checkers has around 10^{40} nodes and for chess around 10^{120}. (It would take around 10^{21} centuries to generate the complete checker tree even assuming that a successor could be generated in $\frac{1}{3}$ of a nanosecond.) Furthermore, ordered search techniques do not reduce the effective branching factor sufficiently to help. Therefore, for complex games, we must accept the fact that search to termination is impossible; that is, we must abandon the idea of *proving* that a win or draw can be obtained (except perhaps during the end-game).

Our goal in searching a game tree might be instead merely to find a "good" first move. We could then make the indicated move, await the opponent's reply, and search again to find a good first move from this new position.

Each of the tree searches would proceed as in ordinary AND/OR search. We can use either breadth-first, depth-first, or ordered-search methods except that the termination conditions must now be modified. Several artificial termination conditions can be specified based on such factors as a time limit, a storage-space limit, and the depth of the deepest tip node in the search tree. It is also usual in chess, for example, not to terminate if any of the tip nodes represent "live" positions, that is, positions (for example) in which there is no immediate advantageous swap.

After tree search terminates, we must extract from the search tree an estimate of the "best" first move. This estimate can be made by applying a *static evaluation function* to the tip nodes of the search tree. The evaluation function measures the "worth" of a tip node position and is based on various features thought to influence this worth. For example, in checkers some useful features measure the relative piece advantage, control of the center, control of the center by kings, and so forth. It is customary in analyzing game trees to adopt the convention that game positions favorable to PLUS cause the evaluation function to have a positive value, while positions favorable to MINUS cause the evaluation function to have a negative value. Values near zero correspond to game positions not particularly favorable to either PLUS or MINUS.

A good first move can then be extracted by a procedure called the *minimax procedure*. We assume that were PLUS to choose among tip nodes, he would choose that node having the largest evaluation. Therefore, the (AND node) parent of OR tip nodes is assigned a *backed-up value* equal to the *maximum* of the evaluations of the tip nodes. On the other hand, if MINUS were to choose among tip nodes, he would presumably choose that node having the smallest evaluation (that is, the most negative). Therefore, the (OR node) parent of AND tip nodes is assigned a backed-up value equal to the *minimum* of the evaluations of the tip nodes. After the parents of all tip nodes have been assigned backed-up values, we back up values another level, assuming that PLUS would choose that node with the largest backed-up value while MINUS would choose that node with the smallest backed-up value.

We continue to back up values, level by level, until finally the successors of the start node are assigned backed-up values. We assume it is PLUS's turn to move at the start (i.e., the successors of the start node are OR nodes), so PLUS should choose as his first move that corresponding to the successor having the *largest* backed-up value.

The utility of this whole procedure rests on the presumption that the backed-up values of the start node's successors are more reliable measures of the ultimate relative worth of these positions than are the values that would be obtained by applying the static evaluation function directly to these positions. The backed-up values are, after all, based on "looking ahead" in the game tree and therefore depend on features occurring nearer the end of the game.

A simple example using the game of tic-tac-toe will illustrate the minimaxing method. Let us suppose that PLUS marks crosses (X) and MINUS marks circles (O) and that it is PLUS's turn to play first. We shall conduct a breadth-first search, until all of the nodes at level 2 are generated, and then we shall apply a static evaluation function to the positions at these nodes. Let our evaluation function $e(p)$ of a position p be given simply by:

If p is not a winning position

$e(p)$ = (number of complete rows, columns, or diagonals that are still open for PLUS) − (number of complete rows, columns, or diagonals that are still open for MINUS)

If p is a win for PLUS

$e(p) = \infty$ (∞ denotes a very large positive number)

If p is a win for MINUS

$e(p) = -\infty$

Thus, if p is [grid] we have $e(p) = 6 - 4 = 2$. We shall make use of symmetries in generating successor positions; thus

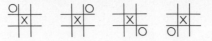

are all considered to be identical. (Early in the game, the branching factor of the tic-tac-toe tree is kept small by symmetries; late in the game it is kept small by the small number of open spaces available.)

In Fig. 5-10, we show the tree generated by a search to depth 2. Static evaluations are shown below the tip nodes, and backed-up values are circled. Since ⊞ has the largest backed-up value, it is chosen as the first move. (Coincidentally, this is PLUS's best first move.)

Now let us suppose that PLUS makes this move and MINUS replies with ⊞. (A bad move for poor MINUS, who must not be using a good search strategy.) Next PLUS searches to depth 2 (below ⊞) yielding the search tree shown in Fig. 5-11. PLUS makes the indicated best move, and MINUS makes the move that avoids his immediate defeat, yielding ⊞. PLUS then searches again, yielding the tree shown in Fig. 5-12. Some of the tip nodes in this tree (for example, the one marked A) represent wins for MINUS and thus have evaluations equal to $-\infty$. When these evaluations are backed up, we see that PLUS's best move is also the only one that avoids his immediate defeat. Now even MINUS can see that PLUS must win on his next move, so MINUS gracefully resigns.

5-12 THE ALPHA-BETA PROCEDURE

The search procedure that we have just described separates completely the process of search-tree *generation* from the process of position *evaluation*. Only after tree generation is completed does position evaluation begin. It happens that this separation results in a grossly inefficient strategy. Remarkable reductions (amounting sometimes to many orders of magnitude) in the amount of search needed (to discover the *same* best move) are possible if one performs tip-node evaluations and calculates backed-up values simultaneously with tree generation.

Consider the search tree of Fig. 5-12 (the last stage of our tic-tac-toe search). Suppose that a tip node is evaluated *as soon as it is generated*. Then after the node marked A is generated and evaluated, there is no point in generating (and evaluating) nodes B, C, and D. For

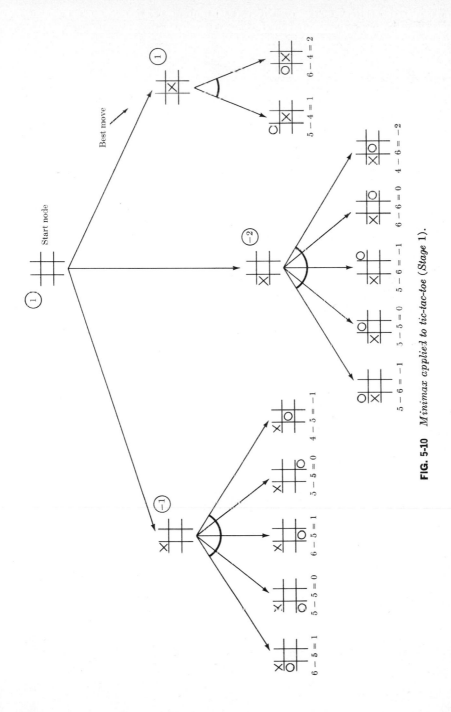

FIG. 5-10 *Minimax applied to tic-tac-toe (Stage 1).*

141

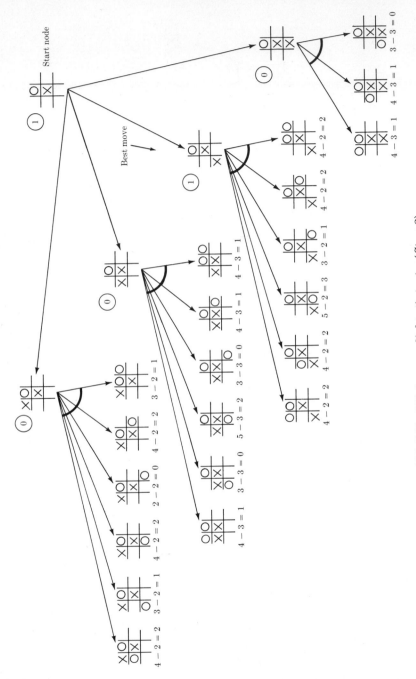

FIG. 5-11 *Minimax applied to tic-tac-toe (Stage 2).*

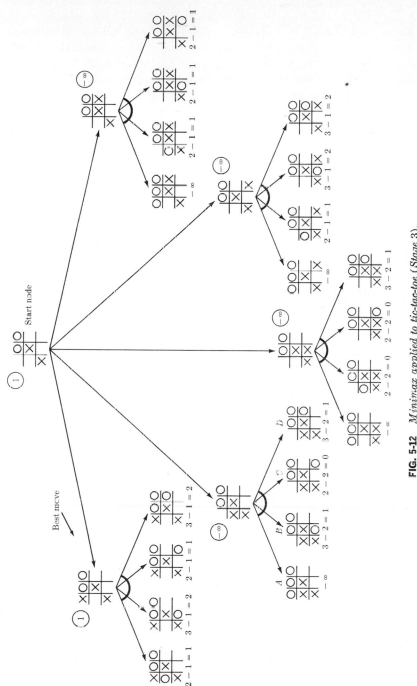

FIG. 5-12 *Minimax applied to tic-tac-toe (Stage 3).*

143

since MINUS has A available and MINUS could prefer nothing to A, we know immediately that MINUS will choose A. We can then assign A's parent the backed-up value of $-\infty$ and proceed with the search, having saved the search effort of generating and evaluating nodes B, C, and D. (Note that the savings in search effort would have been even greater if we were searching to greater depths; for then none of the *descendants* of nodes B, C, and D would have to be generated either.) It is important to observe that failing to generate nodes B, C, and D can in no way affect what will turn out to be PLUS's best first move.

In this example, the search savings depended on the fact that node A represented a win for MINUS. The same kind of savings can be achieved, however, even when none of the positions in the search tree represent wins for either PLUS or MINUS.

Consider the first stage of the tic-tac-toe tree shown in Fig. 5-10. We repeat part of this tree in Fig. 5-13. Suppose search had progressed in a depth-first manner, and that whenever a tip node is generated its static evaluation is computed. Also suppose that whenever a position can be given a backed-up value, this value is computed. Now consider the situation occurring at that stage of the depth-first search immediately after node A and all of its successors have been generated but before node B is generated. Node A is now given the backed-up value of -1. At this point the start node can be given a *provisional* backed-up value

FIG. 5-13 *Part of the first stage tic-tac-toe tree.*

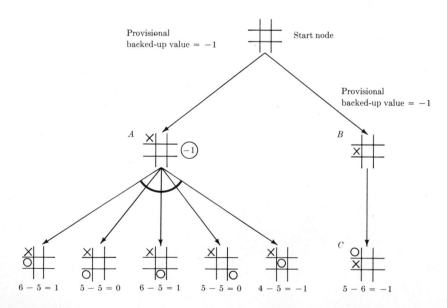

(PBV) of —1. Depending on the backed-up values of the other successors of the start node, the final backed-up value of the start node may be *greater* than this provisional value of —1, but it cannot be less.

Now let depth-first search proceed until node B and its first successor node C are generated. Node C is then given the static value of —1. Node B can now be given the *provisional* backed-up value (PBV) of —1. Depending on the static values of the rest of node B's successors, the final backed-up value of node B can be *less* than —1 but it cannot be greater. We note at this point, therefore, that the final backed-up value of node B cannot ever exceed the PBV of the start node and therefore we can discontinue search below node B. We are guaranteed that node B will not turn out to be preferable to node A.

This reduction in search effort was achieved by keeping track of provisional backed-up values. In general, as successors of a node are given backed-up values, the PBV of a node must be revised. But we note that:

1. The PBV of AND nodes (including the start node) can never decrease, and
2. The PBV of OR nodes can never increase

Because of these constraints we can state the following rules for discontinuing search:

(a)   Search can be discontinued below any OR node having a PBV *less than or equal to* the PBV of any of its AND node ancestors (including the start node). This OR node can then be assigned its PBV as a final backed-up value.[1]
(b)   Search can be discontinued below any AND node having a PBV *greater than or equal to* the PBV of any of its OR node ancestors. This AND node can then be assigned its PBV as a final backed-up value.[1]

During search, PBVs are computed as follows:

1.   The PBV of an AND node (including the start node) is set equal to the currently *largest* of the final backed-up values of its successors.
2.   The PBV of an OR node is set equal to the currently *smallest* of the final backed up values of its successors.

The PBVs of AND nodes are usually called alpha values, and the PBVs of OR nodes are usually called beta values. When search is discontinued under rule (a) above we say that an *alpha cutoff* has

---

[1] Note that these may not be "true" backed-up values for these nodes, but they are bounds that result in the appropriate PBV computations for their ancestors.

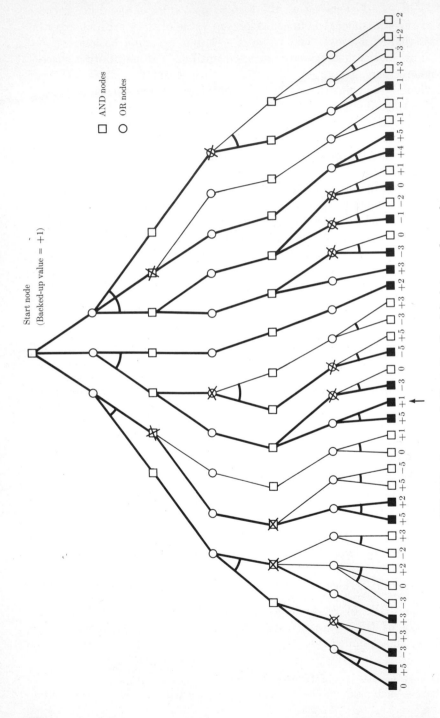

FIG. 5-14 *An example illustrating the alpha-beta search procedure.*

occurred, and when search is discontinued under rule (*b*), we say that a *beta cutoff* has occurred. The whole process of keeping track of PBVs and making cutoffs when possible is usually called the *alpha-beta procedure*. The procedure terminates when all of the successors of the start node have been given final backed-up values, and the best first move is then the one creating that successor having the highest backed-up value. We note that employing this procedure always results in finding the same best first move as would have been found by the simple minimax method of the same depth. The only difference is that the alpha-beta procedure finds the best first move after usually much less search.

An application of the alpha-beta procedure is illustrated by Fig. 5-14. In Fig. 5-14 we show a search tree generated to a depth of 6. (For convenience, AND nodes are depicted by a square □ and OR nodes are depicted by a circle ○.) The tip nodes have the static values indicated. Now suppose we conduct a depth-first search employing the alpha-beta procedure. (Again, our convention is to generate the left-most nodes first.) The subtree generated by the alpha-beta procedure is indicated by darkened branches. Those nodes cut off have *X*'s drawn through them. Note that only 18 of the original 41 tip nodes had to be evaluated. The reader can test his understanding of the procedure by attempting to duplicate the alpha-beta search on this example.

5-13 THE SEARCH EFFICIENCY OF THE ALPHA-BETA PROCEDURE

In order to perform cutoffs, at least some part of the search tree must be generated to maximum depth, because PBVs must be based on the static values of tip nodes. Therefore some type of a depth-first search is usually employed when using the alpha-beta procedure. Furthermore, the number of cutoffs that can be made during a search depends on the degree to which the early provisional values approximate the final backed-up values.

The final backed-up value of the start node is identical to the static value of one of the tip nodes. If this tip node could be reached first in a depth-first search, the number of cutoffs would be maximal. When the number of cutoffs is maximal, we need generate and evaluate a minimal number of tip nodes.

Suppose a tree has depth D, and every node (except a tip node) has exactly B successors. Such a tree will have precisely B^D tip nodes. Suppose an alpha-beta procedure generated successors in the order of their true backed-up values—the highest valued successors first for OR nodes and the lowest valued successors first for AND nodes. (Of course, these backed-up values are not typically known at the time of successor generation, so this order could never really be achieved except perhaps accidentally.)

It happens that this order maximizes the number of cutoffs that will occur and minimizes the number of tip nodes generated. Let us denote this minimal number of tip nodes by N_D. It can be shown that

$$N_D = 2B^{D/2} - 1 \qquad \text{for even } D$$

and

$$N_D = B^{(D+1)/2} + B^{(D-1)/2} - 1 \qquad \text{for odd } D$$

That is, the number of tip nodes of depth D that would be generated by optimal alpha-beta search is about the same as the number of tip nodes that would have been generated at depth $D/2$ without alpha-beta. Therefore, for the same storage requirements, the alpha-beta procedure with *perfect* successor ordering allows search depth to be doubled. Even though perfect ordering cannot be achieved in search problems (if it could, we wouldn't need the search process at all!), the large potential payoff makes it important to use the best ordering function available.

5-14 COMBINED ALPHA-BETA AND ORDERING PROCEDURES

Two procedures for generating successors in the order *estimated* to be best come easily to mind:

Fixed ordering

A depth-first procedure can be employed in which that successor estimated to be the best move (for either player) is generated first. We shall say that such a procedure employs *fixed ordering*. Thus, if node 1, say, is estimated to be the best of the start node successors (from PLUS's viewpoint), it is generated first and selected for expansion. Then if node 11, say, is estimated to be the best of node 1's successors (from MINUS's viewpoint), it is generated next and selected for expansion. We continue this process until a tip node is reached at which point cutoffs become possible. Depth-first search (with alpha-beta) continues in the standard manner, still generating successors in order of their estimated worth.

Estimates of the worth of a node can be made in a number of ways. One might use the static evaluation function itself for ranking successors. Or perhaps a simpler (and less reliable) evaluation function might be used. Alternatively, a relatively shallow search might be carried out below each successor, and then these successors can be ranked according to the backed-up values obtained from this shallow search. Of course, for any of these methods the extra effort incurred by ordering the successors must be weighed against the search savings gained by the increased number of cutoffs that result from the ordering. Usually, some experimentation is needed to obtain a balance.

Dynamic ordering

The fixed-ordering, alpha-beta procedure just described has the virtue of simplicity, but it might happen that while pursuing a certain course down the search tree, it becomes evident that search should be continued at some higher, now more promising, node. A modification of the ordered-search algorithm, for searching AND/OR trees, would allow search to advance in that section of the tree thought to be most promising until maximum depth is reached. We shall say that the modified ordered-search algorithm employs *dynamic ordering*.

The modifications are quite simple. At any stage during the search, the search tree will have tip nodes. Instead of computing an $\hat{h}$ value for these nodes (measuring estimated *cost*), an evaluation function e will be employed to measure the estimated worth of the corresponding game positions. Then, in analogy with computing $\hat{h}$ values, backed-up evaluations, or e-values, will be computed for the nontip nodes in the search tree. (Note that a game tree generally will not have costs associated with its arcs; the backed-up evaluation will thus be computed in the same way as in the minimax procedure.)

Based on these backed-up e-values, the chain of best moves is followed down this tree until one of its tip nodes is reached. This node is then expanded next. (The best move below an AND node is to the OR node successor having the largest backed-up e-value; the best move below an OR node is to the AND node successor having the smallest backed-up e-value.) When maximum depth is finally reached, we are able to compute PBVs and can then look for cutoffs. [Performing cutoffs is then analogous to the process of removing nodes from OPEN in steps (7) and (12) of the ordered-search algorithm (pages 130, 131).]

Here again, the worth of a position at the tip of a search tree can be estimated by a static evaluation function or by a shallow search. Also we can allow a burst of tree growth below a node selected for expansion before making a new τ_0 computation. In several experiments [Slagle and Dixon (1969)] using the game of kalah, it has been verified that the alpha-beta method employing some form of dynamic ordering is more efficient than either alpha-beta with fixed ordering or (of course) simple minimaxing without alpha-beta.

5-15   POSSIBLE IMPROVEMENT ON MINIMAX-BASED METHODS

The basic philosophy of minimax-based methods (including those using alpha-beta) assumes that MINUS will respond with a best move *as defined by* PLUS's *search*. Assuming MINUS has the same search resources as does PLUS, his search will actually delve one level deeper in the game tree than did that of PLUS. Therefore after MINUS conducts his search, he can base his response on backed-up values that are more reliable than are the corresponding ones that PLUS had computed. Consequently MINUS's best move may not be the same as that computed earlier by PLUS.

Some insurance against this difficulty can be provided by altering slightly the minimax method of backing up values. Instead of backing up that value corresponding to the maximum (or minimum) of the values of successors, we can back up some more complex *function* of the values of the successors. For example, it has been suggested that a *bonus* be added to the backed-up value of AND nodes if there is more than one high-valued OR successor. Similarly, a bonus would be subtracted from OR node values if there is more than one good (for MINUS) AND node successor.

This strategy of allowing bonus values to be added or subtracted acknowledges the added worth of positions from which several good moves can be made. Experiments [Slagle and Dixon (1970)] with this strategy indicate that its use does indeed result in better play, at least in the game of kalah.

5-16   BIBLIOGRAPHICAL AND HISTORICAL REMARKS

Development of AND/OR graph-searching techniques

The search strategies of many of the early programs that generated subproblem trees employed only rather simple ordering methods. Early versions of GPS used a depth-first strategy and a means for measuring problem difficulty; backtracking occurred when a successor problem was judged more difficult than any of its ancestors. Slagle's SAINT program used depth-of-function nesting as a measure of problem difficulty and generally worked on the easiest problems first.

Slagle and his coworkers experimented with many search strategies for game trees and AND/OR trees during the 1960s. The game-tree strategies were summarized in a paper by Slagle and Dixon (1969). The most complex of these involved a dynamic ordering of node expansions. In their problem-solving system called MULTIPLE (MULTIpurpose Program that LEarns), Slagle and Bursky (1968) incorporated a general strategy for searching AND/OR trees. This strategy uses the notion of the "probability that a proposition is true" and then defines a "merit function" over the open nodes of the tree. That node having greatest effect on the probability that the original proposition is true is said to have the largest "merit"; this node is the one selected for expansion.

Amarel (1967) proposed an "attention control" strategy for ordering node expansions in an AND/OR tree. This strategy attempted to find a minimal-cost solution. The present author [Nilsson (1969)] also suggested a cost-minimizing strategy and later realized that it was essentially identical to Amarel's. In Nilsson (1969) a proof is given that the strategy does indeed find minimal cost solutions; this proof and the proof given in this chapter are based on the similar one for state-space graphs by Hart, Nilsson, and Raphael (1968). The Amarel-Nilsson strategy differs little from the dynamic ordering method of Slagle and Dixon. The exposition of the ordered-search algorithm in this chapter is merely an attempt to describe this basic strategy in a clear and general manner.

Development of game tree-searching techniques

Claude Shannon (1950) discussed some of the problems inherent in programming a machine to play a complex game such as chess. He suggested a minimax search procedure to be used in conjunction with a static evaluation function. Newell, Shaw, and Simon (1958) used several of these ideas in constructing an early chess-playing program; they also give an excellent discussion of this area of research. Additional discussion on chess-playing programs together with a "Five-Year Plan" for automatic chess can be found in an article by Good (1968) that also lists several references.

Later, Samuel (1959) described a checker-playing program that incorporated polynomial evaluation functions, minimax search methods, and various "learning" strategies for improving play.[1] Samuel's program plays an excellent checker game and beats all but the very best players. It continues to be one of the outstanding examples of the application of artificial intelligence techniques. Later work on this program is described in Samuel (1967). One of the features of more recent versions of Samuel's program is a dynamic ordering search procedure somewhat similar to that of Slagle and Dixon (1969).

The alpha-beta procedure is usually thought to be a rather obvious

[1] Samuel later stated (personal communication) that his program also used the alpha-beta procedure, but at the time he thought its use too straightforward to merit discussion in the paper.

elaboration of the minimaxing technique and was thus "discovered" independently by many workers. It is first described by Newell, Shaw, and Simon (1958) and was the subject of much investigation by McCarthy and his students [Edwards and Hart (1963)] at M.I.T. Few clear expositions of the method and its properties exist. Samuel's second checkers paper [Samuel (1967)] contains a good description as does the paper by Slagle and Dixon (1969). The results on the search efficiency of the alpha-beta procedure were first stated by Edwards and Hart (1963), based on a theorem that they attribute to Michael Levin. Later Slagle and Dixon (1969) give what they consider to be the first published proof of this theorem. Slagle and Dixon discuss several variations of the alpha-beta procedure, culminating with one employing dynamic ordering. The performance of these various strategies is compared, using the ancient game of kalah.

Our discussion about improvements on minimax-based methods is taken from some proposals by Slagle (1963b) and Slagle and Dixon (1970). The latter paper describes experiments with an "M & N Tree Searching Program" that adds (or subtracts) a bonus when backing up scores.

Some representative game-playing programs

Chess

Kister, et al. (1957) describe the earliest chess system programmed on a computer (MANIAC I at Los Alamos). It used a reduced board (6 by 6) and played rather poorly.

Bernstein, et al. (1958) describe a chess system programmed at IBM. It also played rather poorly but on a full (8 by 8) board.

Newell, Shaw, and Simon (1958) present another early chess program under development at Carnegie.

Kotok (1962) discussed an early M.I.T. program later taken to Stanford by John McCarthy and modified slightly. This one achieved the level of mediocre play.

Adelson-Velskii, et al. (no paper available) wrote a program at the Institute for Theoretical and Applied Physics in Moscow. This program beat the Kotok-McCarthy program in a tournament. (See SICART Newsletter, no. 4, p. 11, June 1967.)

Greenblatt, et al. (1967) describe an M.I.T. program now called Mac Hac. Its level of play can be described as "middle-amateur." It is an honorary member of the Massachusetts chess society and has earned a class C rating. For some example games see the following SIGART Newsletters: no. 6, p. 8, October 1967 (here, the computer beat H. Dreyfus, who earlier doubted that a machine could beat even an amateur player); no. 9, pp. 9–10, April 1968; no. 15, pp. 8–10, April 1969; and no. 16, pp. 9–11, June 1969.

Checkers
Samuel (1959, 1967) continues to improve a program that plays excellent checkers but can't quite beat the world champion.

Kalah
Russell (1964) wrote an early kalah program.

Slagle and Dixon (1969) describe experiments using the game of kalah.

Slagle and Dixon (1970) discuss more experiments using kalah to test the "M & N" procedure.

(The kalah programs are probably unbeatable by human players.)

Go
Zobrist (1969) has written a program to play this ancient and difficult game. It plays rather poorly by human standards and does no tree searching. For an example of how Zobrist's program performs, see SIGART Newsletter no. 18, pp. 20–22, October 1969.

PROBLEMS

5-1 In the induction step of Lemma 5-1, we obtained a proof for the case in which the successors of the start node were OR nodes and stated that a similar argument could be given if the successors of the start node were AND nodes. Present a proof for this case, thus finishing the proof of Lemma 5-1.

5-2 (For chess players)   Select a chess end-game problem (say, from a newspaper column on chess) and solve it by generating a game tree to termination. Write down the search tree showing all of the moves you considered and mark the AND/OR solution subtree. What special chess heuristics did you use while generating the search tree?

5-3 † Construct an ordered-search algorithm for AND/OR graphs (generalizing the one for trees described in Sec. 5-7).

5-4 Conduct an alpha-beta search of the game tree shown in Fig. 5-14 by generating nodes in the order *right-most* node first. Indicate where cutoffs occur and compare with Fig. 5-14 in which nodes were generated in a left-most node first order.

5-5   † (For LISP programmers)   Write a LISP function SEARCH (START, DEPTH) that generates a game tree by applying a LISP legal move generator LEGALS(POSITION) first to a starting position START and then to its successors, etc., down to some maximum depth equal to DEPTH. (Assume that it is PLUS's move from START and that play alternates thereafter.) The function SEARCH should apply a static evaluation function VAL(POSITION) to nodes of depth equal to DEPTH and conduct an alpha-beta search to find the best move from position START. The value of SEARCH should be a list of the form (BPOSITION, VALUE) where BPOSITION is the best successor position to START, and VALUE is the backed-up value for PLUS.

5-6   † Write a computer program to play three-dimensional tic-tac-toe (sometimes called Qubic). This game is played by two or *more* players on a $4 \times 4 \times 4$ cube divided into 64 cells. Each player, in turn, places one of his markers in one of the unoccupied cells. The first player to have four of his markers aligned in any row, column, or diagonal of any plane of the cube or along any major diagonal of the cube wins. Your program can use any reasonable search strategy but should employ some heuristic means for restricting the generation of successor positions in the game tree. Note that the notions of a game tree and of game-tree search must be generalized to cover n-person games, $n \geq 2$.

REFERENCES

Amarel, S. (1967): An Approach to Heuristic Problem-Solving and Theorem Proving in the Propositional Calculus, in J. Hart and S. Takasu (eds.), "Systems and Computer Science," University of Toronto Press, Toronto, 1967.

Bernstein, A., et al. (1958): A Chess-Playing Program for the IBM 704 Computer, *Proc. West. Joint Computer Conf.*, pp. 157–159, 1958.

Edwards, D., and T. Hart (1963): The α-β Heuristic, *M.I.T. Artificial Intelligence Memo* no. 30 (revised), Oct. 28, 1963 [originally printed as The Tree Prune (TP) Algorithm, Dec. 4, 1961].

Good, I. (1968): A Five-Year Plan for Automatic Chess, in E. Dale and D. Michie (eds.), "Machine Intelligence 2," pp. 89–118, American Elsevier Publishing Company, Inc., New York, 1968.

Greenblatt, R., et al. (1967): The Greenblatt Chess Program, *Proc. AFIPS Fall Joint Computer Conf.*, pp. 801–810, Anaheim, Calif., 1967.

Hart, P., N. Nilsson, and B. Raphael (1968): A Formal Basis for the Heuristic Determination of Minimum Cost Paths, *IEEE Trans. Sys. Sci. Cybernetics*, vol. SSC-4, no. 2, pp. 100–107, July 1968.

Kister, J., et al. (1957): Experiments in Chess, *J. ACM*, vol. 4, no. 2, pp. 174–177, April 1957.

Kotok, A. (1962): "A Chess Playing Program for the IBM 7090," unpublished B.S. thesis, Massachusetts Institute of Technology, Cambridge, Mass., 1962.

Newell, A., J. Shaw, and H. Simon (1958): Chess Playing Programs and the Problem of Complexity, *IBM J. Res. and Develop.*, vol. 2, pp. 320–335, October 1958. Reprinted in E. Feigenbaum and J. Feldman (eds.), "Computers and Thought," pp. 39–70, McGraw-Hill Book Company, New York, 1963.

Nilsson, N. (1969): Searching Problem-Solving and Game-Playing Trees for Minimal Cost Solutions, in A. J. H. Morrell (ed.), "Information Processing 68," vol. 2, pp. 1556–1562, North-Holland Publishing Company, Amsterdam, 1969.

Russell, R. (1964): Kalah—The Game and The Program, *Stanford University Artificial Intelligence Project Memo* no. 22, Sept. 3, 1964.

Samuel, A. (1959): Some Studies in Machine Learning Using the Game of Checkers, *IBM J. Res. Develop.*, vol. 3, pp. 211–229, 1959. Reprinted in E. Feigenbaum and J. Feldman (eds.), "Computers and Thought," pp. 71–105, McGraw-Hill Book Company, New York, 1963.

―――― (1967): Some Studies in Machine Learning Using the Game of Checkers II. Recent Progress, *IBM J. Res. Develop.*, vol. 11, no. 6, pp. 601–617, November 1967.

Shannon, C. (1950): Programming a Digital Computer for Playing Chess, *Philosophy Magazine*, vol. 41, pp. 356–375, March, 1950. Reprinted in J. R. Newman (ed.), "The World of Mathematics," vol. 4, Simon and Schuster, New York, 1954.

Slagle, J. (1963b): Game Trees, M & N Minimaxing, and the M & N Alpha-Beta Procedure, *Artificial Intelligence Group Rept.* no. 3, UCRL-4671, University of California Lawrence Radiation Laboratory, Livermore, Calif., November 1963.

―――― and P. Bursky (1968): Experiments with a Multipurpose, Theorem-Proving Heuristic Program, *J. ACM*, vol. 15, no. 1, pp. 85–99, January 1968.

―――― and J. Dixon (1969): Experiments with Some Programs That Search Game Trees, *J. ACM*, vol. 16, no. 2, pp. 189–207, April 1969.

―――― and ―――― (1970): Experiments with the M & N Tree Searching Program, *Commun. ACM*, vol. 13, no. 3, p. 147, March 1970.

Zobrist, A. (1969): A Model of Visual Organization for the Game of Go, *Proc. AFIPS Spring Joint Computer Conf.*, pp. 103–112, 1969.

CHAPTER SIX

THEOREM PROVING IN THE PREDICATE CALCULUS

6-1 PREDICATE CALCULUS AS A LANGUAGE FOR PROBLEM SOLVING

We mentioned in the first chapter that the solution to many problems might require logical analysis. In order to do automatic logical reasoning, we need some kind of formal language in which we can state premises and make valid logical deductions. What is required is a language powerful enough to express the problems of interest and a means for *searching* for the appropriate steps in the deduction process.

The *first-order predicate calculus* is a system of logic in which it is possible to express much of mathematics and many statements of everyday English The system has rules of inference that allow us to make valid logical deductions of new statements from a set of given ones. Because of its generality and logical power, the predicate calculus is an important candidate language in which to perform deductions. In this chapter, we shall digress temporarily from our main purpose of studying problem-solving processes to present a summary of the predicate calculus and techniques based on the *resolution principle* for making deductions in this system. Then in Chapter 7, we shall return to the subject of problem solving to give some examples of the role of the predicate calculus in problem solving. Finally, in Chapter 8, we shall explain some of the more efficient means for searching for desired deductions.

A language, such as that used in the predicate calculus, is defined by its *syntax*. To specify a syntax we must specify the alphabet of symbols to be used in the language and how these symbols are to be put together into legitimate expressions in the language. An important class of expressions of the predicate calculus are called the well-formed formulas (wffs).

We use a language to make assertions about some domain of interest. The relationships between the language itself and the domain of discourse is specified by the *semantics* of the language. The wffs of the predicate calculus are the expressions that we shall use to stand for assertions about the domain of interest. The wffs are said to have the value T or F, depending on whether or not the assertions are true or false of the domain. Techniques for manipulating wffs thus allow us to "reason" about a domain, and therefore these techniques can be of value in problem-solving processes requiring such reasoning.

In the next section we shall specify the syntax of one version of the predicate calculus. Then we shall show how this language can be used to make assertions about domains of discourse.

6-2 SYNTAX

The syntax of our predicate-calculus system involves

The specification of an alphabet of symbols.

The definitions of various useful expressions that can be constructed from these symbols.

We shall begin by introducing a rather primitive system[1] in order to explain some of the basic ideas. Later we shall add to the alphabet other symbols that help abbreviate some of the expressions.

[1] Specifically, we shall temporarily exclude quantifiers and variables.

The basic alphabet consists of the following sets of symbols:

1. Punctuation marks: , ( )
2. Logical symbols: $\sim$ $\Rightarrow$ (The symbol $\sim$ is read *not*, and the symbol $\Rightarrow$ is read *implies*.)
3. n-adic function letters: f_i^n ($i \geq 1$, $n \geq 0$) (The f_i^0 are called *constant* letters. For simplicity, it is conventional to use the lower case letters a,b,c in place of the f_i^0, and the lower case letters f,g,h without superscripts in place of other f_i^n.)[1]
4. n-adic predicate letters: p_i^n ($i \geq 1$, $n \geq 0$) (The p_i^0 are called proposition letters; we include them for completeness, but our examples later won't be using them. For simplicity we shall use various capital letters such as P,Q,R without superscripts in place of the p_i^n.)

From these symbols we can construct various expressions. The classes of interesting expressions can be defined recursively as follows:

1. Terms
   a. Each constant letter is a term.
   b. If $t_1\ t_2, \ldots, t_n$ ($n \geq 1$) are terms, then so is f_i^n ($t_1, t_2, \ldots, t_n$).
   c. No other expressions are terms.

   (Note that when $g(t_1, t_2, \ldots, t_n)$ is used as a term, it is used in place of some f_i^n ($t_1, \ldots, t_n$). A superscript on the g would be superfluous.)

2. Atomic formulas
   a. The proposition letters are atomic formulas.
   b. If $t_1, t_2, \ldots, t_n$ ($n \geq 1$) are terms, then the expression p_i^n ($t_1, t_2, \ldots, t_n$) is an atomic formula.
   c. No other expressions are atomic formulas.

3. Well-formed formulas (wffs)
   a. An atomic formula is a wff.
   b. If A is a wff, then so is ($\sim A$).
   c. If A and B are wffs, then so is ($A \Rightarrow B$).
   d. No other expressions are wffs (for the moment).

Some examples[2] of wffs are:

$$\sim P(a,g(a,b,a))$$
$$P(a,b) \Rightarrow (\sim Q(c))$$
$$(\sim(P(a) \Rightarrow P(b))) \Rightarrow P(b)$$
$$\sim P(a) \Rightarrow Q(f(a))$$

---

[1] The reader may wonder why the function letters were not defined to be the letters a,b,c, f,g,h in the first place. The reason is that in our formal definitions we want to provide for an arbitrarily large set of function letters, thus the f_i^n. In specific examples, however, we usually have only a few function letters and can therefore use the simpler finite set $\{a,b,c, f,g,h\}$.

[2] Parentheses are omitted whenever their omission causes no confusion.

Some examples of expressions that are not wffs are:

$\sim f(a)$

$f(P(a))$

$Q(f(a),\ (P(b) \Rightarrow Q(c)))$

The first additions to our alphabet of symbols are the logic symbols $\wedge$ (*and*) and $\vee$ (*or*), which abbreviate more complex wffs involving $\sim$ and $\Rightarrow$. Let X_1 and X_2 be any wffs. Then the expressions $X_1 \wedge X_2$ and $X_1 \vee X_2$ are also wffs and are defined as follows:

$$X_1 \wedge X_2 = \sim(X_1 \Rightarrow \sim X_2)$$
$$X_1 \vee X_2 = (\sim X_1) \Rightarrow X_2$$

6-3 SEMANTICS

In order to give a wff "meaning" we must interpret it as making some assertion about a domain of discourse. For our purposes, a *domain* is some (possibly infinite) nonempty set. It may be the set of integers, or the set of all configurations of the 8-puzzle, or the set of all mathematicians, etc. The assertions of interest will involve relations among the elements of the domain. For example, we may wish to assert that "John is the father of Bill." Then the domain is the set of persons and the relation is the diadic one, "father-of."

It is also useful to allow the use of *functions* over the domain. If the domain is D, an n-adic function maps each n-tuple of elements of D into an element of D. Thus the function *plus* maps pairs of integers into integers according to the well-known addition operation.

It is precisely these aspects of a domain—its elements, its functions, and its relations—that we wish to talk about in our predicate-calculus language. In order for a wff to make a meaningful assertion, we must associate with the wff some nonempty domain D and then

For every constant symbol in the wff we associate some particular element of D.

For every function letter in the wff we associate some particular function over D (n-adic function letters corresponding to n-adic functions).

For every predicate letter in the wff we associate some particular relation among the elements of D (n-adic predicate letters corresponding to n-adic relations).

The specification of a domain and these associations constitute an *interpretation* or a *model* of the wff.

Given a wff and some interpretation, we can assign a *value* T or F to each atomic formula in the wff. These values can then, in turn, be used to assign a value T or F to the entire wff. The process by which a value is assigned to an atomic formula is particularly simple: If the terms of the predicate letter correspond to elements of D that satisfy the associated relation, the value of this atomic formula is T; otherwise it is F.

As an example, consider the atomic formula

$P(a,f(b,c))$

and the following interpretation:

D is the set of integers
a is the integer 2
b is the integer 4
c is the integer 6
f is the addition function
P is the relation *greater than*

With this interpretation our atomic formula asserts "2 is greater than the sum of 4 plus 6." In this case we recognize that the assertion is false, and we say that $P(a,f(b,c))$ has the *value* F for this interpretation. If the interpretation is changed so that a is the integer 11, then $P(a,f(b,c))$ will have the value T. Obviously there are many other interpretations for which this atomic formula has the value T just as there are many others for which it has the value F, but in any interpretation it is either T *or* F and never both.

The value of a nonatomic wff can be computed recursively from the values of its component formulas. In this computation we use the following definitions:

If X_1 is any wff, then $\sim X_1$ has value T when X_1 has value F, and $\sim X_1$ has value F when X_1 has value T.

If X_1 and X_2 are any wffs, then the values of $(X_1 \lor X_2)$, $(X_1 \land X_2)$, and $(X_1 \Rightarrow X_2)$ are given by the following *truth table:*

X_1	X_2	$X_1 \lor X_2$	$X_1 \land X_2$	$X_1 \Rightarrow X_2$
T	T	T	T	T
F	T	T	F	T
T	F	T	F	F
F	F	F	F	T

This method of computation is called the *truth-table method*. Given an interpretation for a wff (and thus the values of each atomic formula contained in the wff), we can always compute the value of the wff (T or F) using the truth table. If the value of a wff is T for a given interpretation, we say that this interpretation *satisfies* the wff. A nonatomic wff and its value serve to define some new relation among the elements of D; the wff makes an assertion about the elements of D that is true whenever the value of the wff is T.

6-4 VARIABLES AND QUANTIFIERS

Consider the wff

$$P(a,b)$$

and the interpretation

D (the domain) is the finite set of integers $\{1,2, \ldots ,99,100\}$
a is the integer 30
b is the integer 1
P is the relationship *greater than or equal to*

Under this interpretation, the wff asserts that "30 is greater than or equal to 1." The assertion is obviously true, and the wff has value T under this interpretation. Using the same domain, suppose we assign the values $1,2, \ldots ,100$, respectively, to the constant letters $f_1^0, f_2^0, \ldots ,f_{100}^0$. With each letter we could construct a wff of the form

$$P(f_i^0, f_1^0)$$

Furthermore, each of these wffs would have the value T under this interpretation.

Frequently, it happens that we wish to make an assertion about *every* element in a domain. Such an assertion could be made by a conjunction[1] of wffs with each wff in the conjunction asserting something about one of the elements. In our example above we might form the wff

$$P(f_1^0, f_1^0) \wedge P(f_2^0, f_1^0) \wedge \cdots \wedge P(f_{100}^0, f_1^0)$$

to assert "each integer between 1 and 100 is greater than or equal to 1." Since each $P(f_i^0, f_1^0)$ has the value T, we determine (by the truth-table method) that the conjunction has the value T also.

It is cumbersome to express assertions involving the words *each* or *for all* by large conjunctions. To abbreviate these expressions we introduce

[1] The wff $X_1 \wedge X_2 \wedge \cdots \wedge X_n$ is called a *conjunction* of the wffs $X_1, X_2, \ldots , X_n$.

the symbol $\forall$ (meaning *for all*) and the *individual variables* x_i ($i \geq 1$) to our language. (Sometimes we use the letters u, v, w, x, y, z in place of the x_i.) The variables x_i are understood to range over the domain of the interpretation. Then, in our example, instead of writing a conjunction containing a wff for every element of the domain, we write instead

$$(\forall x)P(x,f_1{}^0)$$

The $\forall$ sign is called a *universal quantifier*, and the variable occurring immediately after a $\forall$ sign is a *universally quantified variable*. All occurrences of this variable within the *scope* of the quantifier are also said to be universally quantified. Universally quantified variables within the scope of their quantifiers are said to be *bound* by that quantifier.

We now have a new class of wffs, those in which universally quantified variables may appear as terms. For finite domains, the truth values of these wffs can be evaluated by the truth-table method (using the conjunction for which the wff with the quantifier stands). Quantifiers are also used in the same way for infinite domains; however, then truth-table methods cannot be used to evaluate the truth value of infinite conjunctions. The concept is still useful though because sometimes the truth values of wffs possessing quantifiers can be calculated without the need for evaluating infinite conjunctions. (For example, by the truth table, the simple wff

$$[(\forall x)P(x) \Rightarrow (\forall x)P(x)]$$

has the value T regardless of the interpretation.)

Sometimes we want to make an assertion about all pairs of elements in a domain or all triples, etc. Then we employ several variables and a $\forall$ sign for each variable. Thus the wff corresponding to the assertion "for all pairs of integers between 1 and 100, the first is greater than the second" might be written

$$(\forall x)(\forall y)P(x,y)$$

This wff (really a double conjunction) obviously has the value F under our present interpretation.

A similar abbreviation exists for disjunctions[1] naming every element in a domain. Suppose we have the disjunction

$$Q(f_1{}^0) \vee Q(f_2{}^0) \vee Q(f_3{}^0) \vee \cdots$$

where the $f_1{}^0$, $f_2{}^0$, etc. represent the elements of a domain D. By the truth table, the wff has the value T when the assertion "at least one element of D has property Q" is true.

---

[1] The wff $X_1 \vee X_2 \vee \cdots \vee X_n$ is called a *disjunction* of the wffs $X_1, X_2, \ldots, X_n$.

We use the $\exists$ sign with a variable to stand for disjunctions mentioning every element in the domain. Thus our disjunction above is written

$$(\exists x)Q(x)$$

The $\exists$ sign (meaning *there exists*) is called an *existential quantifier*, and the variable occurring immediately after an $\exists$ sign is said to be *existentially quantified*. All occurrences of this variable within the *scope* of the quantifier are also said to be existentially quantified. Existentially quantified variables within the scope of their quantifiers are said to be *bound* by that quantifier.

By truth-table methods (for finite domains) we can show that $\sim(\forall x)W(x)$ always has the same truth value as does $(\exists x)\{\sim W(x)\}$. Similarly, $\sim\exists(x)W(x)$ and $(\forall x)\{\sim W(x)\}$ are equivalent. We use these equivalences for infinite domains also.

In combining universal and existential quantifications, the existential quantification may "depend" on any previous universal quantifiers. Thus to assert "for every integer, there exists an integer that is larger" we might write

$$(\forall x)(\exists y)P(y,x)$$

Obviously the y "that exists" must depend on x if the wff is to have the value T.

In wffs consisting of more than a single predicate letter, we shall use braces to denote the scope of quantifiers; thus $(\forall x)\{\quad\}$ universally quantifies every occurrence of x within the braces.

6-5 VALIDITY AND SATISFIABILITY

If a wff has the value T for *all* interpretations, it is called *valid*. Thus by the truth table, the wff $P(a) \Rightarrow (P(a) \vee P(b))$ has the value T regardless of the interpretation, and therefore it is valid. By the truth-table method, one can always determine the validity of any wff that does not contain quantifiers. One merely checks whether the wff has the value T for all possible valuations (of T and F) of the atomic formulas contained in the wff.

When quantifiers occur, one cannot always determine the validity of a wff. It has been shown to be impossible to find a general method to evaluate the values of all of the infinite formulas represented by the quantifiers. For this reason the predicate calculus is said to be *undecidable*.

The validity of certain kinds of formulas containing quantifiers can be determined, and thus one may speak of *decidable subclasses* of the predicate calculus. Furthermore, it has been shown that if a wff is in fact valid, then a procedure exists for verifying the validity of the wff. (This same procedure applied to wffs that are not valid may never terminate.) Thus it can be said that the predicate calculus is *semidecidable*.

If the same interpretation makes each wff in a set of wffs have the value T, then we say that this interpretation *satisfies* the set of wffs. A wff W *logically follows* from a set of wffs S if every interpretation satisfying S also satisfies W. Thus, trivially, $(\forall x \forall y)\{P(x) \vee Q(y)\}$ logically follows from the set $\{(\forall x \forall y)\{P(x) \vee Q(y)\}, (\forall z)\{R(z) \vee Q(a)\}\}$. Also, $P(a)$ logically follows from $\{(\forall x)P(x)\}$. Less trivially, $(\forall x)Q(x)$ logically follows from the set $\{(\forall x)\{\sim P(x) \vee Q(x)\}, (\forall x)P(x)\}$.

It is the concept of *logically follows* that we take to underlie the notion of proof. A *proof* that some wff W is a logical consequence of a given set of wffs S is a demonstration that W logically follows from S. The main concern of these chapters is to present the basis of what appears to be the most promising mechanical method for finding a proof that a given wff logically follows from a set of wffs and to show how these methods can be applied to problem solving.

The fact that the predicate calculus is "undecidable" also implies that given an arbitrary wff W and an arbitrary set of wffs S, there can exist no effective procedure that will always decide whether or not W logically follows from S. If W does follow from S, then there are procedures that will eventually report this fact. However, if W does not follow from S, then these same procedures will unfortunately not always be able to detect it.

Nevertheless, being able to demonstrate that W logically follows from S (when in fact it does) is useful enough, and we shall concentrate on this subject. Suppose W does logically follow from S; then every interpretation satisfying S also satisfies W. But note that these interpretations do not satisfy $\sim W$. Therefore, no interpretation can satisfy the union of S and $\{\sim W\}$. If a set of wffs cannot be satisfied by *any* interpretation, then we say that the set is *unsatisfiable*. Thus, if W logically follows from S, the set $S \cup \{\sim W\}$ is unsatisfiable. Conversely, if $S \cup \{\sim W\}$ is unsatisfiable, then W must logically follow from S.

We shall use this result to cast all proof problems into the same form: To show that W logically follows from S, we will show that $S \cup \{\sim W\}$ is unsatisfiable. In order to show that a set of wffs is unsatisfiable, we must demonstrate that *no* interpretation exists for which each of the wffs in the set has value T. Formidable as this task sounds, some very powerful procedures do exist for accomplishing it. These procedures demand that the wffs in the set first be put in a special, convenient form called *clause form*.

6-6   CLAUSE FORM

In general, any wff in the predicate calculus can be put into clause form by applying a sequence of simple operations. Our next step is to show how to put an arbitrary wff into clause form. We shall illustrate this process with the wff

$$(\forall x)\{P(x) \Rightarrow \{(\forall y)\{P(y) \Rightarrow P(f(x,y))\} \wedge \sim(\forall y)\{Q(x,y) \rightarrow P(y)\}\}\}$$

The process consists of the following steps:

Eliminate implication signs   Clause form predicate calculus will use explicitly only the connectives $\vee$ and $\sim$. The implication sign may be eliminated by making the substitution[1] "$\sim A \vee B$" for "$A \Rightarrow B$" throughout the statement. In our example wff this substitution yields

$$(\forall x)\{\sim P(x) \vee \{(\forall y)\{\sim P(y) \vee P(f(x,y))\}$$
$$\wedge \sim(\forall y)\{\sim Q(x,y) \vee P(y)\}\}\}$$

Reduce scopes of negation signs   We want each negation sign $\sim$ to apply to at most one predicate letter. By making repeated use of the following substitutions, we may reduce the scope of each $\sim$ until it applies only to a single predicate letter:

Replace $\sim(A \wedge B)$	by $\sim A \vee \sim B$
Replace $\sim(A \vee B)$	by $\sim A \wedge \sim B$
Replace $\sim\sim A$	by A
Replace $\sim(\forall x)A$	by $(\exists x)\{\sim A\}$
Replace $\sim(\exists x)A$	by $(\forall x)\{\sim A\}$

Making use of these rules, our example wff becomes first

$$(\forall x)\{\sim P(x) \vee \{(\forall y)\{\sim P(y) \vee P(f(x,y))\}$$
$$\wedge (\exists y)\{\sim\{\sim Q(x,y) \vee P(y)\}\}\}\}$$

and then

$$(\forall x)\{\sim P(x) \vee \{(\forall y)\{\sim P(y) \vee P(f(x,y))\}$$
$$\wedge (\exists y)\{Q(x,y) \wedge \sim P(y)\}\}\}$$

Standardize variables   Within the scope of any quantifier symbol a variable bound by that symbol is a dummy variable. It can be uniformly

---

[1] The reader should convince himself that these substitutions preserve the truth value of the original wff. In a more formal presentation we would have to show that "$\sim A \vee B$" logically follows from "$A \Rightarrow B$" and that "$A \Rightarrow B$" logically follows from "$\sim A \vee B$," and similarly for the other substitutions we shall be making.

replaced by any other variable throughout the scope of the quantifier without changing the truth value of the wff. Standardizing variables within a wff means to rename the dummy variables to ensure that each quantifier has its own unique dummy variable. Thus, instead of writing $(\forall x)\{P(x) \Rightarrow (\exists x)Q(x)\}$, we should write $(\forall x)\{P(x) \Rightarrow (\exists y)Q(y)\}$. Standardizing our example wff yields

$$(\forall x)\{\sim P(x) \vee \{(\forall y)\{\sim P(y) \vee P(f(x,y))\} \\ \wedge \ (\exists w)\{Q(x,w) \wedge \sim P(w)\}\}\}$$

Eliminate existential quantifiers   Consider the wff

$$(\forall y \exists x)P(x,y)$$

which might be interpreted, say, as "For all y, there exists an x (possibly depending on y) such that x is greater than y." Note that because the existential quantifier $(\exists x)$ is within the scope of a universal quantifier $(\forall y)$, we allow for the possibility that the x that exists might depend on the value of y. Let this dependence be explicitly defined by some function $g(y)$, which maps each value of y into the x that "exists." Such a function is called a *Skolem function*. If we use the Skolem function in place of the x that "exists," we can eliminate the existential quantifier altogether and write $(\forall y)P(g(y),y)$.

The general rule for eliminating an existential quantifier from a wff is to replace each occurrence of its existentially quantified variable by a Skolem function whose arguments are those universally quantified variables that are bound by universal quantifiers whose scopes include the scope of the existential quantifier being eliminated. Function letters used for Skolem functions must be "new" in the sense that they cannot be ones that already occur in the wff.

Thus we can eliminate the $(\exists z)$ from

$$\{(\forall w)Q(w)\} \Rightarrow (\forall x)\{(\forall y)\{(\exists z)\{P(x,y,z) \Rightarrow (\forall u)R(x,y,u,z)\}\}\}$$

to yield

$$\{(\forall w)Q(w)\} \Rightarrow (\forall x)\{(\forall y)\{P(x,y,g(x,y)) \Rightarrow (\forall u)R(x,y,u,g(x,y))\}\}$$

If the existential quantifier being eliminated is not within the scope of any universal quantifiers, we use a Skolem function of no arguments, which is just a constant. Thus $(\exists x)P(x)$ becomes $P(a)$, where a is the constant that we know "exists."

To eliminate all of the existentially quantified variables from a wff, we use the above procedure on each one in turn. Eliminating the existential quantifiers (there is just one) in our example wff yields

$$(\forall x)\{\sim P(x) \lor \{(\forall y)\{\sim P(y) \lor P(f(x,y))\}$$
$$\land \{Q(x,g(x)) \land \sim P(g(x))\}\}\}$$

where $g(x)$ is a Skolem function.

Convert to prenex form   At this stage there are no remaining existential quantifiers, and each universal quantifier has its own variable. We may now move all of the universal quantifiers to the front of the wff and let the scope of each quantifier be the entire rest of the wff following it. The resulting wff is said to be in *prenex form*. A wff in prenex form consists of a string of quantifiers called a *prefix* followed by a quantifier-free formula called a *matrix*. The prenex form of our wff is

$$(\forall x \forall y) \underbrace{\begin{array}{l} \{\sim P(x) \lor \{\{\sim P(y) \lor P(f(x,y))\} \\ \qquad\qquad\qquad \land \{Q(x,g(x)) \land \sim P(g(x))\}\}\} \end{array}}_{}$$

$$\underbrace{(\forall x \forall y)}_{\text{prefix}} \qquad\qquad \underbrace{}_{\text{matrix}}$$

Put matrix in conjunctive normal form   Any matrix may be written as the conjunction of a finite set of disjunctions of predicates and/or negations of predicates. Such a matrix is said to be in *conjunctive normal form*. Examples of matrices in conjunctive normal form are

$$\{P(x) \lor Q(x,y)\} \land \{P(w) \lor \sim R(y)\} \land Q(x,y)$$
$$P(x) \lor Q(x,y)$$
$$P(x) \land Q(x,y)$$
$$\sim R(y)$$

We may put any matrix into conjunctive normal form by repeatedly using the rule:

Replace $A \lor \{B \land C\}$ by $\{A \lor B\} \land \{A \lor C\}$

When the matrix of our example wff is put in conjunctive normal form, our wff becomes

$$(\forall x \forall y)\{\{\sim P(x) \lor \sim P(y) \lor P(f(x,y))\}$$
$$\land \{\sim P(x) \lor Q(x,g(x))\} \land \{\sim P(x) \lor \sim P(g(x))\}\}$$

Eliminate universal quantifiers   Since all of the variables in a wff must be bound, we are assured that all the variables remaining at this step are universally quantified. Furthermore, the order of universal quantification is unimportant, so we may eliminate the explicit occurrence of universal quantifiers and assume by convention that all variables in the matrix are universally quantified. We are left now with just a matrix in conjunctive normal form.

Eliminate *and* **Signs**   We may now eliminate the *and* signs $\wedge$ by replacing $A \wedge B$ with the *two* wffs A,B. The result of repeated replacements is to obtain a finite set of wffs, each of which is a disjunction of atomic formulas and/or negations of atomic formulas. We shall use the word *literal* to denote either an atomic formula or its negation, and we shall call any wff consisting solely of a disjunction of literals a *clause*. Then every wff in our set will be a clause.

Our example wff becomes the following clauses:

$$\sim P(x) \vee \sim P(y) \vee P(f(x,y))$$
$$\sim P(x) \vee Q(x,g(x))$$
$$\sim P(x) \vee \sim P(g(x))$$

We note that the literals of a clause may contain variables, but that these variables are always understood to be universally quantified. If expressions not involving variables are substituted for the variables in a literal, we obtain what is called a *ground instance* of the literal. Thus $Q(a,f(g(b)))$ is a ground instance of $Q(x,y)$.

Our procedure for showing that some set S of wffs is unsatisfiable begins by converting each wff in S into clauses. The result of this operation is to produce some set S' of clauses. It can be shown that if S is unsatisfiable, so is S', and conversely. For the remainder of this chapter we shall describe methods for showing that an unsatisfiable set of clauses is in fact unsatisfiable. These methods are completely general, since any set of wffs can be expressed in clause form.

6-7   THE HERBRAND UNIVERSE

Consider an unsatisfiable, finite set S of clauses. In order to demonstrate that S is unsatisfiable, we must show that there exists *no* interpretation that satisfies it. As part of the specification of an interpretation for S we must first select a domain D. Next, we must associate with each constant symbol in S an element of D and with each function symbol in S a function over D, etc. Obviously we cannot enumerate all possible domains and associations to show that each resulting interpretation fails to satisfy S. But we can enumerate an adequate list of names for domain elements such that if we show that there exists no satisfying interpretation over domains whose elements can be named by the names on our list, then we shall have shown that there exists no satisfying interpretation at all. One such list of names adequate for a set S of clauses is called the *Herbrand universe* of S.

The Herbrand universe $H(S)$ of a set of clauses S is defined recursively as follows:

1. Let the set of all constant letters $\{f_i{}^0\}$ mentioned in S be in $H(S)$. If $\{f_i{}^0\}$ is empty, we allow some arbitrary constant letter, say a, to be in $H(S)$.

2. Suppose the terms $t_1, \ldots, t_n$ are in $H(S)$. Then the expressions $f_i{}^n(t_1,t_2, \ldots, t_n)$ are also in $H(S)$, where $f_i{}^n$ is any function letter mentioned in S.

3. No other terms are in $H(S)$.

It should be clear that in assigning valuations of T or F to the literals of S, we would never need any other names for domain elements regardless of the interpretation. In this sense $H(S)$ is itself a most general domain; if we show that S is unsatisfiable over the domain $H(S)$, we are assured that it is unsatisfiable over any domain.

The Herbrand universe is, in general, infinite, but only countably infinite so its members can always be ordered in some fashion. As an example, consider the following set S of clauses:

$$\{P(x) \vee Q(a) \vee \sim P(f(x)), \sim Q(b) \vee P(g(x,y))\}$$

The constant terms are $\{a,b\}$ and the functions are $\{f,g\}$. $H(S)$ is then the (countably) infinite set of expressions $\{a,b,f(a),f(b),g(a,a),$ $g(a,b),g(b,a),g(b,b),f(f(a)),f(f(b)),g(a,f(a)), \ldots\}$.

6-8 THE HERBRAND BASE

When we specify an interpretation [over $H(S)$] for a clause in S, values (of T or F) are assigned to its atomic formulas. Suppose P is an n-adic predicate letter in S. The valuation of an atomic formula $P(x_1,x_2, \ldots ,x_n)$ is fixed by assigning T or F independently to all of the ground instances of $P(x_1,x_2, \ldots ,x_n)$ that are obtained by substituting the elements of $H(S)$ for the variables $x_1,x_2, \ldots ,x_n$. Of course there may be an infinite number of ground instances of each atomic formula in S, so one could really never finish the task of computing a valuation in this way. But, remarkably, it happens that even before completing a valuation for each atomic formula in S, it will become readily apparent that no interpretation can satisfy S even though all ground instances have not yet been assigned truth values!

The *Herbrand base* of S is defined to be the set of all ground instances of all atomic formulas in S where we use the Herbrand universe to name the elements of the domain. We shall call the elements of the Herbrand base *atoms*. Obviously it is only after each atom in the Herbrand base has been assigned a truth value that an interpretation over $H(S)$ is complete for all clauses in S. The Herbrand base is a countable set also, and thus its elements can be ordered in some fashion. Suppose the ordered Herbrand base of S is written as the ordered sequence $\{p_1, p_2, p_3, \ldots\}$.

6-9 CONSTRUCTING A SEMANTIC TREE

A *semantic tree* is a binary[1] tree extending below a *root* node. Corresponding to each way in which we can assign truth values to the atoms p_i of the Herbrand base, we shall follow a certain path down the tree. If we assign T to p_1, we shall branch left immediately below the root node; if we assign F to p_1, we shall branch right. Then, regardless of which of the two nodes immediately below the root node we have branched to, if we assign T to p_2, we branch left, and if we assign F to p_2, we branch right. This process continues until we have assigned a truth value to each element of the Herbrand base. Obviously if the Herbrand base is infinite, any complete interpretation will result in an infinite path down through the nodes of the tree. The complete tree containing all possible paths then represents all possible interpretations for the clauses in S; hence the name *semantic tree*.

As an example, consider the unsatisfiable set S of clauses

$$P(x) \lor Q(y)$$
$$\sim P(a)$$
$$\sim Q(b)$$

In this case the Herbrand universe is a finite set

$$H(S) = \{a, b\}$$

The Herbrand base is also finite. It can be ordered thus:

$$\{P(a), Q(a), P(b), Q(b)\}$$

The semantic tree for this set of clauses is finite in this case and is shown in Fig. 6-1. Every edge connecting a node with one of its successors represents a decision about the truth value of one of the atoms in the Herbrand base. By convention, for an edge at which an atom is assigned the value T, we write that atom next to the edge; if it is assigned the value F, we write the negation of the atom next to the edge. Tracing down a path from the root node to a tip (i.e., a node at the bottom of the tree), provides one interpretation for the set S. This interpretation can be unambiguously represented by the set of atoms encountered along the path. Thus the interpretation obtained by tracing from the root to the tip node marked 1 in Fig. 6-1 is given

---

[1] Each node in a binary tree has exactly two successors if it has any successors at all. It is possible to generalize the definition of semantic trees to allow nodes to have more than two successors.

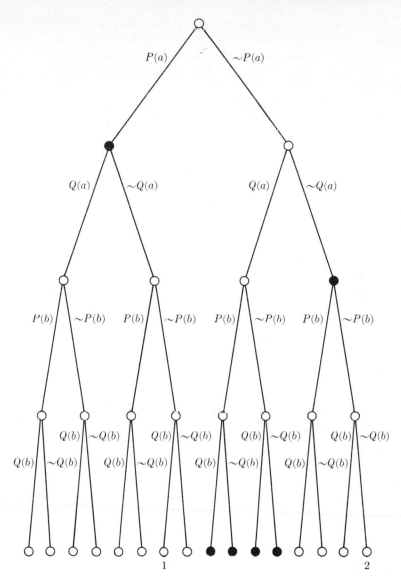

FIG. 6-1 *A semantic tree for the set of clauses* $\{P(x) \lor Q(y), \sim P(a), \sim Q(b)\}$.

by the set

$$M_1 = \{P(a), \sim Q(a), \sim P(b), Q(b)\}$$

We shall call such a set a *model* for the set of clauses.

We say that a model fails to satisfy a clause if there exists a ground instance of the clause (using terms from the Herbrand universe) having the value F, using the valuations specified by the model. Thus, M_1 does not satisfy either of the clauses $\sim P(a)$ or $\sim Q(b)$. Similarly, $M_2 = \{\sim P(a), \sim Q(a), \sim P(b), \sim Q(b)\}$ does not satisfy the clause $P(x) \vee Q(y)$, since the ground instance $P(a) \vee Q(b)$ has the value F.

If there is a clause in S not satisfied by an interpretation or model, then this model fails to satisfy S. Thus M_1 and M_2 do not satisfy our example set; furthermore, we can eliminate each of the 16 possible interpretations in turn to conclude that this example set is unsatisfiable.

6-10 FAILURE NODES

A crucial fact about semantic trees is that it is possible to determine that certain interpretations will not satisfy a set of clauses without having to trace infinitely far down the tree. In our example of Fig. 6-1, just below and to the left of the root node we assign $P(a)$ the value T. Immediately we observe that none of the eight possible interpretations with $P(a)$ having the value T can satisfy S; to satisfy S, $P(a)$ must have the value F. Thus we don't have to trace farther down the left side of the tree. We indicate by solid nodes ($\bullet$) in Fig. 6-1 those nodes in the tree at which it *first* is determined that interpretations will fail to satisfy S. Such nodes are called *failure nodes*.

Certainly, even when the Herbrand base is infinite, every possible interpretation must eventually be cut off by a failure node if the set of clauses is unsatisfiable. For if even one interpretation were never cut off by a failure node, then we could continue tracing down this path forever, and thus an interpretation would exist satisfying the set of clauses—contrary to our hypothesis. We say that a semantic tree for a set of clauses S having all paths cut off by failure nodes is *closed* for S. Thus we have a key result on which our methods for testing for unsatisfiability are based. *A semantic tree for an unsatisfiable set S of clauses is closed for S and contains a finite number of nodes above the failure nodes.*[1]

In Fig. 6-2 we show a partial semantic tree for the unsatisfiable set of clauses

$$S = \begin{Bmatrix} \sim P(x) \vee Q(x) \\ P(f(y)) \\ \sim Q(f(y)) \end{Bmatrix}$$

The Herbrand universe is

$$H(S) = \{a, f(a), f(f(a)), f(f(f(a))), \ldots\}$$

[1] This statement can be shown to be equivalent to the famous theorem of Herbrand (1930).

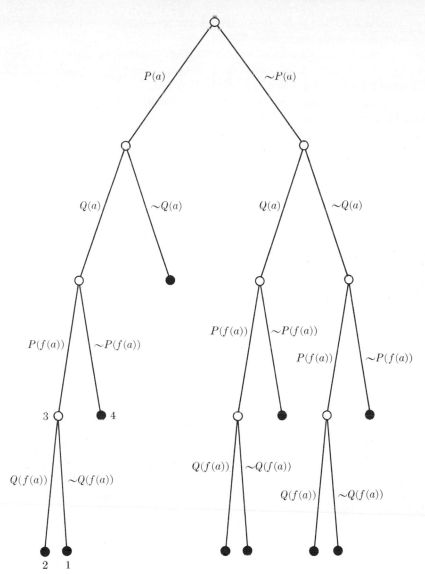

FIG. 6-2 *Closed semantic tree for the unsatisfiable set* $\{\sim P(x) \vee Q(x), P(f(y)),$
$\sim Q(f(y))\}$

and the Herbrand base can be ordered as follows:

$$\{P(a), Q(a), P(f(a)), Q(f(a)), P(f(f(a))), \ldots\}$$

Even though the Herbrand base is infinite, and thus every complete
interpretation corresponds to an infinite path in the semantic tree, we
know that the semantic tree must be closed by failure nodes if S is

unsatisfiable. That part of the semantic tree above and including the failure nodes is shown in Fig. 6-2.

It is seldom practical to detect the unsatisfiability of a set of clauses by a process of actually trying to construct a semantic tree. Practical procedures for detecting unsatisfiability have lately been devised using the resolution principle. In the next sections we shall explain and justify this principle, using the semantic tree ideas already described.

6-11 INFERENCE NODES

Consider again our example of Fig. 6-2. Every one of the failure nodes in the semantic tree has the property that any completion of the partial interpretation defined up to that failure node would fail to satisfy one of the clauses in the set. Below the failure node marked 1 in Fig. 6-2 are interpretations guaranteed not to satisfy the clause $\sim P(x) \vee Q(x)$; below the node marked 2 are interpretations guaranteed not to satisfy the clause $\sim Q(f(y))$. Thus we say that node 1 *fails for* $\sim P(x) \vee Q(x)$ and node 2 fails for $\sim Q(f(y))$. Also we say that the clauses $\sim P(x) \vee Q(x)$ and $\sim Q(f(y))$ *fail at* nodes 1 and 2, respectively.

If a node in a semantic tree is not a failure node, and if both of its successors are failure nodes, then we say that such a node is an *inference node*. In Fig. 6-2, the node marked "3" is an inference node because there is a way of *inferring* a new clause that logically follows from the clauses $\sim P(x) \vee Q(x)$ and $\sim Q(f(y))$, failing at the failure nodes immediately below. Furthermore, the new clause would itself have failed at or above the inference node. (Of course, this new clause was not in S, for otherwise node 3 or a node above would have been a failure node.)

What could we infer from the two clauses $\sim P(x) \vee Q(x)$ and $\sim Q(f(y))$ that would logically follow from them? Let I be an arbitrary interpretation satisfying both of the clauses $\sim P(x) \vee Q(x)$ and $\sim Q(f(y))$. Since I satisfies $\sim P(x) \vee Q(x)$, it would also satisfy any clause derived from it by substituting some other expression for the variable x. In particular, I would satisfy $\sim P(f(y)) \vee Q(f(y))$. But the literal $Q(f(y))$ cannot be satisfied by I since we have assumed that its negation $\sim Q(f(y))$ is satisfied by I. Therefore, if I satisfies $\sim P(f(y)) \vee Q(f(y))$, it must be because I satisfies $\sim P(f(y))$. In this case then we can validly infer $\sim P(f(y))$ from the two clauses. Furthermore, we note that the assignment of truth values to the complementary literals $Q(f(a))$ and $\sim Q(f(a))$ does not affect the valuation of the inferred clause $\sim P(f(y))$. This inferred clause already has failed at the inference node (node 3).

The inferred clause $\sim P(f(y))$ is called a *resolvent* of the two clauses $\sim P(x) \vee Q(x)$ and $\sim Q(f(y))$. When two clauses possess resolvents (they may have more than one), the process of obtaining them depends on being able to make certain substitutions of terms for variables such that the clauses that result from the substitutions contain *complementary* literals. We shall discuss this process in detail shortly. Let us assume now, however, that we have such an inference process and that it possesses the property that resolvents fail at or above inference nodes.

Any closed semantic tree for an unsatisfiable set S of nonempty clauses must have at least one inference node; for otherwise every node would have at least one nonfailure descendant, contradicting the assumption that the tree is closed. Suppose we had a process of inferring a resolvent C from two other clauses failing below an inference node n such that C fails at or above n. Now we could form a new (still) unsatisfiable set $S' = \{C\} \cup S$ of clauses. The semantic tree for S would also be a semantic tree for S' except that for S', node n (or a node above it) is now a failure node. Certainly the number of nodes above the failure nodes in the tree for S' is strictly less than the number of nodes in the tree for S. But still the tree for S' must have at least one inference node giving rise to a new resolvent C'. This process can be repeated, and at each step the number of nodes above the failure nodes in the new (but still closed) semantic tree is reduced. After at most a finite number of inferences, the tree will have *no* nodes above the failure nodes; i.e., the root will be a failure node. Since assignments of truth values are made below the root, the root fails only for the empty clause (i.e., a clause containing no literals).

Given a process for obtaining resolvents that fail at or above inference nodes, we could then use this process to detect that an unsatisfiable set S of clauses is unsatisfiable. We would first compute all possible resolvents between pairs of clauses in S. Since the semantic tree for S must have at least one inference node, one of these resolvents must fail at or above this inference node. Thus, the semantic tree for $S' = S \cup \{$all resolvents between pairs in $S\}$ is still closed and has a smaller number of nodes above its failure nodes. Continuing this process by computing all resolvents between pairs of clauses in S' and so on must then eventually produce an occurrence of the empty clause. Furthermore, if we show that a resolvent of a pair of clauses logically follows from the pair, then obviously if the empty clause is ever produced by this process, the original set S must have been unsatisfiable. (The empty clause is trivially unsatisfiable; its Herbrand base is empty and thus there can exist no model that satisfies it.)

6-12 UNIFICATION

We must next discuss a process called *unification*, which is a basic part of the formal manipulations performed in obtaining resolvents.

The terms of a literal can be variable letters, constant letters, or expressions consisting of function letters and terms. A *substitution instance* of a literal is obtained by substituting terms for variables in the literal. Thus four instances of $P(x,f(y),b)$ are

$P(z,f(w),b)$
$P(x,f(a),b)$
$P(g(z),f(a),b)$
$P(c,f(a),b)$

The first instance is called an *alphabetic variant* of the original literal because we have merely substituted different variables for the variables appearing in $P(x,f(y),b)$. The last of the four instances mentioned above is called a *ground instance* or *atom* since none of the terms in the literal contains variables.

In general, we can represent any substitution by a set of ordered pairs $\theta = \{(t_1,v_1),(t_2,v_2), \ldots ,(t_n,v_n)\}$. The pair (t_i,v_i) means that *term* t_i is substituted for *variable* v_i throughout. We insist that a substitution be such that each occurrence of a variable have the same term substituted for it; that is, $i \neq j$ implies $v_i \neq v_j$, i, $j = 1, \ldots ,n$. The substitutions used above in obtaining the four instances of $P(x,f(y),b)$ are

$\alpha = \{(z,x),(w,y)\}$
$\beta = \{(a,y)\}$
$\gamma = \{(g(z),x),(a,y)\}$
$\delta = \{(c,x),(a,y)\}$

To denote a substitution instance of a literal P using a substitution θ, we write P_θ. Thus $P(z,f(w),b) = P(x,f(y),b)_\alpha$. The composition of two substitutions α and β is denoted by $\alpha\beta$ and is that substitution obtained by applying β to the *terms* of α and then adding any pairs of β having variables not occurring among the variables of α. Thus

$$\{(g(x,y),z)\}\{(a,x),(b,y),(c,w),(d,z)\} = \{(g(a,b),z),(a,x),(b,y),(c,w)\}$$

It can be shown that applying α and β successively to a literal P is the same as applying $\alpha\beta$ to P, that is, $(P_\alpha)_\beta = P_{\alpha\beta}$. It can also be shown that the composition of substitutions is associative:

$$(\alpha\beta)\gamma = \alpha(\beta\gamma)$$

If a substitution θ is applied to every member of a set $\{L_i\}$ of literals, we denote the set of substitution instances by $\{L_i\}_\theta$. We say that a set $\{L_i\}$ of literals is *unifiable* if there exists a substitution θ such that $L_{1\theta} = L_{2\theta} = L_{3\theta} = $ etc. In such a case θ is said to be a *unifier* of $\{L_i\}$ since its use collapses the set to a singleton. For example, $\theta = \{(a,x),(b,y)\}$ unifies $\{P(x,f(y),b),P(x,f(b),b)\}$ to yield $\{P(a,f(b),b)\}$.

Although $\theta = \{(a,x),(b,y)\}$ is a unifier of the set $\{\Gamma(x,f(y),b),$ $P(x,f(b),b)\}$, in some sense it is not the simplest unifier. We note that we really did not have to substitute a for x to achieve unification. The most-general (or simplest) unifier (mgu) λ of $\{L_i\}$ has the property that if θ is any unifier of $\{L_i\}$ yielding $\{L_i\}_\theta$, then there exists a substitution δ such that $\{L_i\}\lambda\delta = \{L_i\}_\theta$. Furthermore, the common instance produced by a most general unifier is unique except for alphabetic variants.

There is an algorithm called the *unification algorithm* that produces a most-general unifier λ for any unifiable set $\{L_i\}$ of literals and reports failure when the set is not unifiable. The general idea of how the algorithm works can be described as follows: The algorithm starts with the empty substitution and constructs, in a step-by-step process, a most-general unifier if one exists. Suppose at the kth step, the substitution so far produced is λ_k. If all of the literals in the set $\{L_i\}$ become identical after employing the substitution λ_k on each, then $\lambda = \lambda_k$ is a most-general unifier of $\{L_i\}$. Otherwise we regard each of the literals in $\{L_i\}\lambda_k$ as a string of symbols and detect the first symbol position in which not all of the literals have the same symbol. We then construct a *disagreement set* containing the well-formed expressions from each literal that begins with this symbol position. (A well-formed expression is either a term or a literal.) Thus, the disagreement set of

$$\{P(a,f(a,g(z)),h(x)),P(a,f(a,u),g(w))\} \text{ is } \{g(z),u\}$$
$$\uparrow \qquad\qquad\qquad \uparrow$$

Now the algorithm attempts to modify the substitution λ_k in such a way as to make two elements of the disagreement set equal. This can be done only if the disagreement set contains a variable that can be set equal to one of its terms. (If the disagreement set contains no variables at all, $\{L_i\}$ cannot be unified. For example, we note that at the first step of the algorithm, the disagreement set may be $\{L_i\}$ itself, and certainly then no element is a variable.)

Let s_k be any variable in the disagreement set and let t_k be a term (possibly another variable) in the disagreement set such that t_k does not contain s_k. (If no such t_k exists, then again $\{L_i\}$ is not unifiable.) Next we create the modified substitution $\lambda_{k+1} = \lambda_k\{(t_k,s_k)\}$ and perform another step of the algorithm.

It can be proven [Robinson (1965a) and Luckham (1967)] that the unification algorithm finds a most general unifier of a set of unifiable literals and reports failure when the literals are not unifiable; we shall not present the proof here.

As examples, we list the most general common substitution instances (those obtained by the mgu) for a few sets of literals.

SETS OF LITERALS	MOST GENERAL COMMON SUBSTITUTION INSTANCES
$\{P(x),P(a)\}$	$P(a)$
$\{P(f(x),y,g(y)),P(f(x),z,g(x))\}$	$P(f(x),x,g(x))$
$\{P(f(x,g(a,y)),g(a,y)),P(f(x,z),z)\}$	$P(f(x,g(a,y)),g(a,y))$

It is customary to regard clauses as sets of literals. Thus a clause containing the set $\{L_i\}$ of literals can be denoted by $\{L_i\}$.

If a subset of the literals in a clause $\{L_i\}$ is unifiable by mgu λ, then we call the clause $\{L_i\}_\lambda$ a *factor* of $\{L_i\}$. Some example factors of the clause $P(f(x)) \vee P(x) \vee Q(a,f(u)) \vee Q(x,f(b)) \vee Q(z,w)$ are

$$P(f(z)) \vee P(z) \vee Q(a,f(u)) \vee Q(z,f(b))$$

and

$$P(f(a)) \vee P(a) \vee Q(a,f(b))$$

In the first factor we unified only the last two occurrences of Q, and in the second we unified all three. Note that the two occurrences of P cannot be unified within the clause. In general, a clause may have more than one factor, but certainly it can have only finitely many.

6-13 RESOLVENTS

We can now define the process by which we can sometimes infer a new clause from two other clauses (called *parent clauses*). Let the prospective parent clauses be given by $\{L_i\}$ and $\{M_i\}$ and assume that the variables occurring in $\{M_i\}$ do not occur in $\{L_i\}$, and vice versa.[1] Suppose that $\{\ell_i\} \subseteq \{L_i\}$ and $\{m_i\} \subseteq \{M_i\}$ are two subsets of $\{L_i\}$ and $\{M_i\}$, respectively, such that a most general unifier λ exists for the set $\{\ell_i\} \cup \{\sim m_i\}$. (That is, $\{m_i\}_\lambda$ contains a single literal equal to the negation of the single literal in $\{\ell_i\}_\lambda$.) Then we say that the two clauses $\{L_i\}$ and $\{M_i\}$ *resolve* and that the new clause

$$[\{L_i\} - \{\ell_i\}]_\lambda \cup [\{M_i\} - \{m_i\}]_\lambda$$

is a *resolvent* of the two clauses.

The resolvent is an *inferred clause*, and the process of forming a resolvent from two "parent" clauses is called *resolution*. If two clauses resolve, they may have more than one resolvent because there may be more than one way in which to choose $\{\ell_i\}$ and $\{m_i\}$. In any case, they can have at most a finite number of resolvents. Next we give some

---

[1] For an arbitrary pair of clauses we can always rename variables so that this assumption is met.

examples of resolution and attempt to relate it intuitively to more familiar inference rules.

Consider the two clauses

$$\{L_i\} = P(x,f(a)) \vee P(x,f(y)) \vee Q(y)$$

and

$$\{M_i\} = {\sim}P(z,f(a)) \vee {\sim}Q(z)$$

With

$$\{\ell_i\} = \{P(x,f(a))\} \qquad \text{and} \qquad \{m_i\} = \{{\sim}P(z,f(a)\}$$

we obtain the resolvent

$$P(z,f(y)) \vee {\sim}Q(z) \vee Q(y)$$

With

$$\{\ell_i\} = \{P(x,f(a)),P(x,f(y))\} \qquad \text{and} \qquad \{m_i\} = \{{\sim}P(z,f(a))\}$$

we obtain the resolvent

$$Q(a) \vee {\sim}Q(z)$$

There are altogether four different resolvents of these two clauses. Three of these are obtained by *resolving on P* and one by resolving on Q.

Resolution is a general rule of inference that combines substitution, *modus ponens*, and various types of syllogisms. Consider the resolvent $Q(a)$ of the two clauses ${\sim}P(a) \vee Q(a)$ and $P(a)$.

If the first clause is written $P(a) \rightarrow Q(a)$, we see that in this case, resolution is the same thing as *modus ponens*.

Next consider the resolvent ${\sim}P(x) \vee Q(x)$ of the two clauses

$${\sim}P(x) \vee R(x)$$

and

$${\sim}R(x) \vee Q(x)$$

In more conventional notation and in English this chain of reasoning goes:

CONVENTIONAL LOGIC	ENGLISH
$(\forall x)\{P(x) \Rightarrow R(x)\}$	Everything with property P has property R.
$(\forall x)\{R(x) \Rightarrow Q(x)\}$ Therefore:	Everything with property R has property Q. Therefore:
$(\forall x)\{P(x) \Rightarrow Q(x)\}$	Everything with property P has property Q.

Such an inference is one type of syllogism.

6-14 THE RESOLUTION PRINCIPLE

Let us briefly recapitulate the line of development in this chapter. We desire to be able to find a proof that a wff W in the predicate calculus logically follows from some set S of wffs. We indicated that it is equivalent to show that the combined set $\{\sim W\} \cup S$ is unsatisfiable. Processes for showing the unsatisfiability of a set of clauses are generally called *refutation processes*.

Anticipating the use of a specialized refutation process applicable to wffs in clause form, we then showed how a sequence of simple operations would put any wff into clause form. Next we introduced the concept of a domain called the Herbrand universe for a set S of clauses and showed how semantic trees constructed from it could be used to represent all possible interpretations for the clauses in S. If S is unsatisfiable, there is of course no interpretation that makes each wff in S true. Such unsatisfiability of S is indicated by its semantic tree being closed. We then showed how a general rule of inference called resolution could be used to create new clauses. We shall soon show that when these clauses are added to S, the new set (still unsatisfiable) has a semantic tree with fewer nodes above the failure nodes, until finally there is just the root node left, corresponding to a failure for the empty clause.

We conclude that if we continue to perform resolutions on a set of unsatisfiable clauses, we will eventually generate the empty clause. This result allows us to use the resolution rule alone without explicit reference to semantic trees in refutation processes. Let us denote by $\mathcal{R}(S)$ the union of S with the set of all resolvents obtainable between pairs of clauses in S. Then by $\mathcal{R}^2(S)$ we mean $\mathcal{R}(\mathcal{R}(S))$, etc. If S is unsatisfiable, we are guaranteed for some finite n (called the *level* or *depth* of the refutation) that the empty clause will be contained in $\mathcal{R}^n(S)$. Furthermore, each $\mathcal{R}^i(S)$ is finite if S is, so that this simple strategy for obtaining a refutation is a finite (even if long) process.

The generation of $\mathcal{R}(S)$, $\mathcal{R}^2(S)$, . . . etc. corresponds to a breadth-first search for a refutation. In Chapter 8 we shall discuss various search strategies that are more efficient than this simple one.

Refutations using resolution (sometimes just simply called resolution proofs) can be simply illustrated by graph-like structures in which every node is labeled by a clause. The clauses in S label *tips* of the graph; if the clauses at two tip nodes resolve, the resolvent labels an *immediate descendant* node connected to these tips by edges. The root of a resolution-refutation graph (these graphs are usually shown with the root at the bottom) is the empty clause (denoted by nil).

In Fig. 6-3 we illustrate an example refutation graph for a set of unsatisfiable clauses. In this case three resolutions are required in

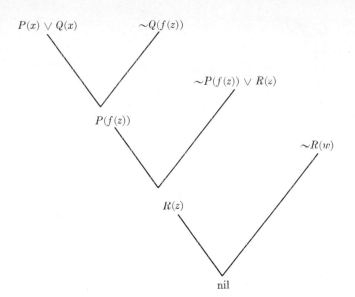

FIG. 6-3 *A refutation graph for the unsatisfiable set* $\{P(x) \lor$
$Q(x), \sim Q(f(z)), \sim P(f(z)) \lor R(z), \sim R(w)\}$.

the refutation. Another example is shown in Fig. 6-4. (Note that in
Fig. 6-4 the clause $C(x)$ is used twice in the graph. Sometimes these
graphs are depicted as trees by repeating the subtrees that occur more
than once.)

6-15 SOUNDNESS AND COMPLETENESS OF RESOLUTION

In this section we shall show that the resolution principle is *sound* and
complete. It is called sound because if the empty clause is ever produced,
the original set must have been unsatisfiable. It is called complete because if the original set is unsatisfiable, the empty clause will eventually
be produced.

In order to show that the resolution principle is sound, we need to
prove that a resolvent of two clauses logically follows from these clauses.
Using our previous notation we must show that the resolvent $[\{L_i\} -$
$\{\ell_i\}]_\lambda \cup [\{M_i\} - \{m_i\}]_\lambda$ logically follows from $\{L_i\}$ and $\{M_i\}$. Note that
every interpretation satisfying $\{L_i\}$ and $\{M_i\}$ satisfies both $\{L_i\}_\lambda$ and
$\{M_i\}_\lambda$. But since *no* interpretation can satisfy *both* $\{\ell_i\}_\lambda$ and $\{m_i\}_\lambda$,
we see that every interpretation satisfying $\{L_i\}$ and $\{M_i\}$ also satisfies
their resolvent. Thus the resolvent logically follows from the parent
clauses.

In order to show that the resolution principle is complete, we have

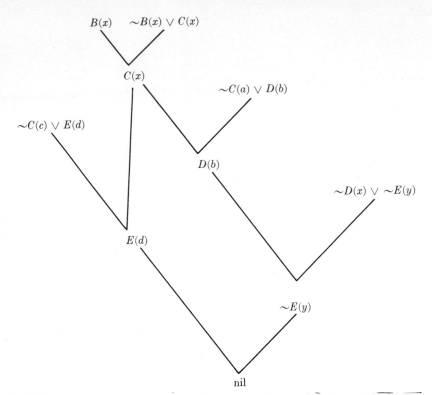

FIG. 6-4 *A refutation graph for the unsatisfiable set* $\{\bar{B}(x),\ \sim\overline{B(x) \vee C(x)},$
$\sim C(a) \vee D(b),\ \sim C(c) \vee E(d),\ \sim D(x) \vee \sim E(y)\}.$

only to show that it has the desired property with respect to inference
nodes in semantic trees.

Suppose Tr is a closed semantic tree for an unsatisfiable set S of
clauses, and let n be an inference node in Tr such that n_1 and n_2 are failure nodes immediately below n but that no clause in S fails at n or above.
Suppose a clause $\{A_i\}$ in S fails at n_1 and a clause $\{B_i\}$ in S fails at n_2.
Then specifically to show that resolution is complete we must show that
there exists a resolvent of $\{A_i\}$ and $\{B_i\}$, say $\{C_i\}$, such that $\{C_i\}$ fails
at n or above.

But the existence of such a resolvent is easily demonstrated.
Suppose L is the element of the Herbrand base whose truth value is
assigned just below node n. Say L is true for node n_1 and false for
node n_2. Although neither $\{A_i\}$ nor $\{B_i\}$ failed at n, $\{A_i\}$ fails at n_1
and $\{B_i\}$ fails at n_2. Let us consider $\{A_i\}$ first. Since it failed at n_1, it
must contain at least a unifiable subset, say $\{a_i\}$, having $\sim L$ as a
common ground instance. Let σ be a unifier such that $\{a_i\}_\sigma = L$.

Furthermore, $\{A_i\} - \{a_i\}$ must fail at n (or above), since in going from n to n_1 we only specify the truth value of L, and $\{A_i\}$ fails at n_1.

Similarly, since $\{B_i\}$ fails at n_2, it must contain a unifiable subset, say $\{b_i\}$, having L as a common ground instance. Let τ be a unifier such that $\{b_i\}\tau = L$. Also, $\{B_i\}$ $\{b_i\}$ must fail at n (or above).

Now the unifiers σ and τ can be combined, since the variables in $\{A_i\}$ and $\{B_i\}$ can be presumed to be different. Let us call this combined unifier ω. Thus, since $\{a_i\}\omega = L$ and $\{b_i\}\omega = \sim L$, $\{A_i\}$ and $\{B_i\}$ have a resolvent

$$[\{A_i\} - \{a_i\}]_\lambda \cup [\{B_i\} - \{b_i\}]_\lambda$$

where λ is a most-general unifier of $\{a_i\} \cup \{\sim b_i\}$. Since λ is a most-general unifier, $[\{A_i\} - \{a_i\}]_\omega$ is an instance of $[\{A_i\} - \{a_i\}]_\lambda$ and $[\{B_i\} - \{b_i\}]_\omega$ is an instance of $[\{B_i\} - \{b_i\}]_\lambda$. Then since both $[\{A_i\} - \{a_i\}]_\omega$ and $[\{B_i\} - \{b_i\}]_\omega$ fail at the inference node n (or above), so must both $[\{A_i\} - \{a_i\}]_\lambda$ and $[\{B_i\} - \{b_i\}]_\lambda$. Obviously their union, the resolvent, does also—completing the argument.

As an illustration of the relationship between resolution and semantic trees, consider again the set S of clauses whose semantic tree is shown in Fig. 6-2. We have already indicated that node 1 failed for the clause $\sim P(x) \wedge Q(x)$, node 2 failed for the clause $\sim Q(f(y))$, and that their resolvent, $\sim P(f(y))$, failed for node 3, an inference node. Now the semantic tree for the set $S' = \{\sim P(f(y))\} \cup S$ has nodes 3 and 4 as failure nodes. Node 4 fails for the clause $P(f(y))$. Resolving $P(f(y))$ with $\sim P(f(y))$ of course yields the empty clause (which fails at the root), and our proof of the unsatisfiability of S is finished after just these two resolutions.

6-16   BIBLIOGRAPHICAL AND HISTORICAL REMARKS

Fundamentals of logic

Our rather superficial treatment of mathematical logic can be augmented by consulting some of the standard textbooks. Two excellent ones are those of Mendelson (1964) and Robbin (1969). For the specialist there is the classic by Alonzo Church (1956). These treat what might be called *classical logic;* the resolution principle (or indeed any discussion of automatic theorem proving) has not yet found its way into textbooks on logic.

We have based this chapter on the first-order predicate calculus with resolution because of its apparent importance in automatic problem solving. A notable omission, however, is any special discussion of the equality relation. It is still not clear how the equality relation (and other standard, ubiquitous relations) ought to be "built-in" to automatic theorem provers. A discussion of these complexities would have been beyond the scope of this book. One scheme for building the equality relation into a resolution theorem prover is discussed by Robinson and Wos (1969).

It also is becoming clear that complex, general problem solvers will need facilities for higher-order logics. For a discussion of the application of higher-order logics to problem solving, see McCarthy and Hayes (1969). Robbin's book (1969) contains a section on second order logic, and some papers by J. A. Robinson (1969*a*, 1969*b*) discuss the general problem of proof procedures for higher-order logics.

The steps that we have outlined for converting any wff into clause form are based on the procedure of Davis and Putnam (1960). Clause form is also called quantifier-free, conjunctive-normal form.

Herbrand proof procedures and resolution

The resolution principle in automatic theorem proving is based on the proof procedure of Herbrand (1930). A direct implementation of Herbrand's procedure would be grossly inefficient; improvements due to Prawitz (1960) and others ultimately led to the resolution principle of J. A. Robinson (1965*a*). Our exposition of resolution proof methods, using the notion of semantic trees, is based on that of Kowalski and Hayes (1969). [See also J. A. Robinson (1968).] This semantic-tree formulation makes obvious the relationship between resolution and Herbrand methods and also can be used to justify the use of inference rules more general than simple resolution. Our proof of the completeness of resolution is a special case of a proof of the completeness of a more general inference rule given by Kowalski and Hayes (1969).

A clearly written, concise review of the resolution principle with proofs of its soundness and completeness can be found in a paper by Luckham (1967). J. A. Robinson's initial paper (1965*a*) also contains proofs of the soundness and completeness of resolution. Both of these last-mentioned papers also contain proofs of the "correctness" of the unification algorithm. J. A. Robinson (1970) has also written an excellent survey entitled "An Overview of Mechanical Theorem-Proving."

PROBLEMS

6-1 Convert the following wffs into clause form:

   a. $(\forall x)\{P(x) \Rightarrow P(x)\}$

   b. $\{\sim\{(\forall x)P(x)\}\} \Rightarrow (\exists x)\{\sim P(x)\}$

c. $\sim\{(\forall x)\{P(x) \Rightarrow \{(\forall y)\{P(y) \Rightarrow P(f(x,y))\} \wedge \sim(\forall y)\{Q(x,y)$
$\Rightarrow P(y)\}\}\}\}$

d. $(\forall x \exists y)\{\{P(x,y) \Rightarrow Q(y,z)\} \wedge \{Q(y,x) \rightarrow S(x,y)\}\}$
$\Rightarrow (\exists x \forall y)\{P(x,y) \Rightarrow S(x,y)\}$

6-2 Under what circumstances will the Herbrand universe for a set S of clauses be finite?

6-3 † Write a program that converts an arbitrary wff into clause form.

6-4 Let S be a set of literals and let ρ be a substitution. Write a program that computes $S\rho$.

6-5 The propositional calculus can be considered as a specialization of the predicate calculus in which the only predicate letters allowed are proposition letters p_i^0 (see page 158). Define how one calculates the resolvent of two clauses in the propositional calculus. Negate each of the following formulas of the propositional calculus and use the resolution principle to show that the set of clauses obtained from each negation is unsatisfiable.

a. $(P \vee Q) \Rightarrow (Q \vee P)$

b. $(P \Rightarrow Q) \Rightarrow ((R \vee P) \Rightarrow (R \vee Q))$

c. $(\sim P \Rightarrow P) \Rightarrow P$

d. $(\sim Q \Rightarrow \sim P) \Rightarrow ((\sim Q \Rightarrow P) \Rightarrow Q)$

e. $((P \rightarrow Q) \Rightarrow P) \Rightarrow P$

6-6 † Define precisely (say by a flow chart) a unification algorithm that operates according to our general description in Sec. 6-12. Employ this algorithm to find a unifier for

$\{P(x,z,y),P(w,u,w),P(a,u,u)\}$

(Note: Be careful to use correctly the definition for the composition of substitutions.) Does your algorithm correctly indicate that the set $\{P(x),P(f(x))\}$ is not unifiable? Using your algorithm, write a program that computes: If S is unifiable, then the most general unifier of S; else nil.

6-7 Let C_1 and C_2 be two clauses. Show how to use the programs of problems 6-4 and 6-6 to write a program that computes the set of all resolvents of C_1 and C_2.

6-8 Negate each of the following theorems of the predicate calculus and use the resolution principle to find a contradiction for each:

a. $(\forall x)\{P(x) \Rightarrow P(x)\}$

b. $\{\sim\{(\forall x)P(x)\}\} \Rightarrow (\exists x)\{\sim P(x)\}$

c. $\{(\forall x)\{P(x) \land Q(x)\} \Rightarrow \{(\forall x)P(x)\} \land \{(\forall y)Q(y)\}$

d. $\{(\exists x)(\forall y)P(x,y)\} \Rightarrow \{(\forall y)(\exists x)P(x,y)\}$

REFERENCES

Church, A. (1956): "Introduction to Mathematical Logic," vol. 1, Princeton University Press, Princeton, N.J., 1956.

Davis, M., and H. Putnam (1960): A computing Procedure for Quantification Theory, *J. ACM*, vol. 7, no. 3, pp. 201–215, July, 1960.

Herbrand. J. (1930): Recherches sur la théorie de la démonstration, *Trav. Soc. Sci. Lettres Varsovie, Classe III Sci. Math. Phys.*, no. 33, 1930.

Kowalski, R., and P. Hayes (1969): Semantic Trees in Automatic Theorem-Proving, in B. Meltzer and D. Michie (eds.), "Machine Intelligence 4," pp. 87–101, American Elsevier Publishing Company, Inc., New York, 1969.

Luckham, D. (1967): The Resolution Principle in Theorem-Proving, in N. Collins and D. Michie (eds.), "Machine Intelligence 1," pp. 47–61, American Elsevier Publishing Company, Inc., New York, 1967.

McCarthy, J., and P. Hayes (1969): Some Philosophical Problems from the Standpoint of Artificial Intelligence, in B. Meltzer and D. Michie (eds.), "Machine Intelligence 4," pp. 463–502, American Elsevier Publishing Company, Inc., New York, 1969.

Mendelson, E. (1964): "Introduction to Mathematical Logic," D. Van Nostrand Company, Inc., Princeton, N.J., 1964.

Prawitz, D. (1960): An Improved Proof Procedure, *Theoria*, vol. 26, pp. 102–139, 1960.

Robbin, J. (1969): "Mathematical Logic: A First Course," W. A. Benjamin, Inc., New York, 1969.

Robinson, G., and L. Wos (1969): Paramodulation and Theorem-Proving in First-Order Theories with Equality, in B. Meltzer and D. Michie (eds.), "Machine Intelligence 4," American Elsevier Publishing Company, Inc., New York, 1969.

Robinson, J. A. (1965a): A Machine-Oriented Logic Based on the Resolution Principle, *J. ACM*, vol. 12, no. 1, pp. 23–41, January 1965.

——— (1968): The Generalized Resolution Principle, in D. Michie (ed.), "Machine Intelligence 3," pp. 77–93, American Elsevier Publishing Company, Inc., New York, 1968.

——— (1969a): New Directions in Mechanical Theorem Proving, in A. J. H. Morrell (ed.), "Information Processing 68," vol. 1, pp. 63–67, North-Holland Publishing Company, Amsterdam, 1969.

——— (1969b): Mechanizing Higher Order Logic, in B. Meltzer and D. Michie (eds.), "Machine Intelligence 4," pp. 151–170, American Elsevier Publishing Company, Inc., New York, 1969.

——— (1970): An Overview of Mechanical Theorem Proving, in R. Banerji and M. Mesarovic (eds.), "Theoretical Approaches to Non-Numerical Problem Solving," pp. 2–20, Springer-Verlag New York, Inc., New York, 1970.

CHAPTER SEVEN

APPLICATIONS OF THE PREDICATE CALCULUS IN PROBLEM SOLVING

7-1 THE PREDICATE CALCULUS IN PROBLEM SOLVING

In this chapter we shall discuss some of the ways in which predicate-calculus theorem proving can be applied in problem solving. For some of these applications we merely want to know whether or not some wff W logically follows from some set S of wffs. If W does not follow from S, we may want to determine if $\sim W$ follows from S. Of course, since the predicate calculus is undecidable, we cannot always find out whether or not W (or $\sim W$) follows from S. We can attempt to find a proof of each, and if no proof is found after a certain amount of effort or time has been expended, we can only conclude that no answer can be given (within our resource limit) to the question of whether or not W (or $\sim W$) follows from S. Often, of course, one or the other of the two proofs will be found, and the question will be settled.

In other applications of the predicate calculus we want the value (if any) of some element x such that a given wff W (containing x as an argument) logically follows from a set S of wffs. That is, we want to know if the wff $(\exists x)W(x)$ logically follows from S, and, if it does, we want an instance of the x that exists. The problem of finding a proof for $(\exists x)W(x)$ from S is an ordinary predicate-calculus theorem-proving problem, but producing the satisfying instance requires that the proof method be "constructive."

We note that the possibility of producing satisfying instances for existentially quantified variables allows the posing of some quite general questions. For example, we could ask "Does there exist a solution sequence to a certain 15-puzzle"? If a constructive proof that there does exist a solution can be found, then we could produce the desired solution also. We could even ask quite complex questions such as "Does there exist a program that will perform a certain computation?" From the constructive proof of its existence we could produce the program. (Obviously, we must remember that complex questions will generally have complex proofs, possibly so complex that our automatic proof-finding procedures will not find them.)

The main concern of this chapter will be to describe a process by which a satisfying instance of an existentially quantified variable in a wff can be extracted from a proof of that wff. The problem-solving applications of this process in particular and of the predicate calculus in general will then be illustrated by some examples. We shall postpone until the next chapter any discussion of search processes for finding the proofs themselves.

Often the statements of problems are initially given as sentences in a natural language such as English. One might naturally ask therefore under what circumstances can one carry out automatic translations from English into wffs in the first-order predicate calculus. Although such a translation process would constitute a key part of a complete problem solver, we shall not deal with this matter here. Programs have been written that are able to translate limited subsets of English into predicate calculus, but the ability to deal with natural language is still in quite an unsatisfactory state. There are two major difficulties that we might mention: (1) the choice of which relations to use in translating an English sentence, and (2) the unambiguous transformation of the intended meaning of the sentence into wffs using predicate letters standing for these relations. Often ambiguities can only be resolved by referring to the "context" of the sentence, which involves difficult and not yet sufficiently understood mechanisms. The problem of transforming English into wffs is no easier than, for example, the problem of transforming English into state descriptions, operators, and so forth. In this book, we are forced to ignore these translation problems (important as they are) and to concentrate on the process of solving already-formulated problems.

7-2 AN EXAMPLE

Consider the following trivially simple problem: "If Marcia goes wherever John goes, and John is at school, where is Marcia?" Quite clearly the problem specifies two "facts" and then asks a question whose answer presumably can be deduced from these facts. The facts might simply be translated into the set S of wffs

1. $(\forall x)\{AT(John,x) \Rightarrow AT(Marcia,x)\}$

and

2. $AT(John,school)$

where the predicate letter AT is given the obvious interpretation.

The question "where is Marcia?" could be answered if we could first prove that the wff

$(\exists x)AT(Marcia,x)$

followed from S and could then find an instance of the x "that exists." The key idea here is to convert the question into a wff containing an existential quantifier such that the existentially quantified variable stands for an answer to the question. If the question can be answered from the facts given, the wff created in this manner will logically follow from S. After obtaining a proof, we then try to extract an instance of the existentially quantified variable to serve as an answer. In our example we will easily be able to prove that $(\exists x)AT(Marcia,x)$ follows from S. We can also show that a relatively simple process extracts the appropriate answer.

The proof is obtained in the usual manner by first negating the wff to be proved, adding this negation to the set S, converting all of the members of this enlarged set to clause form, and then, by resolution, showing that this set of clauses is unsatisfiable. A refutation tree for our example is shown in Fig. 7-1. The wff to be proved is called the *conjecture* and the clauses resulting from the wffs in S are called *axioms*.

Note that the negation of $(\exists x)AT(Marcia,x)$ produces

$(\forall x)[\sim AT(Marcia,x)]$

whose clause form is simply $\sim AT(Marcia,x)$.

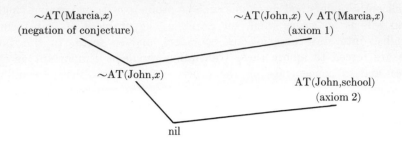

FIG. 7-1 *Refutation tree for example problem.*

Next we must extract an answer to the question "Where is Marcia?" from this refutation tree. The process for doing so in this case is as follows:

(1) Append to each clause arising from the negation of the conjecture its own negation. Thus $\sim$AT(Marcia,x) becomes the tautology[1] $\sim$AT(Marcia,x) $\vee$ AT(Marcia,x).

(2) Following the structure of the refutation tree, perform the same[2] resolutions as before until some clause is obtained at the root.

In our example this process produces the proof tree shown in Fig. 7-2 with the clause AT(Marcia school) at the root.

(3) Convert the clause at the root back to the conventional predicate-calculus form and use it as an *answer statement*. This wff can

---

[1] A tautology is any wff of the form $W \vee \sim W$.
[2] We shall make the phrase *the same resolutions* more precise later.

FIG. 7-2 *The modified proof tree for example problem.*

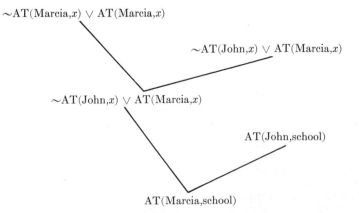

then be translated back into English, say, as an answer to the question. In our example it is obvious that AT (Marcia,school) is the appropriate answer to the problem.

We note that the answer statement has a form similar to that of the conjecture. In this case, the only difference is that in place of the existentially quantified variable in the conjecture, we have a constant (the answer) in the answer statement.

Before going on to discuss the applications of this method we must deal somewhat more thoroughly with the answer-extraction process. In the next section we shall justify the validity of the process itself and discuss how it should be employed if the conjecture contains universal as well as existential quantifiers.

7-3 THE ANSWER-EXTRACTION PROCESS

Answer extraction involves converting a refutation graph (with nil at the root) to a proof graph having some statement at the root that can be used as an answer. Since the conversion involves converting every clause arising from the negation of the conjecture into a tautology, the converted proof graph is a proof that the statement at the root logically follows from the axioms plus tautologies. Hence it also follows from the axioms alone. Thus the converted proof graph itself justifies the extraction process! Later we shall make it clear that the statement at the root of the modified refutation tree can always be used as an answer.

Although the method is simple there are some fine points that can be clarified by considering some additional examples.

Example 1   Consider the following set of wffs:

1. $(\forall x \forall y)\{P(x,y) \wedge P(y,z) \Rightarrow G(x,z)\}$

and

2. $(\forall y \exists x)\{P(x,y)\}$

We might interpret these as follows:

"For all x and y if x is the parent of y and y is the parent of z, then x is the grandparent of z."
and

"Everyone has a parent."

Given these wffs as hypotheses, suppose we wanted to ask the question "Do there exist individuals x and y such that $G(x,y)$?" (*That is, are there x and y such that x is the grandparent of y?*)

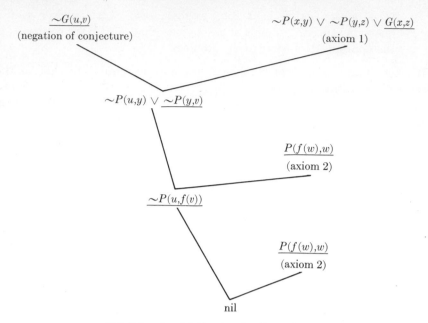

FIG. 7-3 *A refutation tree for Example 1.*

We pose the question as a conjecture to be proved:

$(\exists x \exists y)G(x,y)$

The conjecture is easily proved by a resolution refutation showing the unsatisfiability of the set of clauses obtained from the axioms and the negation of the conjecture. The refutation tree is shown in Fig. 7-3. The literals that are unified in each resolution are marked by underlining. We shall call the subset of literals in a clause that is unified during a resolution the *unification set*.

Note that the clause $P(f(w),w)$ contains a Skolem function f introduced to eliminate the existential quantifier in Axiom 2: $(\forall y \exists x)\{P(x,y)\}$. This function is defined so that $(\forall y)P(f(y),y)$. (The function f can be interpreted as a function that is defined to name the parent of any individual.)

The modified proof tree is shown in Fig. 7-4. The negation of the conjecture is transformed into a tautology, and the resolutions follow those performed in the tree of Fig. 7-3. *Each resolution in the modified tree uses unification sets that correspond precisely to the unification sets of the refutation tree.* Again the unification sets are indicated by underlining.

The proof tree of Fig. 7-4 has $G(f(f(v)),v)$ at the root. This clause corresponds to the wff $(\forall v)\{G(f(f(v)),v)\}$, which is the answer statement.

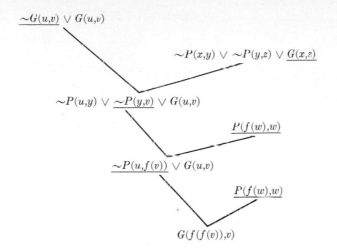

FIG. 7-4   *The modified proof tree for Example* 1.

The answer statement provides a complete answer to the question "Are there x and y such that x is the grandparent of y?" The answer in this case involves the definitional function f: Any v and the parent of the parent of v are examples of individuals satisfying the conditions of the question. Again the answer statement has a form similar to that of the conjecture.

Example 2   In this example we shall illustrate the way in which more complex clauses arising from the negation of the conjecture are transformed into tautologies.

Consider the following set of clauses:

$\sim A(x) \vee F(x) \vee G(f(x))$
$\sim F(x) \vee B(x)$
$\sim F(x) \vee C(x)$
$\sim G(x) \vee B(x)$
$\sim G(x) \vee D(x)$
$A(g(x)) \vee F(h(x))$

We desire to prove from these axioms the conjecture

$(\exists x \exists y)\{\{B(x) \wedge C(x)\} \vee \{D(y) \wedge B(y)\}\}$

The negation of this conjecture produces two clauses, each with two literals

$\sim B(x) \vee \sim C(x)$

and

$\sim B(x) \vee \sim D(x)$

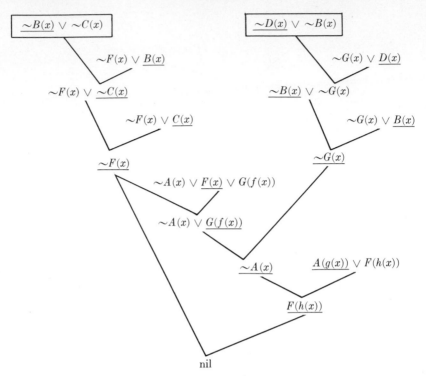

FIG. 7-5 *A refutation graph for Example 2.*

A refutation graph for this combined set of clauses is shown in Fig. 7-5.

Now to transform this graph we must convert the clauses coming from the negation of the conjecture (shown in boxes in Fig. 7-5) into tautologies by appending their own negations. In this case, the negated clauses involve $\wedge$ signs. For example, the clause $\sim B(x) \vee \sim C(x)$ is converted to the formula $\sim B(x) \vee \sim C(x) \vee (B(x) \wedge C(x))$. This formula is not a clause because of the occurrence of the conjunction $(B(x) \wedge C(x))$. Nevertheless we shall treat this conjunction as a single literal and proceed formally as if the formula were a clause (none of the elements of this conjunction are ever in any unification sets). Similarly, we transform the clause $\sim D(x) \vee \sim B(x)$ into the tautology $\sim D(x) \vee \sim B(x) \vee (D(x) \wedge B(x))$.

Performing the resolutions dictated by corresponding unification sets, we then produce the proof graph shown in Fig. 7-6. Here the root clause is the wff

$$\{(\forall x)[B(g(x)) \wedge C(g(x))] \vee [D(f(g(x))) \wedge B(f(g(x)))]$$
$$\vee [B(h(x)) \wedge C(h(x))]\}$$

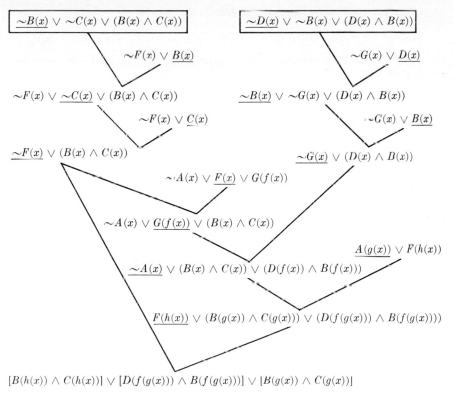

FIG. 7-6 *The modified proof graph for Example 2.*

We note that, here, the answer statement has a form somewhat different than the form of the conjecture. The underlined part of the answer statement is readily seen to be similar to the entire conjecture, with $g(x)$ taking the place of the existentially quantified variable x in the conjecture, and $f(g(x))$ taking the place of the existentially quantified variable y in the conjecture. But, in this example, there is the extra disjunct $[B(h(x)) \wedge C(h(x))]$ in the answer statement. This disjunct is seen to be similar to one of the disjuncts of the conjecture with $h(x)$ now taking the place of the existentially quantified variable x of the conjecture.

In general, if the conjecture itself is in disjunctive normal form, then our answer-extraction process will produce a statement that is a disjunction of expressions, each of which is similar in form either to the entire conjecture or to one or more disjuncts of the entire conjecture. For this reason we claim that this statement can be used as an "answer" to the question represented by the conjecture.

The general situation can be precisely described as follows: Suppose we are to prove a conjecture of the form

$$(\exists x_1) \cdots (\exists x_n)[W_1(x_1, \ldots, x_n) \vee \cdots \vee W_m(x_1, \ldots, x_n)]$$

where each W_i is a conjunction of literals. That is, each W_i can be written as

$$W_i = L_{i1} \wedge L_{i2} \wedge \cdots \wedge L_{ik_i}$$

where we have suppressed explicit mention of the variables. Now, the negation of the conjecture will yield the following clauses:

$$\sim L_{11} \vee \sim L_{12} \vee \cdots \vee \sim L_{1k_1}$$

.
.
.

$$\sim L_{m1} \vee \sim L_{m2} \vee \cdots \vee \sim L_{mk_m}$$

After a refutation tree is obtained, we convert every occurrence of any of these clauses into a tautology by appending the negation of the clause. That is, we append formulas of the form

$$L_{i1} \wedge L_{i2} \wedge \cdots \wedge L_{ik_i} = W_i(x_1, x_2, \ldots, x_n)$$

Therefore, at the root of the transformed refutation tree we will have collected an answer statement consisting of a disjunction of the W_i with various substitution instances occurring in place of the $x_1, \ldots, x_n$. It should be obvious that each W_i may be represented once, several times, or not at all in the answer statement. Thus it is not necessary that the answer statement have a form exactly similar to that of the conjecture.

7-4 CONJECTURES CONTAINING UNIVERSALLY QUANTIFIED VARIABLES

A problem arises when the conjecture to be proven contains universally quantified variables. These universally quantified variables become existentially quantified in the negation of the conjecture, causing Skolem functions to be introduced. What is to be the interpretation of these Skolem functions if they should eventually appear as terms in the answer statement?

We shall illustrate this problem with another example. Let the clause form of the axioms be

$C(x, p(x))$ meaning "for all x, x is the child of $p(x)$." (That is, p is a function mapping a child of an individual into the individual.)

and

> $\sim C(x,y) \lor P(y,x)$, meaning "for all x and y, if x is the child of y, then y is the parent of x."

Now suppose we wish to ask the question "For all x, who is the parent of x?" The conjecture corresponding to this question is

$$(\forall x \exists y)P(y,x)$$

Converting the negation of this conjecture to clause form, we obtain first

$$(\exists x \forall y) \sim P(y,x)$$

and then

$$\sim P(y,a)$$

where a is a Skolem function of no arguments (i.e., a constant) introduced to eliminate the existential quantifier occurring in the negation of the conjecture. (The negation of the conjecture alleges that some individual named a has no parent.) A modified proof tree with answer statement at the root is shown in Fig. 7-7.

Here we obtain the somewhat difficult-to-interpret answer statement $P(p(a),a)$, containing the Skolem function a. The interpretation should be that regardless of the Skolem function a, hypothesized to "spoil" the validity of the conjecture, we have been able to prove

FIG. 7-7 *A modified proof tree for an answer statement.*

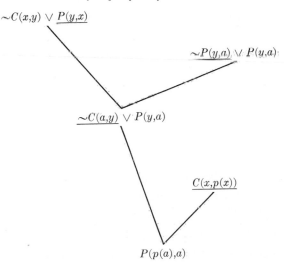

$P(p(a),a)$. That is, *any* individual a, thought to spoil the conjecture, actually satisfies the conjecture. The constant a could have been a variable without invalidating the proof shown in Fig. 7-7.

It can be shown [Luckham and Nilsson (1971)] that in the answer-extracting process it is correct to replace any Skolem functions in the clauses coming from the negation of the conjecture by new variables. These new variables will never be substituted for in the modified proof and will merely trickle down to occur in the final answer statement. Resolutions in the modified proof will still be limited to those defined by those unification sets corresponding to the unification sets occurring in the original refutation. Variables might be renamed during some resolutions so that, possibly, a variable used in place of a Skolem function may get renamed and thus might be the "ancestor" of several new variables in the final answer statement.

We shall illustrate some of the things that might happen in this case by two simple examples.

Example 3 Suppose S consists of the single axiom (in clause form)

$$P(b,w,w) \lor P(a,u,u)$$

and we wish to prove the conjecture

$$(\exists x \forall z \exists y)P(x,z,y)$$

A refutation tree is shown in Fig. 7-8*a*. Here the clause coming from the negation of the conjecture contains the Skolem function $g(x)$. In Fig. 7-8*b* we show the modified proof tree in which the variable t is used in place of the Skolem function $g(x)$. Here we obtain a proof of the answer statement $P(a,t,t) \lor P(b,z,z)$ that is identical (except for variable names) to the single axiom. This example illustrates how new variables introduced by renaming the variables in one clause during a resolution can finally appear in the answer statement.

Example 4 As another example, suppose we wish to prove the same conjecture as before, but now from the single axiom $P(z,u,z) \lor P(a,u,u)$. The refutation tree is shown in Fig. 7-9*a*. Here the clause coming from the negation of the conjecture contains the Skolem function $g(x)$.

In Fig. 7-9*b* we show the modified proof tree in which the variable w is used in place of the Skolem function $g(x)$. Here we obtain a proof of the answer statement

$$P(z,w,z) \lor P(a,w,w)$$

which is identical (except for variable names) to the single axiom. Care-

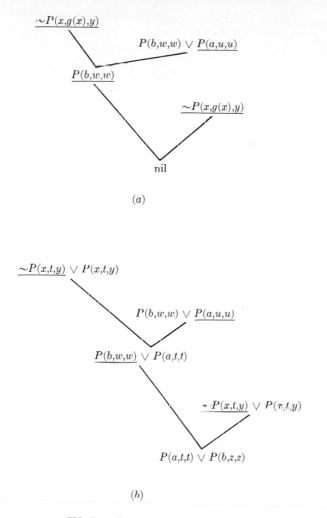

FIG. 7-8 *Proof trees for Example 3.*

ful analysis of the unifying substitutions in this example will show that although the resolutions in the modified tree are constrained by corresponding unification sets, the substitutions used in the modified tree can be more general than those in the original refutation tree.

In conclusion we shall list the steps of the answer-extracting process:

1. A resolution-refutation graph is found by some search process. The unification subsets of the clauses in this graph are marked.

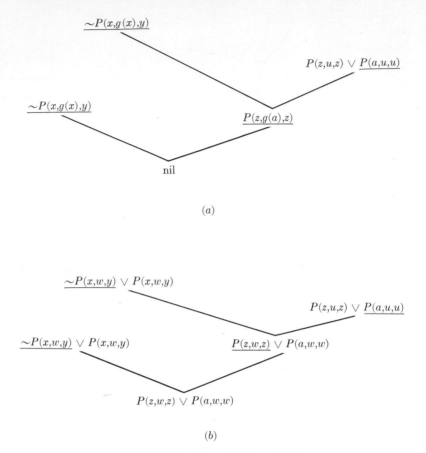

(a)

(b)

FIG. 7-9 *Proof trees for Example* 4.

2. New variables are substituted for any Skolem functions occurring in the clauses coming from the negation of the conjecture.

3. The clauses coming from the negation of the conjecture are converted into tautologies by appending to them their own negations.

4. A modified proof graph is produced following the structure of the original refutation graph. Each resolution in the modified graph uses a unification set determined by the unification set used by the corresponding resolution in the refutation graph.

5. The clause at the root of the modified graph is the answer statement extracted by this process.

Obviously the answer statement depends upon the refutation from which it is extracted. It is possible that several different refutations might exist for the same problem. From each refutation we could extract an answer, and, although some of these answers might be identical, it is possible that some answer statements might be more general than others. Usually we would have no way of knowing whether or not the answer statement extracted from a given proof is the most general answer possible. We could, of course, continue to search for proofs until we found one producing a sufficiently general answer. Because of the undecidability of the predicate calculus, though, we would not always know whether we have found all of the possible proofs for a wff W from a set S. This difficulty is probably mainly of theoretical interest; in the following examples, the answers obtained are perfectly adequate.

7-5 AN AUTOMATIC PROGRAM-WRITING EXAMPLE

With the proper formalization, the answer-extraction process can be used to produce automatically some simple computer programs. At the present state of development of these techniques, automatic proof-finding methods are still inadequate to produce any but the simplest of programs. Even for these, the process requires some human guidance. We include the following example mainly as an illustration of the method; the general problem of automatic program synthesis is still beyond the power of any available techniques.

Suppose we want to produce a program that takes x as input and produces as output some y that satisfies a particular relation $R(x,y)$. We assume that the interpretation of the predicate letter R is suitably defined by some set of axioms. The definitions of primitive functions out of which we will construct our program (by function composition) are given by other axioms. Using the answer-extraction process, a theorem-proving system will produce the desired program if it can prove that the conjecture $(\forall x \exists y) R(x,y)$ logically follows from the axioms. When a proof is found, the answer statement will display the conjectured y as a composition of primitive functions. This composition of functions then is the program.

In order to write interesting programs, we must have available primitive functions that allow conditional branching and either iteration or recursion. The use of a programming language such as LISP[1] makes it possible to write recursive programs. Formalizing the effects of functions that allow conditional branching (such as the LISP function "cond") requires either the ability to deal with the equality relation or special inference rules. We have not treated the special subject of the equality relation in this book; it is still not clear which (if any) of several proposed methods for handling equality can be made feasible.

[1] The programming language LISP is well described in a book by Weissman (1967).

In certain cases, we can work around this difficulty and produce recursive programs that branch on a test for the terminating condition. The technique used in these cases can best be described by considering a specific example.

Suppose that we want to produce a program that will sort an input list of numbers. The output is to be another list containing just the numbers on the input list in ascending numerical order. For this example we shall allow the program to be constructed out of the primitive functions "car," "cdr," "cons," and "merge." The first three of these functions are primitive functions of the LISP programming language. They are defined as follows:

car(x) has as its value the first element of the list x

cdr(x) has as its value the rest of the list x after the first element has been removed

cons(x,y) has as its value the list formed by putting the element x at the front of the list y

As a consequence of these definitions we note that cons(car(x), cdr $(x)) = x$.

One can immediately see the utility of these primitive functions as components of more complex operations on lists, such as the "sort" program we desire to produce. The other primitive function, merge, that we shall allow ourselves in this example is really quite complex compared with car, cdr, and cons. The merge function has two arguments: The first is an element, and the second is a sorted list. The value of merge(x,y) is a new list containing the element x and all of the members of the list y, and in addition this new list is a sorted list. That is, merge(x,y) finds the correct place in the sorted list y to place x such that the resulting list is sorted.

Now we must state some "axioms" that formalize the definitions we have just made and also formalize the desired input/output relation $R(x,y)$.

First we define the sort relation $R(x,y)$ in terms of two other relations:

1. $(\forall x \forall y)\{\{R(x,y) \Rightarrow \{S(y) \wedge I(x,y)\}\} \wedge \{\{S(y) \wedge I(x,y)\} \Rightarrow R(x,y)\}\}$

The intuitive meaning of $S(y)$ is "the list y is a sorted list." The meaning of $I(x,y)$ is "the two lists x and y contain precisely the same elements (but not necessarily in the same order)." Next we offer (recursive) definitions of S and I in terms of primitive functions:

2. $(\forall x \forall y \forall u)\{I(x,y) \Rightarrow I(\text{cons}(u,x),\text{merge}(u,y))\}$

3. I(nil,nil) (The symbol *nil* denotes the empty list.)

4. $(\forall x \forall y)\{S(y) \Rightarrow S(\text{merge}(x,y))\}$

5. S(nil)

Actually these last four definitions are somewhat weaker than the corresponding intuitive ones we have given, but nevertheless they are sufficient to produce a proof.[1]

The set of clauses corresponding to wffs 1 to 5 above are as follows:

1*a.* $\sim R(x,y) \vee S(y)$

1*b.* $\sim R(x,y) \vee I(x,y)$

1*c.* $\sim S(y) \vee \sim I(x,y) \vee R(x,y)$

2. $\sim I(x,y) \vee I(\text{cons}(u,x),\text{merge}(u,y))$

3. I(nil,nil)

4. $\sim S(y) \vee S(\text{merge}(x,y))$

5. S(nil)

Our strategy will be to attempt to prove $(\forall x \exists y)R(x,y)$ by induction. We shall prove the conjecture for lists of length zero, then assume its truth for lists of length $n \geq 0$, and prove its truth for lists of length $n + 1$. The result will be a recursive function that sorts a list of arbitrary length.

In handling the proof in this manner, we are essentially aiding the writing of a program by "building in" a conditional branch testing for $x = $ nil. If this test is satisfied, we branch to the program produced by the proof for input lists of length $n = 0$. Otherwise we branch to the program produced by the proof employing the induction hypothesis. This scheme simplifies our example to the extent that it releases us from the task of formalizing conditional functions and bringing in the necessary equality relations.

In the case of lists of length $n = 0$, the conjecture may be stated as $(\exists y)R(\text{nil},y)$. The negation of the conjecture is $\sim R(\text{nil},y)$. A refutation tree is shown in Fig. 7-10. Extracting an answer from this tree yields the answer statement

R(nil,nil)

Therefore we have the somewhat trivial result, "If the list x is of length zero, $y = $ nil."

We next state the induction hypothesis: For any nonempty list x, cdr(x) can be sorted. We imagine that we have some function "sort"

---

[1] The axiomatization presented here is virtually identical to that originally proposed by Robert Yates at the Stanford Research Institute.

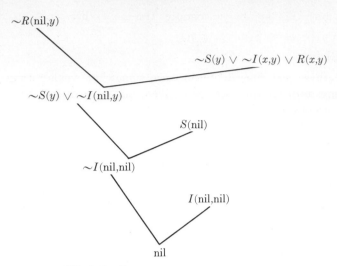

FIG. 7-10 *Refutation tree for $(\exists y)R(\text{nil},y)$.*

that is able to accomplish the sorting of the smaller list. The clause form of the induction hypothesis is

6. $R(\text{cdr}(x),\text{sort}(\text{cdr}(x)))$

In this part of the proof we are of course assuming $x \neq \text{nil}$, and the program produced by this part of the proof is that part of the total sort-program entered when the $x = \text{nil}$ test fails.

In order now to prove $(\forall x \exists y)R(x,y)$, we will need the following relation between car, cons, and cdr:

$$\forall x\{\text{cons}(\text{car}(x),\text{cdr}(x)) = x\}$$

Again, merely to avoid the complexities of equality predicates, we introduce this fact in terms of the following clause:

7. $\sim R(\text{cons}(\text{car}(x),\text{cdr}(x)),y) \vee R(x,y)$

(We note that this clause becomes a tautology after performing the substitution $x = \text{cons}(\text{car}(x),\text{cdr}(x))$ justified by the definitions of car, cons, and cdr.)

The negation of the conjecture is given by

8. $\sim R(a,y)$

In this clause, a is the usual Skolem function that occurs when the conjecture has universally quantified variables. A refutation tree is given in Fig. 7-11. Eliminating the Skolem function a and transforming

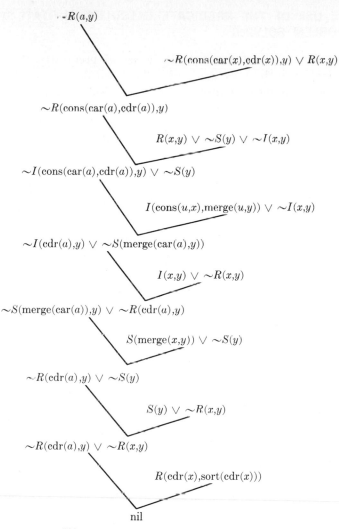

FIG. 7-11 *Refutation tree for* $(\forall x \exists y) R(x,y)$.

the refutation tree in the usual manner, we obtain the answer statement

$$R(x, \text{merge}(\text{car}(x), \text{sort}(\text{cdr}(x))))$$

Combining the conditional branch provided by us ahead of time and the pieces provided by the theorem prover, we finally get the recursive program

$$\text{sort}(x) = \begin{cases} \text{if } x = \text{nil, then nil} \\ \text{else merge}(\text{car}(x), \text{sort}(\text{cdr}(x))) \end{cases}$$

7-6 THE USE OF THE PREDICATE CALCULUS IN STATE-SPACE PROBLEM SOLVING

If we can define a problem state by a set of predicate-calculus wffs, then we can let such a set constitute the state description for use in a state-space approach to problem solving. Using a representation of this sort, the state-space operators will be computations that change one set of wffs into another. The set of goal states can then easily be defined as being described by any set of wffs from which some *goal wff* follows. Similarly, we can define the set of states to which a given operator is applicable by an *applicability wff*. Predicate-calculus theorem-proving methods would be used in such a problem-solving system to check the goal and operator applicability conditions.

The state-space representation of the monkey-and-bananas problem given in Chapter 3 can easily be modified so that the states are described by wffs. (Recall that in our monkey-and-bananas problem, a monkey at position **a** is in a room with a box at position **b**. A bunch of bananas hangs out of reach above position **c**.)

The initial state description S_0 can then consist of the following four wffs:

$$S_0 = \begin{Bmatrix} \sim\text{ONBOX} \\ \text{AT(box,}\mathbf{b}) \\ \text{AT(monkey,}\mathbf{a}) \\ \sim\text{HB} \end{Bmatrix}$$

The predicate ONBOX has value T only when the monkey is on top of the box; the predicate HB has value T only when the monkey has the bananas; and the AT predicate has the obvious interpretation. The goal wff is just HB. Any state description from which HB follows corresponds to a goal state.

As before, we have four operators, goto(**u**), pushbox(**v**), climbbox, and grasp. The first two of these are operator schemas; the precise instance of each depends upon the value of the schema variable. There are two main items in the definition of each operator:

An applicability wff stating the condition under which the operator is applicable.

Rules for transforming the set of wffs describing the state to which the operator is applied to a new set of wffs describing the resulting state.

The transformation rules might take the form of a list of wffs to be deleted and a list to be added, assuming that those wffs not deleted remain in the new state description. In these terms our four operators might then be defined as follows:

goto(u)

Applicability wff: $\sim$ONBOX

Transformations

    Delete: AT(monkey,$)

    Add: AT(monkey,**u**)

Here the $ sign stands for any term. The wff AT(monkey,$) is to be deleted regardless of the value of $. Since goto(**u**) is an operator schema, its application will produce a state-description schema containing the variable **u**. Assigning some particular (constant) value to **u** will produce a particular state description.

pushbox(v)

Applicability wff: $\sim$ONBOX $\wedge$ ($\exists$**x**)[AT(monkey,**x**) $\wedge$ AT(box,**x**)]

Transformations

    Delete: AT(monkey,$)

              AT(box,$)

    Add: AT(monkey,**v**)

              AT(box,**v**)

climbbox

Applicability wff: $\sim$ONBOX $\wedge$ ($\exists$**x**)[AT(monkey,**x**) $\wedge$ AT(box,**x**)]

Transformations

    Delete: $\sim$ONBOX

    Add: ONBOX

grasp

Applicability wff: ONBOX $\wedge$ AT(box,**c**)

Transformations

    Delete: $\sim$HB

    Add. HB

When setting up delete and add rules to define the transformations on wffs effected by the operators, one must be careful to make sure that the wffs deleted do not follow from some of the nondeleted wffs, for otherwise the deleted wff could be rederived.

The search for a goal state can now proceed by the standard process of applying applicable operators to the initial state, S_0, and to its successors until a state description containing the goal predicate HB is produced. Because we are employing operator schemas, we shall be producing a graph of state-description schemas (identical to that of Fig. 2-10). The goal test and operator applicability tests on a given state-description schema then are tests to see if the schema has an instance from which the goal wff (or applicability wff) follows.

The first step of the search process is to determine whether or not HB follows from S_0. Formally, this test could be accomplished by negating the wff to be proved and by using resolution proof-finding methods to derive a contradiction. Since a contradiction obviously cannot be derived from $\{S_0\} \cup \sim$HB (no resolutions are possible at all) we conclude that the goal test fails.

The next step of a simple state-space search process is to determine which of the operators is applicable. Here again resolution theorem-proving methods can be employed. For each operator we might attempt to prove that the applicability wff follows from S_0. We will quickly determine that grasp is inapplicable. The applicability wffs for climb-box and pushbox are identical. The negation of this common applicability wff (in clause form) is ONBOX $\vee \sim$AT(monkey,**x**) $\vee \sim$AT (box,**x**). An attempt to derive a contradiction with S_0 will also fail here, and thus climbbox and pushbox are inapplicable to S_0.

Finally, we shall be able to prove that the operator goto is applicable to S_0. Employing the transformation rule for goto(**u**) we see that the application of this operator produces the state-description *schema*:

$$S_1 = \left\{ \begin{array}{l} \sim\text{ONBOX} \\ \text{AT(box,}\mathbf{b}) \\ \text{AT(monkey,}\mathbf{u}) \\ \sim\text{HB} \end{array} \right\}$$

Now the process repeats. We first check to see if there is an instance of the schema S_1 from which the goal wff HB follows. Obviously there isn't. Next we determine the operators that might be applicable to instances of S_1. For example, in checking on the applicability of push-box(**v**) we want to ask if there is an instance of S_1 from which the wff $\sim$ONBOX $\wedge$ ($\exists$**x**)[AT(monkey,**x**) $\wedge$ AT(box,**x**)] follows. We see that substituting **b** for **u** in S_1 gives us an instance in which pushbox is applicable. Let us call this instance S_1'. We must be careful to substitute **b** for *every* occurrence of **u** in S_1. (In this case there is just one occurrence, but there might have been more than one).

Since pushbox is applicable to S_1', so is climbbox, but we see that grasp is not applicable to any instance of S_1. Also, of course, goto(**u**) is applicable to any instance of S_1, but its application does not change the state-description schema.

Now if we apply pushbox $(\mathbf{v})$ to S_1' we obtain the state-description schema

$$S_2 = \begin{cases} \sim\text{ONBOX} \\ \text{AT}(\text{box},\mathbf{v}) \\ \text{AT}(\text{monkey},\mathbf{v}) \\ \sim\text{HB} \end{cases}$$

Another different schema is obtained if we apply climbbox to S_1'. This process continues in this same manner until the goal predicate is satisfied. If we were to continue the process we would produce a graph identical in form to that of Fig. 2-10. The solution sequence of operators (with properly instantiated schema variables) could then easily be extracted.

By making use of differences and key operators as discussed in Chapter 4, we could also have used a problem-reduction approach for solving this problem. Then the subproblems created by attempting to apply the key operators would have as their goal conditions the applicability wffs of the operators. Using the solution suggested by Fig. 4-14, the reader might experiment with a predicate-calculus-oriented problem-reduction solution method.

7-7 A FORMALIZATION FOR STATE-SPACE PROBLEM SOLVING

In the last section the states were described by sets of wffs, and successor state descriptions were produced by operator rules for deleting and adding wffs. Since these operator computations transformed sets of wffs into other sets of wffs, they were like logical inference rules. Actually they were not really inference rules since the successor wffs didn't logically follow from the parents. The operator computations *changed* the state descriptions and were performed outside of the predicate-calculus system for making inferences.

With a slight reformulation it is possible to incorporate the description of the effects of operators into the predicate-calculus formalism. To do so we add a *state term* to each predicate, naming the state to which the predicate applies. Thus, in our previous example, the initial state S_0 would be described by the following set of wffs: $\{\sim\text{ONBOX}(s_0),$ $\text{AT}(\text{box},\mathbf{b},s_0),\ \text{AT}(\text{monkey},\mathbf{a},s_0),\ \sim\text{HB}(s_0)\}$. Here the state term is s_0.

In this formulation we conceive of the operators as functions that map one state into another. Thus the value of grasp(s) is the new state resulting when the operator grasp is applied to state s. The main effect of grasp can be defined by the wff

$$(\forall s)\{\text{ONBOX}(s) \wedge \text{AT}(\text{box},\mathbf{c},s) \Rightarrow \text{HB}(\text{grasp}(s))\}$$

meaning "For all s, if the monkey is on the box, and the box is at

c in state s, then the monkey will have the bananas, in the state attained by applying the operator grasp to state s."

In this manner the operator descriptions are merely additional "axioms" that can be combined with those wffs describing the initial state S_0. If our goal is to produce a state s satisfying some goal wff $W(s)$, we can formally solve the problem by first obtaining a proof for the conjecture $(\exists s)W(s)$ and then using the answer-extraction process to obtain the solution. The answer statement will contain an expression for the goal state in the form of a composition of operator functions.

We shall use a simplified form of the monkey-and-bananas problem to illustrate this approach. Let us assume that there are just three operators—grasp, climbbox, and pushbox—and that their applicability conditions are slightly different than before. (This simplified form is more suitable for illustration purposes. The reader is encouraged to experiment with the four-operator version that we used in the last section.) The effects of these operators are now given by the following wffs:

1. $(\forall x \forall s)\{\sim ONBOX(s) \Rightarrow AT(box,x,pushbox(x,s))\}$, meaning "For all **x** and s, if the monkey is not on the box in state s, then the box will be at position **x** in the state attained by applying the operator pushbox (**x**) to state s."

2. $(\forall s)\{ONBOX(climbbox(s))\}$, meaning "For all s, the monkey will be on the box in the state attained by applying the operator climbbox to state s."

3. $(\forall s)\{ONBOX(s) \wedge AT(box,c,s) \Rightarrow HB(grasp(s))\}$, meaning "For all s, if the monkey is on the box and the box is at **c** in state s, then the monkey will have the bananas in the state attained by applying the operator grasp to state s."

In addition to these axioms, we need to state explicitly other effects of the operators such as "The position of the box does not change when the monkey climbs on the box" and "The monkey is still not on the box after finishing pushing the box." Since our proof merely requires the first of these, we state it formally:

4. $(\forall x \forall s)\{AT(box,x,s) \Rightarrow AT(box,x,climbbox(s))\}$.

For the purposes of this problem, we can adequately describe the initial state S_0 by the simple wff

5. $\sim ONBOX(s_0)$.

Now to pose the question for our formal problem solver we merely state the conjecture

$(\exists s)HB(s)$

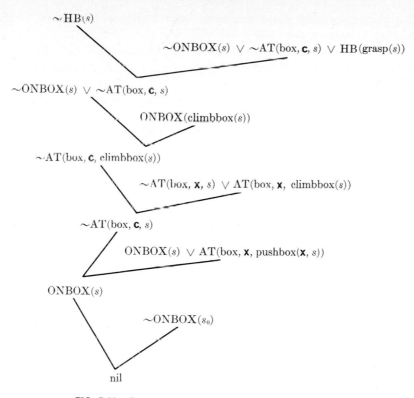

FIG. 7-12 *Proof for monkey-and-bananas problem.*

We next convert the above axioms and the negation of the conjecture to clause form and obtain the refutation tree shown in Fig. 7-12. The answer statement extracted in the usual way from this tree is

HB(grasp(climbbox(pushbox($\mathbf{c}$,s_0))))

We see from this answer statement that the desired state is achieved by the sequence of operators

{pushbox($\mathbf{c}$),climbbox,grasp}

It is of interest to compare this formal approach to problem solving with the state space method (using predicate calculus for goal and operator applicability tests) discussed in the last section. The formal approach has the advantage of not needing any special mechanism to perform the operator computations. These are handled automatically by the deduction mechanism embedded in the theorem prover. Thus no special state space (or problem-reduction) search procedures are needed other than those for finding proofs (to be discussed in the next chapter). But this very uniformity could also be a disadvantage of the formal method. Any special heuristics useful for ordering the operator applications in state-space searches might not easily be incorporated into the formal theorem-prover search procedure.

Another disadvantage of the formal procedure is that one must explicitly describe, by special axioms, those relations *not affected* by the various operators. Thus, in our example, we had to state and use the fact that the position of the box did not change when the operator climbbox was applied. Proving that certain relations are still satisfied in successor states is tedious and greatly increases the effort needed to search for the complete proof. The problem posed by the evident fact that operators affect certain relations and don't affect others is sometimes called the *frame problem*. Our delete-and-add rules of the last section adopted the view that it was easier to name just the wffs that were changed and assume that all others were unaffected. A weakness of the formal approach described in this section is that it uses no such convention, and thus if we need the fact that a certain relation is still satisfied after applying an operator, it must be explicitly proved.

7-8 BIBLIOGRAPHICAL AND HISTORICAL REMARKS

Question-answering systems

The process for extracting answer statements from refutations allows us to apply formal methods to *question-answering* tasks. In general, a question-answering system involves a sophisticated type of information retrieval in which the answers to queries require that logical deductions be made from various facts stored in the data base. The design of question-answering systems also raises the question of how to translate between a natural language, such as English, and a formal language, such as the predicate calculus, used by the deductive system.

An early, general question-answering system was developed by Raphael (1964a, 1964b). Raphael concentrated on the deductive and associative mechanisms needed and largely ignored the issue of natural-language translation. On the other hand, Bobrow (1964a, 1964b) developed a system for solving simple algebra problems stated in English. His system could translate these into the appropriate equations to be solved. Another general question-answering system called DEDUCOM (without English-logic translation abilities) was developed by Slagle (1965). Green and Raphael (1968) collaborated in the development of a question-answering system using resolution and first-order logic. Coles (1968) has developed a limited English-logic translation program that has been added to this question-answering system.

Two good surveys of work on natural-language question-answering systems have been written by Simmons (1965, 1970). Bar Hillel (1969) emphasizes some of the difficulties inherent in processing natural languages and concludes that they may be insuperable.

Answer-extraction processes

Although the subject of computing instances of existentially quantified variables has been discussed in classical proof theory, Green (1969a) was the first to propose a definite procedure for resolution-based systems. The answer-extraction method discussed in this chapter is a generalization of Green's technique and is based on a paper by Luckham and Nilsson (1971).

Our automatic program-writing example illustrating an application of the answer-extraction process is an adaptation of one discussed by Green (1969b, Appendix C). The problem of writing computer programs is related to that of proving them correct. There is a substantial body of work on this latter subject including papers by McCarthy (1962), Floyd (1967b), and Manna (1969). London (1970) gives a good survey of work on proving the correctness of programs. A somewhat different (but still resolution-based) procedure for automatic program writing is described by Waldinger and Lee (1969). An excellent, readable article on the relationship between proof procedures and automatic program writing has been written by Manna and Waldinger (1971).

Applications of the predicate calculus in state-space problem solving

The idea of using sets of wffs as state descriptions in a state-space problem solver is being studied at the Stanford Research Institute. The processes described in our monkey-and-bananas problem of Sec. 7-6 evolved from discussions between Drs. Richard Fikes, Bertram Raphael, John Munson, and the author.

We have already mentioned that techniques for solving state-space problems using formal methods exclusively were stimulated by the "advice taker" memoranda of McCarthy (1958, 1963). Work toward implementing such a system was undertaken by Black (1964). Cordell Green was the first to develop a formal state-space problem solver using a complete inference system (resolution) for first-order logic. Much of this work is described in his dissertation [Green (1969b)] and in two papers [Green (1969a, 1969c)]. Green's system used a "state term" in each predicate, as discussed in Sec. 7-7.

Professor McCarthy continued his investigations on the requirements for a general, formal problem-solving system. He was particularly concerned with the necessity for including higher (than first) order logic features in order to formalize such concepts as situations, future operators, actions, strategies, results of strategies, and knowledge. An excellent discussion of these ideas is contained in the paper by McCarthy and Hayes (1969). Many of the issues raised by McCarthy and Hayes are beyond the scope of an introductory text.

Mathematical theorem proving

One of the most obvious applications of automatic theorem provers (although it is not discussed in this chapter) is proving mathematical theorems. This application has been pursued by Robinson and Wos (1969) and by Guard et al. (1969). In particular, Guard's program (with some human aid) has succeeded in finding the first proof for a conjecture in modular lattice theory.

PROBLEMS

7-1 Argue for or against the following statement: "The use of formal proof procedures will be of little use in any problem-solving system designed to solve significant, practical problems."

7-2 Employ the answer-extraction process to the resolution refutation tree of Fig. 7-11 to obtain the answer statement $R(x,\text{merge}(\text{car}(x),\text{sort}(\text{cdr}(x))))$.

7-3 Write down predicate-calculus wffs containing state variables that describe the applicability conditions and the effects of the four operators goto, pushbox, climbbox, and grasp used in the monkey-and-bananas problem of Sec. 7-6. From these expressions and from predicates describing the initial state S_0, obtain a resolution proof that the monkey can grasp the bananas. Using the answer-extraction process, extract an expression for the goal state. (Note: This exercise is just a more complex version of the example presented in Sec. 7-7.)

7-4 A robot truck driver starting at Universal Plastics, Inc., must deliver baubles, bangles, and beads to Gump's, Macy's, and Sak's, respectively. Assuming some simple operators such as drive(x,y) and unload(z) with appropriate preconditions and results, show how a state-space problem solver using predicate calculus could find a sequence of operators producing a state satisfying

AT (baubles,Gump's) $\land$ AT(bangles,Macy's) $\land$ AT(beads,Sak's)

7-5 †Write a computer program that performs the answer-extraction process on an input resolution refutation tree.

7-6 Formulate as predicate-calculus expressions the facts given and the question asked in the following puzzle. Use the resolution principle with answer extraction to find an answer:

Tony, Mike, and John belong to the Alpine Club. Every member of the Alpine Club is either a skier or a mountain climber or both. No mountain climber likes rain, and all skiers like snow. Mike dislikes whatever Tony likes and likes whatever Tony dislikes. Tony likes rain and snow. Is there a member of the Alpine Club who is a mountain climber but not a skier? Who?

REFERENCES

Bar Hillel, Y. (1969): Universal Semantics and Philosophy of Language: Quandaries and Prospects, in Jaan Puhvel (ed.), "Substance and Structure of Language," University of California Press, Berkeley, 1969.

Black, F. (1964): "A Deductive Question-Answering System," doctoral dissertation, Harvard, June 1964. Reprinted in M. Minsky (ed.), "Semantic Information Processing," pp. 354–402, The M.I.T. Press, Cambridge, Mass., 1968.

Bobrow, D. (1964a): "Natural Language Input for a Computer Problem-Solving System," doctoral dissertation, Massachusetts Institute of Technology, September 1964. Reprinted in M. Minsky (ed.), "Semantic Information Processing," The M.I.T. Press, Cambridge, Mass., 1968.

———— (1964b): A Question-Answering System for High-School Algebra Word Problems, *Proc. AFIPS Fall Joint Computer Conf.*, pp. 591–614, 1964.

Coles, L. S. (1968): An On-Line Question-Answering System with Natural Language and Pictorial Input, *Proc. ACM 23d Natl. Conf.*, 1968, pp. 157–167, Brandon Systems Press, Princeton, N.J., 1968.

Floyd, R. (1967b): Assigning Meanings to Programs, *Proc. Symp. Appl. Math.*, Am. Math. Soc., vol. 19, pp. 19–32, 1967.

Green, C. (1969a): Theorem-Proving by Resolution as a Basis for Question-Answering Systems, in B. Meltzer and D. Michie (eds.), "Machine Intelligence 4," pp. 183–205, American Elsevier Publishing Company, Inc., New York, 1969.

———— (1969b): "The Application of Theorem-Proving to Question-Answering Systems," doctoral dissertation, Electrical Engineering Dept., Stanford University, June 1969. Also printed as *Stanford Artificial Intelligence Project Memo* AI-96, June 1969.

———— (1969c): Application of Theorem-Proving to Problem Solving, in Donald E. Walker and Lewis M. Norton (eds.), *Proc. Intern. Joint Conf. Artificial Intelligence*, Washington, D.C., May 1969.

———— and B. Raphael (1968): The Use of Theorem-Proving Techniques in Question-Answering Systems, *Proc. ACM 23d Natl. Conf.*, pp. 169–181, Brandon Systems Press, Princeton, N.J., 1968.

Guard, J., et al. (1969): Semi-Automated Mathematics, *J. ACM*, vol. 16, no. 1, pp. 49–62, January 1969.

London, R. (1970): Bibliography on Proving the Correctness of Computer

Programs, in B. Meltzer and D. Michie (eds.), "Machine Intelligence 5," pp. 569–580, American Elsevier Publishing Company, Inc., New York, 1970.

Luckham, D., and N. Nilsson (1971): Extracting Information from Resolution Proof Trees, *Artificial Intelligence*, 1971.

Manna, Z. (1969): The Correctness of Programs, *J. Computer Sys. Sci.*, vol. 3, May 1969.

———— and R. Waldinger (1971): Towards Automatic Program Synthesis, *Commun. ACM*, April 1971.

McCarthy, J. (1958): Programs with Common Sense, "Mechanization of Thought Processes," vol. I, pp. 77–84, *Proc. Symp. Natl. Phys. Lab.*, London, Nov. 24–27, 1958. Reprinted in M. Minsky (ed.), "Semantic Information Processing," pp. 403–410, The M.I.T. Press, Cambridge, Mass., 1968.

———— (1962): Towards a Mathematical Science of Computation, *Proc. IFIP Congr.* 62, North-Holland Publishing Company, Amsterdam, 1962.

———— (1963): Situations, Actions and Causal Laws, *Stanford University Artificial Intelligence Project Memo.* no. 2, 1963. Reprinted in M. Minsky (ed.), "Semantic Information Processing," pp. 410–418, The M.I.T. Press, Cambridge, Mass., 1968.

———— and P. Hayes (1969): Some Philosophical Problems from the Standpoint of Artificial Intelligence, in B. Meltzer and D. Michie (eds.), "Machine Intelligence 4," pp. 463–502, American Elsevier Publishing Company, Inc., New York, 1969.

Raphael, B. (1964*a*): "SIR: A Computer Program for Semantic Information Retrieval," doctoral dissertation, Massachusetts Institute of Technology, June 1964. Reprinted in M. Minsky (ed.), "Semantic Information Processing," The M.I.T. Press, Cambridge, Mass., 1968.

———— (1964*b*): A Computer Program Which "Understands," *Proc. AFIPS Fall Joint Computer Conf.*, pp. 577–589, 1964.

Robinson, G., and L. Wos (1969): Paramodulation and Theorem-Proving in First-Order Theories with Equality, in B. Meltzer and D. Michie (eds.), "Machine Intelligence 4," pp. 135–150, American Elsevier Publishing Company, Inc., New York, 1969.

Simmons, R. (1965): Answering English Questions by Computer: A Survey, *Commun. ACM*, vol. 8, pp. 53–70, January 1965.

———— (1970): Natural Language Question Answering Systems: 1969, *Commun. ACM*, vol. 13, no. 1, pp. 15–30, January 1970.

Slagle, J. (1965): Experiments with a Deductive-Question Answering Program, *Commun. ACM*, vol. 8, pp. 792–798, December 1965.

Waldinger, R., and R. Lee (1969): PROW: A Step Toward Automatic Program-Writing, in Donald E. Walker and Lewis M. Norton (eds.), *Proc. Intern. Joint Conf. Artificial Intelligence*, Washington, D.C., 1969.

Weissman, C. (1967): "LISP 1.5 Primer," Dickenson Publishing Company, Inc., Belmont, Calif., 1967.

CHAPTER EIGHT

PREDICATE-CALCULUS PROOF-FINDING METHODS

8-1 SEARCH STRATEGIES

In Chapter 6 we mentioned that a straightforward application of the resolution principle would correspond to a simple breadth-first search for a refutation. Such a search would start with a set of clauses S and add to this set *all* of the resolvents between pairs of clauses in S to produce the set $\mathcal{R}(S)$. Next, all of the resolvents between pairs of clauses in $\mathcal{R}(S)$ would be added to produce the set $\mathcal{R}(\mathcal{R}(S)) = \mathcal{R}^2(S)$, and so on. This type of search is usually impractical because the sets $\mathcal{R}(S)$, $\mathcal{R}^2(S)$, . . . grow too rapidly. Practical proof procedures depend on search *strategies* to speed up the search. These strategies are of three types: simplification strategies, refinement strategies, and ordering strategies. Of these, the ordering strategies correspond most closely to those search methods employed in searching state-space graphs and AND/OR graphs. We shall present a brief discussion of all three types of strategies in this chapter.

8-2   SIMPLIFICATION STRATEGIES

Sometimes a set of clauses can be simplified by elimination of certain clauses or by elimination of certain literals in the clauses. These simplifications are such that the simplified set of clauses is unsatisfiable if and only if the original set is unsatisfiable. Thus the employment of these simplification strategies helps to reduce the rate of growth of new clauses.

Elimination of tautologies

Any clause containing a literal and its complement (such a clause is called a *tautology*) may be eliminated, since any unsatisfiable set containing a tautology is still unsatisfiable after removing it, and conversely. Thus, clauses like $P(s) \vee B(z) \vee \sim B(y)$ and $P(f(a)) \vee \sim P(f(a))$ may be eliminated.

Elimination by evaluating predicates

Sometimes it is possible to *evaluate* the truth value of literals and more convenient to do so than it would be to include the corresponding clauses in S. Often such evaluations can be made easily for ground instances. For example, if the predicate letter E stands for the equality relation, it is a simple matter to evaluate ground instances such as $E(7,3)$ when they occur, whereas we would not want to add to S a complete table containing a large number of ground instances of $E(x,y)$ and $\sim E(x,y)$.

If a literal in a clause evaluates to T, the entire clause can be eliminated without affecting the unsatisfiability of the rest of the set. If a literal evaluates to F, then the occurrence of just that literal in the clause can be eliminated. Thus the clause $P(x) \vee Q(a) \vee E(7,3)$ can be replaced by $P(x) \vee Q(a)$ since $E(7,3)$ evaluates to F.

Elimination by subsumption

By definition, a clause $\{L_i\}$ *subsumes* a clause $\{M_i\}$ if there exists a substitution θ such that $\{L_i\}_\theta \subseteq \{M_i\}$. As examples:

$P(x)$	subsumes $P(y) \vee Q(z)$
$P(x)$	subsumes $P(a)$
$P(x)$	subsumes $P(a) \vee Q(z)$
$P(x) \vee Q(a)$	subsumes $P(f(a)) \vee Q(a) \vee R(y)$

A clause in S subsumed by another clause in S can be eliminated without affecting the unsatisfiability of the rest of the set. Eliminating clauses subsumed by others frequently leads to substantial reductions in the number of resolutions that need to be made in finding a proof.

In general, tautologies may be eliminated as they are generated during the course of a search for a proof, but subsumed clauses should be eliminated only after each "level" has been completed. [See Kowalski (1970).]

8-3 REFINEMENT STRATEGIES

Refinement strategies are based on theoretical results in resolution-proof theory that state that not all of the possible resolutions need to be performed in order to find a refutation. That is, only resolutions between clauses meeting certain criteria need to be performed, We shall denote by $\Re_C(S)$ the union of S with the set of all resolvents between pairs in S meeting criterion C. We note that $\Re_C(S) \subseteq \Re(S)$.

A refinement strategy using criterion C is said to use "resolution relative to C." To apply such a strategy we first compute $\Re_C(S)$, then $\Re_C(\Re_C(S)) = \Re_C{}^2(S)$, etc., until for some n, the empty clause (denoted by nil) is in $\Re_C{}^n(S)$.

The potential value of a refinement strategy is that fewer resolutions need be performed at each level. The level at which the empty clause is produced usually will be increased, however, so refinement strategies typically result in narrower but deeper searches. A refinement strategy is useful only if its use reduces the total search effort, including the effort needed to test against the criterion C.

We shall consider two major refinement strategies that generally do reduce total search effort, plus some special cases of them.

8-4 ANCESTRY-FILTERED FORM PROOFS

Our first refinement strategy can easily be described in terms of the type of refutation graph that it produces. It will be helpful to introduce some definitions first.

A *resolution proof graph* (or tree) is a structure of nodes with each node corresponding to a clause. (For simplicity we shall often speak of a node in such a graph as *being* a clause.) Those nodes in the graph having no ancestors are called *tip nodes*. If the graph displays a resolution proof of some clause (possibly nil) from a set of clauses S, then the tip nodes correspond to clauses in S. These are called the *base clauses* of the proof. The node in the graph having no descendants is called the *root node*. It corresponds to the clause that is proved by the graph.

We shall say that a proof graph is in *vine form* if each of its nodes is either a base clause or the *immediate* descendant of a base clause. (Such a graph will also be a tree, but note that not all trees will be in vine form.) We see that of the examples in Chapter 6, the graph in Fig. 6-3 is in vine form but the graph in Fig. 6-4 is not. If a refutation graph in vine form exists, then in searching for it we need only perform resolutions between pairs of clauses such that at least one member of a pair is a member of S. Such a restriction on resolutions might constitute an excellent refinement strategy if we could be assured that any unsatisfiable set of clauses had a vine-form refutation graph. Unfortunately, a refinement strategy based on vine-form graphs is not complete; but a strategy very much like it is.

To see that vine-form graphs do not always exist for unsatisfiable sets consider the set

$$S = \begin{cases} Q(x) \lor P(a) \\ {\sim}Q(x) \lor P(x) \\ {\sim}Q(x) \lor {\sim}P(x) \\ Q(x) \lor {\sim}P(x) \end{cases}$$

The set is clearly unsatisfiable, as evidenced by the refutation graph in Fig. 8-1. A vine-form refutation graph must (in particular) have a member of S as one of the immediate ancestors of nil at the root. But to produce the empty clause one must either resolve two single-literal clauses or two clauses that factor to single-literal clauses. None of the members of S meet either of these criteria, so therefore there cannot be a vine-form refutation of S.

In Fig. 8-1 we see that one of the resolutions is between the clause ${\sim}P(a)$ and the clause $P(a) \lor P(x)$. Furthermore, the clause $P(a) \lor P(x)$ is also an ancestor of ${\sim}P(a)$ in the refutation graph. The graph of Fig. 8-1 is an example of a graph in *ancestry-filtered (AF) form*.

We shall say that a refutation graph is in *AF* form if each node in the graph corresponds to either

1.   A base clause
2.   An immediate descendant of a base clause
3.   An immediate descendant of two nonbase clauses A and B such that B is an ancestor of A (hence, the name ancestry filter)

The vine form is a special case of the *AF*-form graph using only the first two conditions. A base clause C in an *AF*-form graph is called a *top node* if every other node in the tree is either a base clause or a descendant of C.

The next theorem, which we state without proof, claims that an *AF*-form refutation graph always exists for any unsatisfiable set of

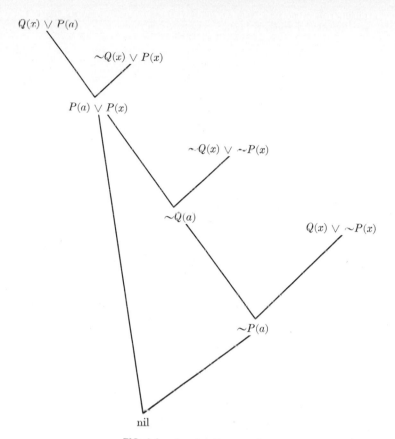

FIG. 8-1   *A refutation graph.*

clauses. Therefore, a refinement strategy based on searching for AF-form graphs is complete.

Theorem 8.1   Let $gr(\text{nil})$ be some refutation graph for an unsatisfiable set S of clauses and let C be a clause in S occurring in $gr(\text{nil})$. Then a refutation graph $gr'(\text{nil})$ in AF form exists for S with C as a top node of $gr'(\text{nil})$.

Often the vine-form special case of AF-form refutation graphs exists. Although the tree in Fig. 6-4 is not in AF form, we illustrate in Fig. 8-2 a vine-form refutation for the same set of clauses with $\sim D(x) \vee \sim E(y)$ as top node. The reader may want to find other AF-form graphs for this set of clauses, having different top nodes.

Since Theorem 8-1 states that an AF-form refutation graph exists for any unsatisfiable set of clauses, we may restrict our search so that we look only for such refutations. The AF-form strategy is a refinement

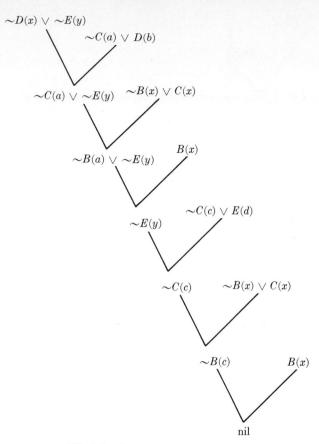

FIG. 8-2 *A vine-form refutation tree.*

strategy that embodies just such a restriction. It uses resolution relative to an ancestry-filter criterion. This criterion can be described as follows: First we note that we have the freedom to select a top node for the *AF* graph. This top node must be one that occurs in *some* refutation graph, so we select it from some subset $K \subseteq S$ that is certain to contain only clauses that occur in some refutation (for example, K might be those clauses originating from the negation of the theorem to be proved). Then the criterion that must be satisfied by a pair of clauses (A,B) in order that they be resolved relative to the *AF* strategy is just

One member of the pair (A,B) belongs to S and the other is either a clause in K or a descendant of a clause in K

or

One member of the pair (A,B) is an ancestor of the other

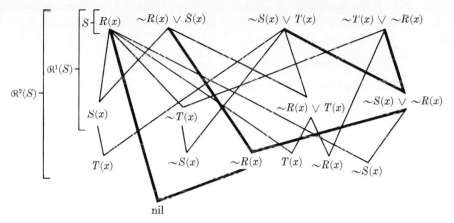

FIG. 8-3 *A search for a refutation using the AF strategy.*

Let us denote by $\mathcal{R}_{AF}(S)$ the union of S with the set of all resolvents between pairs of S allowed by the AF-form strategy. Then as usual we define

$$\mathcal{R}_{AF}^0(S) = S$$

and

$$\mathcal{R}_{AF}^{n+1}(S) = \mathcal{R}_{AF}(\mathcal{R}_{AF}^n(S))$$

By Theorem 8-1 we are guaranteed that if S is unsatisfiable, there will exist some n such that nil ϵ $\mathcal{R}_{AF}^n(S)$.

In Fig. 8-3 we show the result of applying the AF-form strategy to a simple unsatisfiable set of clauses. (In this example, $K = S$.) All of the allowable resolutions are performed at levels 1 and 2 until the empty clause is deduced at level 3. The AF-form graph thus produced is indicated by the darker branches. In this case it is actually a vine.

8-5 SET-OF-SUPPORT STRATEGY

In the *set-of-support* strategy we choose a nonempty subset K of the initial set S of clauses such that $S - K$ is satisfiable. We might, for example, choose K to be the set of clauses originating from the negation of the theorem to be proved. We say that the clauses in K *have support*. In searching for a refutation we then permit only those resolutions between pairs of clauses such that at least one member of the pair has support. Each clause produced by a resolution is also given support.

Since $S - K$ is satisfiable, there is an AF-form refutation graph with one of the members of K as top node. Thus the set-of-support strategy is complete because it allows all of the resolutions allowed by this AF-form strategy (and more).

8-6   MORE RESTRICTIVE STRATEGIES

Actually we can make the AF-form strategy even more restrictive and still preserve completeness. One restriction involves requiring that when A is an ancestor of B, A and B are allowed to resolve only if the resolvent subsumes a substitution instance of B. [See Loveland (1969).] Additional restrictions involving special types of resolutions called *merges* [Andrews (1968); Yates, Raphael, and Hart (1970)] can also be imposed. Of course in deciding on any of these strategies the cost of the extra calculation required to select appropriate resolutions may not necessarily be offset by the possible reduction in the number of resolutions actually performed during search. At present these matters can only be judged by experience.

8-7   MODEL STRATEGIES

Recall that in Chapter 6 we gave a precise meaning to an interpretation by specifying the truth values of the atoms in the Herbrand base. We called such a specification a model. Thus if the Herbrand base consisted of the atoms $\{P(a,b),P(a,a),P(b,b),P(b,a),Q(a),Q(b)\}$, then one possible model would be $\{\sim P(a,b),P(a,a),P(b,b),\sim P(b,a),\sim Q(a),Q(b)\}$. In general, a model is a (possibly infinite) set of literals constructed from the Herbrand base in such a way that each atom in the Herbrand base is contained either negated or unnegated (but not both) in the model.

By definition, a model fails to satisfy a clause C if there exists a ground instance of C (using terms from the Herbrand universe) having the value F, using the valuations specified by the model. Otherwise we say that the model satisfies C.

Usually it is straightforward to determine if a given model M does not satisfy a clause C. For example, $\{\sim P(a,b),P(a,a),P(b,b),\sim P(b,a),\sim Q(a),Q(b)\}$ does not satisfy $\sim Q(x) \vee P(y,x)$, since the substitution $\{(b,x),(a,y)\}$ creates a ground instance having the value F. This model does satisfy the clause $\{\sim Q(x) \vee P(y,y)\}$, since no substitution creates a ground instance having the value F.

A model can often be more compactly specified by listing a set of literals *all* of whose ground instances (over the Herbrand universe) have the value T. Care must be taken to see that in such a specification no conflicts result and that each atom of the Herbrand base is given a truth value. Thus if our set of clauses is

$$S = \begin{cases} \sim Q(x) \vee P(a,f(x)) \\ Q(x) \vee P(f(x),a) \\ \sim P(x,f(x)) \vee R(y) \\ \sim R(a) \end{cases}$$

a model can be specified, for example, by the set $\{Q(x),\sim P(a,f(x)), \sim P(x,f(x)),P(f(x),a),R(x)\}$. In terms of atoms in the Herbrand base this model is the infinite set

$$M = \{R(a),R(f(a)),R(f(f(a))), \ldots ,Q(a),Q(f(a)),Q(f(f(a))),$$
$$\ldots ,\sim P(a,f(a)),\sim P(a,f(f(a))), \ldots ,\sim P(f(a),f(f(a))),$$
$$\ldots ,P(f(a),a),P(f(f(a)),a), \ldots \}$$

Notice that the first and last clauses are not satisfied by this model, whereas the second and third are.

We can use the concept of a model to limit the resolutions needed to find a refutation. The following theorem (which we state without proof) gives the basis for another powerful refinement strategy based on models:

Theorem 8-2   Let S be an unsatisfiable set of clauses and let M be any model defined over the Herbrand base of S. Then a refutation graph for S exists having the property that each node in the graph is either a clause in S or has as one of its immediate ancestors a clause that is *not* satisfied by M.

We shall call the strategy based on Theorem **8-2** the *model* strategy. The criterion that must be satisfied by a pair of clauses (A,B) in order that they be resolved relative to the model strategy is that at least one of (A,B) must not be satisfied by the model.

We shall denote by $\mathcal{R}_M(S)$ the union of S with the set of all resolvents between pairs of S allowed by the model strategy. Again we define

$$\mathcal{R}_M{}^0(S) = S$$

and

$$\mathcal{R}_M{}^{n+1}(S) = \mathcal{R}_M(\mathcal{R}_M{}^n(S))$$

By Theorem 8-2 we are guaranteed that if S is unsatisfiable, there will exist some n such that nil ϵ $\mathcal{R}_M{}^n(S)$.

In Fig. **8-4** we show a refutation graph for the set of unsatisfiable clauses originally given in Fig. **8-1**. Each resolution in the graph satisfies the model criterion with $\{Q(x),P(x)\}$ used to define a model. Those clauses not satisfied by the model are enclosed in boxes. The extent to which the model strategy reduces the number of needed resolutions

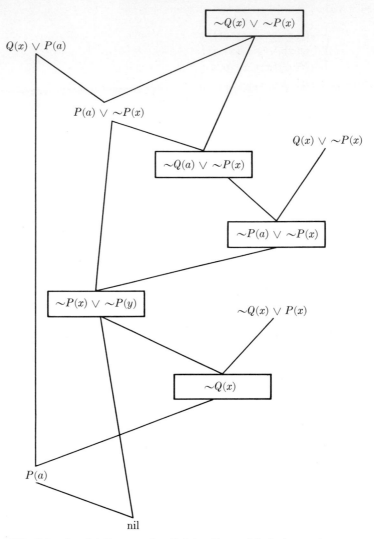

FIG. 8-4 *A refutation graph satisfying the model strategy using* $\{Q(x), P(x)\}$ *to define a model.*

depends of course on the model M; any model M not satisfying *any* of the clauses in S is obviously a bad choice.

The completeness of the set-of-support strategy can also be derived from the completeness of the model strategy: Select a model satisfying every clause in $S - K$ where K has support. By Theorem 8-2 a refutation exists such that no resolution is performed between a pair of clauses both of which are in $S - K$. The model strategy is thus seen as a sharpening of the set-of-support strategy.

8-8 P_1 REFUTATIONS

Let us call a clause *positive* if it has *no* negated literals. Certainly any unsatisfiable set S must have at least one positive clause; if it did not, the model defined by the set of negated atoms from the Herbrand base would satisfy S. A P_1 refutation is one in which every resolution is between clauses at least one of which is positive. It follows from Theorem 8-2 that the P_1 refutation strategy is complete, since we can take the set of negative literals in S to specify a model. Then a clause is false in the model if and only if it is positive.

Variations of P_1 refutations can be found if we just consistently rename the literals in S. In our example of Fig. 8-4, if we replace $Q(x)$ by $\sim R(x)$ and $P(x)$ by $\sim T(x)$, then the refutation shown serves as a P_1 refutation for the renamed set of clauses. The P_1 refutations and their variations are important because the criterion for resolution is easy to test.

8-9 COMBINED STRATEGIES

One is tempted to ask whether or not combining the restrictions on resolutions specified by the AF and model strategies yields a complete strategy. Certainly such a combination could substantially reduce the required resolutions. Unfortunately, the combination is not complete; no refutation of the unsatisfiable set $\{\sim R(a), R(a) \vee \sim Q(a), \sim P(a) \vee R(a), P(a) \vee Q(a)\}$ in AF form exists also satisfying the model restriction with $\{P(a), Q(a), R(a)\}$ as a model. As a heuristic, however, combining the two strategies may often yield efficient searches for refutations.

8-10 ORDERING STRATEGIES

Within the range of resolution choices provided by the various refinement strategies, it is sometimes possible to search for a refutation by careful ordering of the resolutions performed. Ordering strategies do not prohibit any particular types of resolutions but merely provide guidance about which ones should be performed first. Ordering strategies correspond to the heuristic search strategies discussed for graph searching in Chapters 3 and 5. A skillfully ordered search would not necessarily compute all of the members of $\Re(S)$, $\Re^2(S)$, etc. If the shallowest occurrence of the empty clause is in the nth level, one would hope that the search could be focused more or less directly toward it before filling out the lower levels.

Two very efficient ordering strategies are the *unit-preference strategy* and the *fewest-components strategy*. In the unit-preference strategy, one attempts first to resolve units against units (a unit is a clause containing a single literal). If this stage succeeds, we get an immediate refutation. Failing to find a pair of units that will resolve, one next tries to resolve units against doubletons, etc. (Whenever a pair of clauses resolve, the resolvent is checked against the units for a possible resolution before continuing.) To prevent the refutation search from running away along some unprofitable chain of endless unit resolutions, a *level bound* is usually set. If a clause is in $\Re^{\ell}(S)$ but not in $\Re^{\ell-1}(S)$, the clause is said to be of level ℓ. Setting a level bound of ℓ prevents clauses in $\Re^{\ell}(S)$ from being generated. When the level bound allows no more unit resolutions, then some other ordering scheme, such as doubletons against doubletons, etc., can be employed until additional units are generated.

The unit-preference strategy is motivated by the guaranteed shortening in the length of clauses caused by unit resolutions. Since the object of generating resolvents is to produce the empty clause (of length zero), unit preference is an obvious strategy. When combined with level bounds to make other resolutions eventually possible, its use does not preclude finding a refutation (if one exists within the level bound), and usually it significantly speeds up the search.

The fewest-components strategy orders resolutions according to the lengths of the resolvents produced. Thus, those two clauses that will produce the shortest resolvent are resolved first. This strategy is somewhat more expensive to apply since potential resolvent lengths must be computed and ordered before each resolution is performed.

8-11 BIBLIOGRAPHICAL AND HISTORICAL REMARKS

Discussions of search strategies

An excellent discussion of the problem of developing heuristically effective search strategies while maintaining logical completeness is contained in a paper by J. A. Robinson (1967). G. A. Robinson, et al. (1964) give a very clear exposition of several strategies with many examples.

Simplification strategies

The problem of the elimination of subsumed clauses during a search for a proof is more subtle than it might appear. Kowalski (1970a) acknowledges inadequacies in the treatment of this subject by Kowalski and Hayes (1969) and refers the reader to his dissertation [Kowalski (1970*b*)] for a complete discussion.

Refinement strategies

The ancestry-filtered (*AF*) form strategy is the simplest of a family of related strategies. Our Theorem 8-1 states that the *AF*-form strategy is logically complete; a proof of this theorem is given in Luckham (1969). Although we show the completeness of the set-of-support strategy as a corollary of Theorem 8-1, it was in fact first developed and justified by Wos, et al. (1965).

Several elaborations of the *AF*-form strategy are possible. Some of these combine the *AF*-form strategy with a strategy proposed by Andrews (1968) involving *merges*. Among the papers proving the completeness of *AF* form with merging are Kieburtz and Luckham (1971), Yates, Raphael, and Hart (1970), and Anderson and Bledsoe (1970). The first of these contains other results about the properties of *AF*-form proofs, while the last two use rather novel methods of proving completeness that are of independent interest. Anderson and Bledsoe use their method to establish the completeness of other strategies as well. A paper by Loveland (1968) establishes the completeness of another restriction on the *AF*-form strategy.

The model strategies are elaborations of the P_1 deductions originally proposed by J. A. Robinson (1965*b*). Slagle (1967) proved the completeness of some very general model strategies. Our Theorem 8-2 is due to Luckham (1969) and is an easier-understood, special case of one of Slagle's theorems. Meltzer (1966, 1968) provides some additional results about P_1-type deductions.

Ordering strategies

The unit-preference strategy was proposed and justified in a paper by Wos, et al. (1964). It and the set-of-support strategy have been incorporated as basic parts of a number of automatic theorem provers.

The reader probably noticed that all of the search strategies discussed in this chapter involved syntactic rather than semantic rules (that is, search restrictions and orderings were based on the *form* of the clauses and possible deductions rather than on their *meaning*). Semantic guidance could be provided in a number of ways, but there have not yet been many attempts in this direction. One might ask whether it would be possible to use an evaluation function over pairs of clauses that are candidates to be resolved. Presumably this evaluation function could be influenced by the available semantic information as well as by the forms of the candidate clauses. Some theoretical results about the properties of strategies using evaluation functions are contained in a paper by Kowalski (1970a). Kowalski's results on searching "inference-graph" structures parallel those of Hart, et al. (1968) for state-space graph structures.

Examples of implementations

Several automatic theorem-proving programs have now been written. As examples we might mention those of Robinson and Wos (1969), Allen and Luckham (1970), Guard, et al. (1969), and the Green-Raphael-Yates system recently modified by Garvey and Kling (1969).

PROBLEMS

8-1 Indicate which of the following clauses are subsumed by $P(f(x),y)$:

  a. $P(f(a),f(x)) \vee P(z,f(y))$

  b. $P(z,a) \vee \sim P(a,z)$

  c. $P(f(f(x)),z)$

  d. $P(f(z),z) \vee Q(x)$

  e. $P(a,a) \vee P(f(x),y)$

8-2 Find a vine-form refutation for the following unsatisfiable set of clauses:

  a. $\sim P \vee \sim Q \vee R$

  b. $\sim S \vee T$

  c. $\sim T \vee P$

  d. S

  e. $\sim R$

  f. $\sim S \vee U$

  g. $\sim U \vee Q$

Can you find some other refutation (not necessarily of vine form) of lesser depth?

8-3 Find an AF-form refutation for the following unsatisfiable set of clauses:

  a. $\sim A(x) \vee F(x) \vee G(f(x))$

  b. $\sim F(x) \vee B(x)$

c. $\sim F(x) \lor C(x)$

d. $\sim G(x) \lor B(x)$

e. $\sim G(x) \lor D(x)$

f. $A(g(x)) \lor F(h(x))$

g. $\sim B(x) \lor \sim C(x)$

h. $\sim B(x) \lor \sim D(x)$

Compare with the non-AF-form refutation of Fig. 7-5.

8-4 Find a counterexample to the statement: "The unit-preference strategy always finds a refutation of minimal depth."

8-5 Consider the problem of finding an ancestry-filtered form refutation of an unsatisfiable set S of clauses to be a state-space search problem. Suppose the state description consists of an AF-form proof tree and the set S.

a. What is the start node?

b. What is the successor operator?

c. What is the goal test?

d. Suggest an evaluation function $\hat{f}$ that takes into consideration the level of the AF tree, the "generality" of the clauses it contains, depth of function nesting in its clauses, and any other factors that you think may be important.

8-6 Consider the statement "In a closed, associative system with left and right solutions to equations, there is an identity element." We can express the hypotheses as follows:

$\forall x \forall y \exists z P(z,x,y)$ "For all x and y in the system, there is a z in the system such that $z \cdot x = y$."

$\forall x \forall y \exists z P(x,z,y)$ "For all x and y in the system, there is a z in the system such that $x \cdot z = y$."

$\forall x \forall y \exists z P(x,y,z)$ "For all x and y in the system, there is a z in the system such that $x \cdot y = z$ (closure)."

$\forall u \forall v \forall w x y z \{[P(u,v,w) \land P(v,x,y)] \Rightarrow [P(u,y,z) \equiv P(w,x,z)]\}$ (associativity)

(Note: $A = B$ is an abbreviation for $[A \Rightarrow B) \land (B \Rightarrow A)]$.)
The conclusion can be written as follows:

$\exists y \forall x P(x,y,x)$ "There is a right-identity element."

For this theorem, do the following:

a. Convert hypotheses and negation of conclusion to clause form.

b. Obtain a P_1 refutation using these clauses.

c. From this refutation, extract an answer statement (i.e., exhibit an expression for a right-identity element).

REFERENCES

Allen, J., and D. Luckman (1970): An Interactive Theorem-Proving Program, in B. Meltzer and D. Michie (eds.), "Machine Intelligence 5," pp. 321–336, American Elsevier Publishing Company, Inc., New York, 1970.

Anderson, R., and W. Bledsoe (1970): A Linear Format for Resolution with Merging and a New Technique for Establishing Completeness, *J. ACM*, vol. 17, no. 3, July 1970.

Andrews, P. (1968): Resolution with Merging, *J. ACM*, vol. 15, no. 3, pp. 367–381, July 1968. (Also see corrections in *J. ACM*, vol. 15, no. 4, p. 720, October 1968.)

Garvey, T., and R. Kling (1969): User's Guide to QA3.5 Question-Answering System, *Stanford Research Institute Artificial Intelligence Group Technical Note* 15, December 1969.

Guard, J., et al. (1969): Semi-Automated Mathematics, *J. ACM*, vol. 16, no. 1, pp. 49–62, January 1969.

Hart, P., N. Nilsson, and B. Raphael (1968): A Formal Basis for the Heuristic Determination of Minimum Cost Paths, *IEEE Trans. Sys. Sci. Cybernetics*, vol. SSC-4, no. 2, pp. 100–107, July 1968.

Kieburtz, R., and D. Luckham (1971): Compatibility of Refinements of the Resolution Principle, to be published.

Kowalski, R. (1970a): Search Strategies for Theorem-Proving, in B. Meltzer and D. Michie (eds.), "Machine Intelligence 5," pp. 181–201, American Elsevier Publishing Company, Inc., New York, 1970.

——— (1970b): "Studies in the Completeness and Efficiency of Theorem-Proving by Resolution," doctoral dissertation, University of Edinburgh, Edinburgh, 1970.

——— and P. Hayes (1969): Semantic Trees in Automatic Theorem-Proving, in B. Meltzer and D. Michie (eds.), "Machine Intelligence 4," pp. 87–101, American Elsevier Publishing Company, Inc., New York, 1969.

Loveland, D. (1968): "A Linear Format for Resolution," Carnegie-Mellon University Computer Science Dept. Report, December 1968. Also in *Proc. IRIA 1968 Symp. Autom. Demonstration*, Lecture Notes in Mathematics no. 125, Springer-Verlag, New York, Inc., New York, 1970.

Luckham, D. (1969): Refinement Theorems in Resolution Theory, *Stanford Artificial Intelligence Project Memo* AI-81, March 24, 1969. Also in *Proc. IRIA 1968 Symp. Autom. Demonstration*, Lecture Notes on Mathematics no. 125, Springer-Verlag New York, Inc., New York, 1970.

Meltzer, B. (1966): Theorem-Proving for Computers: Some Results on Resolution and Renaming, *Computer J.*, vol. 8, pp. 341–343, 1966.

——— (1968): Some Notes on Resolution Strategies, in D. Michie (ed.), "Machine Intelligence 3," pp. 71–75, American Elsevier Publishing Company, Inc., New York, 1968.

Robinson, G. A., and L. Wos (1969): Paramodulation and Theorem-Proving in First-Order Theories with Equality, in B. Meltzer and D. Michie (eds.), "Machine Intelligence 4," pp. 135–150, American Elsevier Publishing Company, Inc., New York, 1969.

———, L. Wos, and D. F. Carson (1964): Some Theorem-Proving Strategies and Their Implementation, *Argonne Natl. Laboratories Technical Memorandum* no. 72, 1964.

Robinson, J. A. (1965*b*): Automatic Deduction with Hyper-Resolution, *Intern. J. Comp. Math.*, vol. 1, pp. 227–234, 1965.

——— (1967): Heuristic and Complete Processes in the Mechanization of Theorem-Proving, in J. T. Hart and S. Takasu (eds.), "Systems and Computer Science," pp. 116–124, University of Toronto Press, Toronto, 1967.

Slagle, J. (1967): Automatic Theorem-Proving with Renamable and Semantic Resolution, *J. ACM*, vol. 14, no. 4, pp. 687–697, October 1967.

Wos, L., D. Carson, and G. Robinson (1964): The Unit Preference Strategy in Theorem Proving, *Proc. AFIPS 1964 Fall Joint Computer Conf.*, vol. 26, pp. 616–621, 1964.

——— G. Robinson, and D. Carson (1965): Efficiency and Completeness of the Set of Support Strategy in Theorem-Proving, *J. ACM*, vol. 12, no. 4, pp. 536–541, October 1965.

Yates, R., B. Raphael, and T. Hart (1970): Resolution Graphs, *Artificial Intelligence*, vol. 1, no. 4, 1970.

COMBINED REFERENCES
AND AUTHOR INDEX

Allen, J., and D. Luckham (1970): An Interactive Theorem-Proving Program, in B. Meltzer and D. Michie (eds.), "Machine Intelligence 5," pp. 321–336, American Elsevier Publishing Company, New York, 1970. (230)†

Anderson, R., and W. Bledsoe (1970): A Linear Format for Resolution with Merging and a New Technique for Establishing Completeness, *J. ACM*, vol. 17, no. 3, July 1970. (229)

Andrews, P. (1968): Resolution with Merging, *J. ACM*, vol. 15, no. 3, pp. 367–381, July, 1968. (Also see corrections in *J. ACM*, vol. 15, no. 4, p. 720, October 1968.) (224, 229)

Amarel, S. (1965): Problem Solving Procedures for Efficient Syntactic Analysis,

† The numbers following each entry refer to pages on which the entry is cited.

ACM 20th Natl. Conf. [Also printed as *Sci. Rept.* no. 1, AFOSR Contr. no. AF49(638)-1184, 1968.] (10, 39)

———— (1966): More on Representations of the Monkey Problem, *Carnegie Institute of Technology Lecture Notes*, March 1, 1966. (39)

———— (1967): An Approach to Heuristic Problem-Solving and Theorem Proving in the Propositional Calculus, in J. Hart and S. Takasu (eds.), "Systems and Computer Science," University of Toronto Press, Toronto, 1967. (10, 11, 38, 112, 151)

———— (1968): On Representations of Problems of Reasoning About Actions, in D. Michie (ed.), "Machine Intelligence 3," pp. 131–171, American Elsevier Publishing Company, Inc., New York, 1968. (39, 41, 77)

———— (1969): On the Representation of Problems and Goal Directed Procedures for Computers, *Commun. Am. Soc. Cybernetics*, vol. 1, no. 2, 1969. (10, 38)

Ball, W. (1931): "Mathematical Recreations and Essays," 10th ed., Macmillan & Co., Ltd., London, 1931. (15-puzzle, pp. 224–228; Tower-of-Hanoi, pp. 228–229.) (12)

Banerji, R. (1969): "Theory of Problem Solving: An Approach to Artificial Intelligence," American Elsevier Publishing Company, Inc., New York, 1969. (10)

Bar Hillel, Y. (1969): Universal Semantics and Philosophy of Language: Quandaries and Prospects, in Jaan Puhvel (ed.), "Substance and Structure of Language," University of California Press, Berkeley, 1969. (213)

Bellman, R., and S. Dreyfus (1962): "Applied Dynamic Programming," Princeton University Press, Princeton, N.J., 1962. (76)

Bellmore, M., and G. Nemhauser (1968): The Traveling Salesman Problem: A Survey, *Operations Res.*, vol. 16, no. 3, pp. 538–558, May–June 1968. (11, 39)

Berge, C. (1962): "The Theory of Graphs and Its Applications," Dunod, Paris, 1958 (in French); English translation, Alison Doig, John Wiley & Sons, Inc., New York, 1962. (38)

Bernstein, A., et al. (1958): A Chess-Playing Program for the IBM 704 Computer, *Proc. West. Joint Computer Conf.*, pp. 157–159, 1958. (152)

Black, F. (1964): "A Deductive Question-Answering System," doctoral dissertation, Harvard, June 1964. Reprinted in M. Minsky (ed.), "Semantic Information Processing," pp. 354–402, The M.I.T. Press, Cambridge, Mass., 1968. (11, 213)

Bobrow, D. (1964a): "Natural Language Input for a Computer Problem-Solving System," doctoral dissertation, Massachusetts Institute of Technology, September 1964. Reprinted in M. Minsky (ed.), "Semantic Information Processing," The M.I.T. Press, Cambridge, Mass., 1968. (212)

———— (1964b): A Question-Answering System for High-School Algebra Word Problems, in *Proc. AFIPS Fall Joint Computer Conf.*, pp. 591–614, 1964. (212)

Campbell, D. (1960): Blind Variation and Selective Survival as a General Strategy in Knowledge-Processes, in M. Yovits and S. Cameron (eds.),

"Self-Organizing Systems," pp. 205–231, Pergamon Press, New York, 1960. (10)

Church, A. (1956): "Introduction to Mathematical Logic," vol. 1, Princeton University Press, Princeton, N.J., 1956. (183)

Coles, L. S. (1968): An On-Line Question-Answering System with Natural Language and Pictorial Input, *Proc. ACM 23rd Natl. Conf., 1968,* pp. 157–167, Brandon Systems Press, Princeton, N.J., 1968. (212)

Collins, N., and D. Michie (eds.): "Machine Intelligence 1," American Elsevier Publishing Company, Inc., New York, 1967. (12)

Dale, E., and D. Michie (eds.): "Machine Intelligence 2," American Elsevier Publishing Company, Inc., New York, 1968. (12)

Davis, M., and H. Putnam (1960): A Computing Procedure for Quantification Theory, *J. ACM,* vol. 7, no. 3, pp. 201–215, July 1960. (184)

De Russo, P., R. Roy, and C. Close (1965): "State Variables for Engineers," John Wiley & Sons, Inc., New York, 1965. (39)

Dijkstra, E. (1959): A Note on Two Problems in Connection with Graphs, *Numerische Math.,* vol. 1, pp. 269–271, 1959. (71)

Doran, J. (1967): An Approach to Automatic Problem-Solving, in N. Collins and D. Michie (eds.), "Machine Intelligence 1," pp. 105–123, American Elsevier Publishing Company, Inc., New York, 1967. (76)

——— (1968): New Developments of the Graph Traverser, in E. Dale and D. Michie (eds.), "Machine Intelligence 2," pp. 119–135, American Elsevier Publishing Company, Inc., New York, 1968. (76)

——— and D. Michie (1966): Experiments with the Graph Traverser Program, *Proc. Roy. Soc.,* A, vol. 294, pp. 235–259, 1966. (75, 76)

Dreyfus, H. (1965): Alchemy and Artificial Intelligence, Rand Corporation Paper P3244 (AD 625 719), December 1965. (8)

Dreyfus, S. (1969): An Appraisal of Some Shortest Path Algorithms, *Operations Res.,* vol. 17, no. 3, pp. 395–412, May–June 1969. (76)

Dudeney, H. (1958): "The Canterbury Puzzles," Dover Publications, Inc., New York, 1958. (Originally published in 1907.) (12)

——— (1967): "536 Puzzles and Curious Problems," Martin Gardner (ed.), Charles Scribner's Sons, New York, 1967. (A collection from two of Dudeney's books: "Modern Puzzles," 1926, and "Puzzles and Curious Problems," 1931.) (12)

Edwards, D., and T. Hart (1963): The α–β Heuristic, *M.I.T. Artificial Intelligence Memo* no. 30 (revised), Oct. 28, 1963 [originally printed as The Tree Prune (TP) Algorithm, Dec. 4, 1961]. (152)

Ernst, G. (1969): Sufficient Conditions for the Success of GPS, *J. ACM,* vol. 16, no. 4, pp. 517–533, October 1969. (113)

——— and A. Newell (1969): "GPS: A Case Study in Generality and Problem Solving," ACM Monograph Series, Academic Press, Inc., New York 1969. (11, 38, 113)

Feigenbaum, E. (1963): Artificial Intelligence Research, *IEEE Trans. Info. Theory,* vol. IT-9, no. 4, pp. 248–261, October 1963. (12)

——— (1969): Artificial Intelligence: Themes in the Second Decade, in A. J. H. Morrell (ed.), "Information Processing 68," vol. 2, pp. 1008–1022,

North Holland Publishing Company, Amsterdam, 1969. Also printed as *Stanford University Artificial Intelligence Project Memo* no. 67, Aug. 15, 1968. (12)

——, B. Buchanan, and J. Lederberg (1971): Generality and Problem Solving: A Case Study Using the DENDRAL Program, in B. Meltzer and D. Michie (eds.), "Machine Intelligence 6," American Elsevier Publishing Company, Inc., New York, 1971. (11)

—— and J. Feldman (eds.) (1963): "Computers and Thought," McGraw-Hill Book Company, New York, 1963. (12)

Feldman, J., and D. Gries (1968): Translator Writing Systems, *Commun. ACM*, vol. 11, no. 2, pp. 77–113, February 1968. (39)

Fikes, R. (1970): Ref-Arf: A System for Solving Problems Stated as Procedures, *Artificial Intelligence*, vol. 1, no. 1, 1970. (38, 39)

Floyd, R. (1967a): Nondeterministic Algorithms, *J. ACM*, vol. 14, no. 4, pp. 636–644, October 1967. (38)

—— (1967b): Assigning Meanings to Programs, *Proc. Symp. Appl. Math.*, *Am. Math. Soc.*, vol. 19, pp. 19–32, 1967. (213)

Fogel, L., A. Owens, and M. Walsh (1966): "Artificial Intelligence Through Simulated Evolution," John Wiley & Sons, Inc., New York, 1966. (9)

Ford, L., Jr., and D. Fulkerson (1962): "Flows in Networks," Princeton University Press, Princeton, N.J., 1962. (39)

Gardner, M. (1959): "The Scientific American Book of Mathematical Puzzles and Diversions," Simon and Schuster, New York, 1959. (12)

—— (1961): "The Second Scientific American Book of Mathematical Puzzles and Diversions," Simon and Schuster, New York, 1961. (12)

—— (1964, 1965a,b,c): Mathematical Games, *Sci. Am.*, vol. 210, no. 2, pp. 122–130, February 1964; vol. 212, no. 3, pp. 112–117, March 1965; vol. 212, no. 6, pp. 120–124, June 1965; vol. 213, no. 3, pp. 222–236, September 1965. (12)

Garvey, T., and R. Kling (1969): User's Guide to QA3.5 Question-Answering System, *Stanford Research Institute Artificial Intelligence Group Technical Note* 15, December 1969. (230)

Gelernter, H (1959): Realization of a Geometry Theorem-Proving Machine, *Proc. Intern. Conf. Inform. Proc.*, pp. 273–282, UNESCO House, Paris, 1959. Reprinted in E. Feigenbaum and J. Feldman (eds.), "Computers and Thought," pp. 134–152, McGraw-Hill Book Company, New York, 1963. (112)

——, J. Hansen, and D. Loveland (1960): Empirical Explorations of the Geometry Theorem Proving Machine, *Proc. West. Joint Computer Conf.*, vol. 17, pp. 143–147, 1960. Reprinted in E. Feigenbaum and J. Feldman (eds.), "Computers and Thought," pp. 153–167, McGraw-Hill Book Company, New York, 1963. (102, 112)

Golomb, S., and L. Baumert (1965): Backtrack Programming, *J. ACM*, vol. 12, no. 4, pp. 516–524, October 1965. (76)

Good, I. (1968): A Five-Year Plan for Automatic Chess, in E. Dale and D. Michie (eds.), "Machine Intelligence 2," pp. 89–118, American Elsevier Publishing Company, Inc., New York, 1968. (151)

Green, C. (1969a): Theorem-Proving by Resolution as a Basis for Question-Answering Systems, in B. Meltzer and D. Michie (eds.), "Machine Intelligence 4," pp. 183–205, American Elsevier Publishing Company, Inc., New York, 1969. (213)

———— (1969b): "The Application of Theorem-Proving to Question-Answering Systems," doctoral dissertation, Electrical Engineering Dept., Stanford University, June 1969. Also printed as *Stanford Artificial Intelligence Project Memo* AI-96, June 1969. (213)

———— (1969c): Application of Theorem-Proving to Problem Solving, in Donald E. Walker and Lewis M. Norton (eds.), *Proc. Intern. Joint Conf. Artificial Intelligence,* Washington, D. C., May 1969. (213)

———— and B. Raphael (1968): The Use of Theorem-Proving Techniques in Question-Answering Systems, *Proc. ACM 23rd Natl. Conf.,* pp. 169–181, Brandon Systems Press, Princeton, N.J., 1968. (212)

Greenblatt, R., et al. (1967): The Greenblatt Chess Program, *Proc. AFIPS Fall Joint Computer Conf.,* pp. 801–810, Anaheim, Calif., 1967. (152)

Guard, J., et al. (1969): Semi-Automated Mathematics, *J. ACM,* vol. 16, no. 1, pp. 49–62, January 1969. (214, 230)

Hart, P., N. Nilsson, and B. Raphael (1968): A Formal Basis for the Heuristic Determination of Minimum Cost Paths, *IEEE Trans. Sys. Sci. Cybernetics,* vol. SSC-4, no. 2, pp. 100–107, July 1968. (76, 151, 230)

Herbrand, J. (1930): Recherches sur la théorie de la démonstration, *Trav. Soc. Sci. Lettres Varsovie, Classe III Sci. Math. Phys.,* no. 33, 1930. (172, 184)

Jelinek, F. (1969): Fast Sequential Decoding Algorithm Using a Stack, *IBM J. Res. Develop.,* vol. 13, no. 6, pp. 675–685, November 1969. (11)

Kieburtz, R., and D. Luckham (1971): Compatibility of Refinements of the Resolution Principle, to be published. (229)

Kister, J., et al. (1957): Experiments in Chess, *J. ACM,* vol. 4, no. 2, pp. 174–177, April 1957. (152)

Kotok, A. (1962): A Chess Playing Program for the IBM 7090, unpublished B.S. thesis, Massachusetts Institute of Technology, Cambridge, Mass., 1962. (152)

Kowalski, R. (1970a): Search Strategies for Theorem-Proving, in B. Meltzer and D. Michie (eds.), "Machine Intelligence 5," pp. 181–201, American Elsevier Publishing Company, Inc., New York, 1970. (228, 230)

———— (1970b): "Studies in the Completeness and Efficiency of Theorem-Proving by Resolution," doctoral thesis, University of Edinburgh, 1970. (229)

———— and P. Hayes (1969): Semantic Trees in Automatic Theorem-Proving, in B. Meltzer and D. Michie (eds.), "Machine Intelligence 4," pp. 87–101, American Elsevier Publishing Company, Inc., New York, 1969. (184, 228–229)

Lawler, E., and D. Wood (1966): Branch and Bound Methods: A Survey, *Operations Res.,* vol. 14, no. 4, pp. 699–719, July–August 1966. (11, 76)

Lin, Shen (1965): Computer Solutions of the Traveling Salesman Problem, *Bell Syst. Tech. J.,* vol. XLIV, no. 10, December 1965. (11)

———— (1970): Heuristic Techniques for Solving Large Combinatorial Problems on a Computer, in R. Banerji and M. Mesarovic (eds.), "Theoretical Approaches to Non-Numerical Problem-Solving," pp. 410–418, Springer-Verlag New York, Inc., New York, 1970. (11)

London, R. (1970): Bibliography on Proving the Correctness of Computer Programs, in B. Meltzer and D. Michie (eds.), "Machine Intelligence 5," pp. 569–580, American Elsevier Publishing Company, Inc., New York, 1970. (213)

Loveland, D. (1968): "A Linear Format for Resolution," Carnegie-Mellon University Computer Science Dept. Report, December 1968. Also in *Proc. IRIA 1968 Symp. Autom. Demonstration,* Lecture Notes in Mathematics no. 125, Springer-Verlag New York, Inc., New York, 1970. (224, 229)

Luckham, D. (1967): The Resolution Principle in Theorem-Proving, in N. Collins and D. Michie (eds.), "Machine Intelligence 1," pp. 47–61, American Elsevier Publishing Co., Inc., 1967. (177, 184)

———— (1969): Refinement Theorems in Resolution Theory, *Stanford Artificial Intelligence Project Memo* AI-81, March 24, 1969. Also in *Proc. IRIA 1968 Symp. Autom. Demonstration,* Lecture Notes on Mathematics no. 125, Springer-Verlag New York, Inc., New York, 1970. (229)

———— and N. Nilsson (1971): Extracting Information from Resolution Proof Trees, *Artificial Intelligence,* 1971. (198, 213)

Manna, Z. (1969): The Correctness of Programs, *J. Computer Syst. Sci.,* vol. 3, May 1969. (38, 213)

———— (1970): The Correctness of Non-Deterministic Programs, *Artificial Intelligence,* vol. 1, no. 1, 1970. (38, 112)

———— and R. Waldinger (1971): Towards Automatic Program Synthesis, *Commun. ACM,* April 1971. (213)

McCarthy, J. (1958): Programs with Common Sense, in "Mechanization of Thought Processes," vol. I, pp. 77–84, *Proc. Symp., Nat. Phys. Lab.,* London, Nov. 24–27, 1958. Reprinted in M. Minsky (ed.), "Semantic Information Processing," pp. 403–410, The M.I.T. Press, Cambridge, Mass., 1968. (11, 213)

———— (1962): Towards a Mathematical Science of Computation, *Proc. IFIP Congr. 62,* North-Holland Publishing Company, Amsterdam, 1962. (213)

———— (1963): Situations, Actions and Causal Laws, *Stanford University Artificial Intelligence Project Memo.* no. 2, 1963. Reprinted in M. Minsky (ed.), "Semantic Information Processing," pp. 410–418, The M.I.T. Press, Cambridge, Mass., 1968. (11, 213)

———— (1964): A Tough Nut for Proof Procedures, *Stanford University Artificial Intelligence Project Memo* no. 16, 1964. (39, 41)

———— and P. Hayes (1969): Some Philosophical Problems from the Standpoint of Artificial Intelligence, in B. Meltzer and D. Michie (eds.), "Machine Intelligence 4," pp. 463–502, American Elsevier Publishing Company, Inc., New York, 1969. (184, 214)

McCulloch, W. S., and W. Pitts (1943): A Logical Calculus of the Ideas Immanent in Neural Nets, *Bull. Math. Biophys.,* vol. 5, pp. 115–137, 1943. (9)

Meltzer, B. (1966): Theorem-Proving for Computers: Some Results on Resolution and Renaming, *Comp. J.,* vol. 8, pp. 341–343, 1966. (229)

——— (1968): Some Notes on Resolution Strategies, in D. Michie (ed.), "Machine Intelligence 3," pp. 71–75, American Elsevier Publishing Company, Inc., New York, 1968. (229)

——— and D. Michie (eds.) (1969): "Machine Intelligence 4," American Elsevier Publishing Company, Inc., New York, 1969. (12)

——— and ——— (eds.) (1970): "Machine Intelligence 5," American Elsevier Publishing Company, Inc., New York, 1970. (12)

——— and ——— (eds.) (1971): "Machine Intelligence 6," American Elsevier Publishing Company, Inc., New York, 1971. (12)

Mendelson, E. (1964): "Introduction to Mathematical Logic," D. Van Nostrand Company, Inc., Princeton, New Jersey, 1964. (183)

Michie, D. (ed.) (1968): "Machine Intelligence 3," American Elsevier Publishing Company, Inc., New York, 1968. (12)

——— and R. Ross (1970): Experiments with the Adaptive Graph Traverser, in B. Meltzer and D. Michie (eds.), "Machine Intelligence 5," pp. 301–318, American Elsevier Publishing Company, Inc., New York, 1970. (76)

Minsky, M. (1961a): Steps Toward Artificial Intelligence, *Proc. IRE,* vol. 49, pp. 8–30, January 1961. Reprinted in E. Feigenbaum and J. Feldman (eds.), "Computers and Thought," pp. 406–450, McGraw-Hill Book Company, New York, 1963. (9)

——— (1961b): A Selected Descriptor-Indexed Bibliography to the Literature on Artificial Intelligence, *IRE Trans. Human Factors Electron.,* HFE-2, pp. 39–55, March 1961. A revision is reprinted in E. Feigenbaum and J. Feldman (eds.), "Computers and Thought," pp. 453–523, McGraw-Hill Book Company, New York, 1963. (12)

——— (1967): "Computation: Finite and Infinite Machines," Prentice-Hall, Inc., Englewood Cliffs, N.J., 1967. (39)

——— (ed.) (1968): "Semantic Information Processing," The M.I.T. Press, Cambridge, Mass., 1968. (3, 9, 12)

——— and S. Papert (1969): "Perceptrons: An Introduction to Computational Geometry," The M.I.T. Press, Cambridge, Mass., 1969. (9)

Montanari, U. (1970): Heuristically Guided Search and Chromosome Matching, *Artificial Intelligence,* vol. 1, no. 4, 1970. (11)

Moore, E. (1959): The Shortest Path Through a Maze, *Proc. Intern. Symp. Theory Switching, Part II,* April 2–5, 1957; The Annals of the Computation Laboratory of Harvard University 30, Harvard University Press, Cambridge, Mass., 1959. (76)

Moses, J. (1967): "Symbolic Integration," thesis, Project MAC, Report MAC-TR-47, Massachusetts Institute of Technology, December 1967. (112)

Newell, A. (1965): Limitations of the Current Stock of Ideas about Problem Solving, in A. Kent and O. Taulbee (eds.), "Electronic Information Handling," Spartan Books, Washington, D.C., 1965. (39)

——— (1969): Heuristic Programming: Ill-Structured Problems, in J. Aronofsky (ed.), "Progress in Operations Research," vol. 3, John Wiley & Sons, Inc., 1969. (10, 12)

———, J. Shaw, and H. Simon (1957): Empirical Explorations of the Logic

Theory Machine, *Proc. West. Joint Computer Conf.*, vol. 15, pp. 218–239, 1957. Reprinted in E. Feigenbaum and J. Feldman (eds.), "Computers and Thought," pp. 109–133, McGraw-Hill Book Company, New York, 1963. (13, 112)

———, ———, and ——— (1958): Chess Playing Programs and the Problem of Complexity, *IBM J. Res. Develop.*, vol. 2, pp. 320–335, October 1958. Reprinted in E. Feigenbaum and J. Feldman (eds.), "Computers and Thought," pp. 39–70, McGraw-Hill Book Company, New York, 1963. (151, 152)

———, ———, and ——— (1959): Report on a General Problem-Solving Program, *Proc. Intern. Conf. Inform. Process.*, pp. 256–264, UNESCO House, Paris, 1959. (10)

Nilsson, N. (1969): Searching Problem-Solving and Game-Playing Trees for Minimal Cost Solutions, in A. J. H. Morrell (ed.), "Information Processing 68," vol. 2, pp. 1556–1562, North-Holland Publishing Company, Amsterdam, 1969. (151)

O'Beirne, T. H. (1961): Puzzles and Paradoxes, *New Scientist*, no. 245, July 27, 1961, and no. 246, Aug. 3, 1961. (113)

Ore, O. (1962): Theory of Graphs, *Am. Math. Soc. Colloq. Publ.*, vol. XXXVIII, Providence, Rhode Island, 1962. (38)

——— (1963): "Graphs and Their Uses," Random House, New York, 1963. (38)

Papert, S. (1968): The Artificial Intelligence of Hubert L. Dreyfus. A Budget of Fallacies, *M.I.T. Artificial Intelligence Memo* no. 54, January 1968. (9)

Pohl, I. (1969): "Bi-Directional and Heuristic Search in Path Problems," doctoral dissertation, Computer Science Dept., Stanford University, Stanford, Calif., 1969. Also printed as *Stanford Linear Accelerator Center Report* no. 104, May 1969. (76)

——— (1970): First Results on the Effect of Error in Heuristic Search, in B. Meltzer and D. Michie (eds.), "Machine Intelligence 5," pp. 219–236, American Elsevier Publishing Company, New York, 1970. (76)

Polya, G. (1957): "How to Solve It," 2d ed., Doubleday & Company, Inc., Garden City, N.Y., 1957. (10)

Prawitz, D. (1960): An Improved Proof Procedure, *Theoria*, vol. 26, pp. 102–139, 1960. (184)

Quinlan, J., and E. Hunt (1968): A Formal Deductive Problem-Solving System, *J. ACM*, vol. 15, no. 4, pp. 625–646, October 1968. (38)

Raphael, B. (1964a): "SIR: A Computer Program for Semantic Information Retrieval," doctoral dissertation, Massachusetts Institute of Technology, June 1964. Reprinted in M. Minsky (ed.), "Semantic Information Processing, The M.I.T. Press, Cambridge, Mass., 1968. (212)

——— (1964b): A Computer Program Which "Understands," *Proc. AFIPS Fall Joint Computer Conf.*, pp. 577–589, 1964. (212)

Rigney, J. W., and D. M. Towne (1969): Computer Techniques for Analyzing the Microstructure of Serial-Action Work in Industry, *Human Factors*, vol. 11, no. 2, pp. 113–122, 1969. (112)

Risch, R. H. (1969): The Problem of Integration in Finite Terms, *Trans. Am. Math. Soc.*, vol. 139, pp. 167–189, 1969. (112, 114)

Robbin, J. (1969): "Mathematical Logic: A First Course," W. A. Benjamin, Inc., New York, 1969. (183)

Robinson, G. A., L. T. Wos, and D. F. Carson (1964): Some Theorem-Proving Strategies and Their Implementation, *Argonne National Laboratories Technical Memorandum* no. 72, 1964. (228)

——— and ——— (1969): Paramodulation and Theorem-Proving in First-Order Theories with Equality, in B. Meltzer and D. Michie (eds.), "Machine Intelligence 4," pp. 135–150, American Elsevier Publishing Company, Inc., New York, 1969. (184, 214, 230)

Robinson, J. A. (1965a): A Machine-Oriented Logic Based on the Resolution Principle, *J. ACM*, vol. 12, no. 1, pp. 23–41, January 1965. (177, 184)

——— (1965b): Automatic Deduction with Hyper-Resolution, *Intern. J. Comp. Math.* vol. 1, pp. 227–234, 1965. (229)

——— (1967): Heuristic and Complete Processes in the Mechanization of Theorem-Proving, in J. T. Hart and S. Takasu (eds.), "Systems and Computer Science," pp. 116–124, University of Toronto Press, Toronto, 1967. (228)

——— (1968): The Generalized Resolution Principle, in D. Michie (ed.), "Machine Intelligence 3," pp. 77–93, American Elsevier Publishing Co., Inc., New York, 1968. (184)

——— (1969a): New Directions in Mechanical Theorem Proving, in A. J. H. Morrell (ed.), "Information Processing 68," vol. 1, pp. 63–67, North-Holland Publishing Company, Amsterdam, 1969. (184)

——— (1969b): Mechanizing Higher Order Logic, in B. Meltzer and D. Michie (eds.), "Machine Intelligence 4," American Elsevier Publishing Company, Inc., New York, 1969. (184)

——— (1970): An Overview of Mechanical Theorem Proving, in R. Banerji and M. Mesarovic (eds.), "Theoretical Approaches to Non-Numerical Problem Solving," pp. 2–20, Springer-Verlag New York, Inc., New York, 1970. (184)

Rosenblatt, F. (1962): "Principles of Neurodynamics," Spartan Books, New York, 1962. (9)

Russell, R. (1964): Kalah—The Game and the Program, *Stanford University Artificial Intelligence Project Memo* no. 22, Sept. 3, 1964. (152)

Samuel, A. (1959): Some Studies in Machine Learning Using the Game of Checkers, *IBM J. Res. Develop.*, vol. 3, no. 3, pp. 211–229, 1959. Reprinted in E. Feigenbaum and J. Feldman (eds.), "Computers and Thought," pp. 71–105, McGraw-Hill Book Company, New York, 1963. (76, 151, 153)

——— (1967): Some Studies in Machine Learning Using the Game of Checkers II. Recent Progress, *IBM J. Res. and Develop.*, vol. 11, no. 6, pp. 601–617, November 1967. (76, 151, 152, 153)

Sandewall, E. (1969): Concepts and Methods for Heuristic Search, in Donald E. Walker and Lewis M. Norton (eds.), *Proc. Intern. Joint Conf. Artificial Intelligence*, Washington, D.C., 1969. (10)

Schuh, F. (1968): "The Master Book of Mathematical Recreations," W. J. Thieme & Cie., Zutphen, 1943 (in Dutch); English translation, F. Göbel, Dover Publications, Inc., New York, 1968. (12)

Selfridge, O., and J. Kelly, Jr. (1962): Sophistication in Computers: A Disagreement, *IRE Trans. Inform. Theory,* vol. IT-8, no. 2, pp. 78–80, February 1962. (8)

Shannon, C. (1950): Programming a Digital Computer for Playing Chess, *Philosophy Magazine,* vol. 41, pp. 356–375, March, 1950. Reprinted in J. R. Newman (ed.), "The World of Mathematics," vol. 4, Simon and Schuster, New York, 1954. (151)

Shapiro, D. (1966): Algorithms for the Solution of the Optimal Cost Traveling Salesman Problem, Sc.D. thesis, Washington University, St. Louis, Mo., 1966. (11, 76)

Simmons, R. (1965): Answering English Questions by Computer: A Survey, *Commun. ACM,* vol. 8, pp. 53–70, January 1965. (213)

—— (1970): Natural Language Question Answering Systems: 1969, *Commun. ACM,* vol. 13, no. 1, pp. 15–30, January 1970. (213)

Slagle, J. (1961): "A Computer Program for Solving Problems in Freshman Calculus (SAINT)," doctoral dissertation, Massachusetts Institute of Technology, Cambridge, Mass., 1961. Also printed as *Lincoln Laboratory Report* 5G-0001, May 10, 1961. (112, 150)

—— (1963a): A Heuristic Program That Solves Symbolic Integration Problems in Freshman Calculus, *J. ACM,* vol. 10, no. 4, pp. 507–520, October 1963. Also in E. Feigenbaum and J. Feldman (eds.), "Computers and Thought," pp. 191–203, McGraw-Hill Book Company, New York, 1963. (11, 97, 112, 150)

—— (1963b): Game Trees, M & N Minimaxing, and the M & N Alpha-Beta Procedure, *Artificial Intelligence Group Report* no. 3, UCRL-4671, University of California Lawrence Radiation Laboratory, Livermore, Calif., November 1963. (152)

—— (1965): Experiments with a Deductive-Question Answering Program, *Commun. ACM,* vol. 8, pp. 792–798, December 1965. (212)

—— (1967): Automatic Theorem-Proving with Renamable and Semantic Resolution, *J. ACM,* vol. 14, no. 4, pp. 687–697, October 1967. (229)

—— (1970: Heuristic Search Programs, in R. Banerji and M. Mesarovic (eds.), "Theoretical Approaches to Non-Numerical Problem Solving," pp. 246–273, Springer-Verlag New York, Inc., New York, 1970. (113)

—— and P. Bursky (1968): Experiments with a Multipurpose, Theorem-Proving Heuristic Program, *J. ACM,* vol. 15, no. 1, pp. 85–99, January 1968. (112, 113, 150–151)

—— and J. Dixon (1969): Experiments with Some Programs that Search Game Trees, *J. ACM* vol. 16, no. 2, pp. 189–207, April 1969. (76, 149, 150, 151, 152, 153)

—— and —— (1970): Experiments with the M & N Tree Searching Program, *Commun. ACM,* vol. 13, no. 3, p. 147, March 1970. (150, 152, 153)

Solomonoff, R. (1966): Some Recent Work in Artificial Intelligence, *Proc. IEEE,* vol. 54, no. 112, December 1966. (12)

Travis, L. (1963): The Value of Introspection to the Designer of Mechanical Problem-Solvers, *Behav. Sci.,* vol. 8, no. 3, pp. 227–233, July 1963. (9)

——— (1967): Psychology and Bionics: Many Old Problems and a Few New Machines, *Conf. Record 1967 Winter Conv. Aerospace Electron. Sys. (WINCON)*, IEEE Publication no. 10-C-42, vol. VI, February 1967. (9)

Turing, A. M. (1950): Computing Machinery and Intelligence, *Mind*, vol. 59, pp. 433–460, October 1950. Reprinted in E. Feigenbaum and J. Feldman (eds.), "Computers and Thought," pp. 11–35, McGraw-Hill Book Company, New York, 1963. (8)

Waldinger, R., and R. Lee (1969): PROW: A Step Toward Automatic Program-Writing, in Donald E. Walker and Lewis M. Norton (eds.), *Proc. Intern. Joint Conf. Artificial Intelligence*, Washington, D.C., 1969. (213)

Weissman, C. (1967): "LISP 1.5 Primer," Dickenson Publishing Company, Inc., Belmont, Calif., 1967. (201)

Whitney, D. (1969): State Space Models of Remote Manipulation Tasks, in Donald E. Walker and Lewis M. Norton (eds.), *Proc. Intern. Joint Conf. Artificial Intelligence*, pp. 495–507, Washington, D.C., 1969. (11)

Wos, L., D. Carson, and G. Robinson (1964): The Unit Preference Strategy in Theorem Proving, *Proc. AFIPS 1964 Fall Joint Computer Conf.*, vol. 26, pp. 616–621, 1964. (229)

———, G. Robinson, and D. Carson (1965): Efficiency and Completeness of the Set of Support Strategy in Theorem-Proving, *J. ACM*, vol. 12, no. 4, pp. 536–541, October 1965. (229)

Yates, R., B. Raphael, and T. Hart (1970): Resolution Graphs, *Artificial Intelligence*, vol. 1, no. 4, 1970. (224, 229)

Zobrist, A. (1969): A Model of Visual Organization for the Game of Go, *Proc. AFIPS Spring Joint Computer Conf.*, pp. 103–112, 1969. (153)

SUBJECT INDEX

For author index see Combined References and Author Index, pp. 234–244.

Boldface page numbers indicate illustrations.

Italic page numbers indicate exercise problems.

Action schedules, 112
Admissibility:
  of A^*, 59–61
  of ordered-search algorithm for
    AND/OR trees, 131–136

Admissibility (*cont'd*):
  of search algorithms, 59
Advice taker, 11, 213–214
Algebra, solving word problems in, 212
Algorithm A^*, 59

L$1195